Sophomore Organic Chemistry 1 By Inquisition

Kevin Burgess

Texas A & M University

By Inquisition Press

Publisher: *By Inquisition Press*.

Outside cover by Kevin Burgess.

Library of Congress Cataloging-in-Publication Data is available.

ISBN 978-0-692-77443-4

Preface

This is the first of two books intended to accompany courses in sophomore organic chemistry, particularly in The United States and anywhere else using similar curricula. They are intended for "flipped" settings where instructors and students may solve the problems in an interactive way, or as workbooks for students wanting to check their understanding as they take a conventional class. Throughout, I have tried to emphasize the concepts that students need for other classes in the biological and biomedical sciences, and *not* parts of synthetic organic chemistry that have no parallels in the chemistry of living systems.

I thank the friends who have already looked at some of these questions, and have given valuable suggestions for improvements. Special thanks to Dr Anyanee Kamkaew who solved all the problems, hence suggested numerous corrections and improvements, and generated a set of answers that can be found on the web page for By Inquisition Press (www.byinquisition.org). Dr Evamarie Capareda also reviewed the content carefully and gave much help and encouragement. Dr Aurore Loudet, a phenomenal eagle-eyed checker, weeded out many of my stupid mistakes.

There were many others who helped including (in alphabetical order) Dr Ivana Flcischer, Verena Lehner, Santos Pagire, Julietta Yedoyan, from the University of Regensburg where I stayed for two months towards the end of this project, courtesy of The Humboldt Foundation and my host Dr Prof. Oliver Reiser. At TAMU over the years that it took to compose these texts there were many graduate and undergraduate students who checked parts, and some professors, Kenn Harding, GG and Patricio Santander in particular, also gave help and encouragement.

Ideas for the cartoons were mine, and the worst drawings are also mine; the good ones were drawn by artistic friends. Thank you all.

All the errors in this book are mine, too. I welcome constructive criticism (burgess@tamu.edu) that points to corrections, confusing questions, or material to include or exclude.

Kevin Burgess
Rachal Professor of Chemistry
Department of Chemistry
Texas A & M University

www.chem.tamu.edu/rgroup/burgess/

www.byinquisition.org

To Instructors

Philosophy

Angela Duckworth's book *Grit: The Power of Passion and Perseverance* makes excellent points about the psychology of teaching and learning. One of those points is that *focused, targeted practice time* is essential.

For sophomore organic chemistry maybe 40 – 50 hours of that type of practice per semester is enough for a student to get a good grade, provided it is really focused and targeted. The key issue is how to guide students to focus on, and to target parts of the course that have most impact on their understanding. Trying to memorize a textbook, or notes from a textbook, is certainly not optimal.

This is a *workbook*, not a textbook, for students to practice *essential concepts in the first semester of sophomore organic chemistry*. Book 2 in this series covers the second semester.

This first book is organized by concepts (*eg* mechanisms), not by functional groups, but nevertheless follows roughly the same sequence as chemistry textbooks like those by McMurry and Wade. It has features many instructors might recommend for quality study time. It targets key concepts that can be applied repeatedly, and avoids facts that students might think are important to memorize but are not.

Throughout, students are encouraged to research factual information that is easily understood; instructors do not have to teach this. Twenty-first century teenagers do not like to be lectured, especially about the simple and obvious material, but they have no hesitation whipping out their device to research things for themselves.

Students need to compare their answers against model solutions. Consequently, answers for this workbook are available via the *By Inquisition* website (www.byinquisition.org) and will be available in some videos online.

Uses Of This Book

Strategies

- Motivated students can use this text to supplement what they are being taught in sophomore organic chemistry; and,
- instructors implementing "flipped" paradigms may use this book as a template to solve some of the problems in class, and leave others for the students to work off-site.

Flipping Organic Chemistry Classes

About a decade ago, I decided to lecture less and focus more on teaching strategies to empower students to learn organic chemistry more effectively. Before that I dutifully covered syllabi by presenting material from the textbook, expecting students to copy and learn it. I thought that simply showing vast amounts of information would inspire students to learn it. However, when shown a table of functional groups, for instance, most students did not learn most of them until it was far too late. People would emerge from my lectures with only a few memories, and a poor replication of a textbook, containing errors from my lectures and their copying.

Now I teach sophomore organic from a collection of problems that has evolved into these workbooks. In class I introduce concepts colloquially asking questions as I go, and ruthlessly calling students by name. In that way, about 25 % of the problems in these books are solved on-site. In the next lecture there will be a quiz on that material *including problems I did not solve*. Most of the exams and the final also are based on any of the problems distributed. Outside class, students may ask me about concepts, but not answers to specific problems.

The strategy described above "flips" a class: placing the expectations on students to understand material outside of class, while the contact time is focused on solving problems involving new concepts. I enjoy flipped teaching more than lecturing, and overall the students seem to respond better.

Book Structure

Each section in this book is designed to be the focus of one 75 min class period, *ie* ideally about 10 – 15 pages of content. Thus the book is divided into 23 sections, which approximately corresponds to a semester of instruction, with a few class time slots for review and exams. Listening to anyone for 75 min is tough, particularly me, but the quiz breaks the routine and after that I show chemistry videos from the web or demonstrations. If I do not finish all the intended problems in any given lecture, the rest of the questions automatically become homework.

This workbook could be used with *any* decent organic chemistry textbook, including supposedly out-of-date editions obtained cheaply via re-sale. I have tried to make the book attractive but affordable. It is intended to be light enough to carry to class and has space for students to write in answers and keep them organized; they do not necessarily have to bring paper.

Most new textbooks now are sold as a package wherein students pay a lot for on-line problems, and only a little more for the text; this suits publishers because online subscriptions have no resale value. Instructors like the arrangement too for the pedagogical value, and because all the problems are graded automatically. However, it is expensive for the students, and sometimes the online problems not ideal.

These workbooks have *no* online learning component, and I appreciate that many instructors want one. For that reason I suggest students be asked to buy the online component from Sapling Learning (http://www2.saplinglearning.com). Sapling Learning can provide a set of problems earmarked for most sections. To learn more about using Sapling Learning, go to www.meetme.so/SaplingLearning or email support@saplinglearning.com. Combinations of this book, older editions of a textbook, and an online account from Sapling Learning can be more affordable than a conventional textbook/online learning bundle.

Content

Reactions With Parallels *In Vivo*

Approximately 1800 people take sophomore organic chemistry each semester at the university where I teach, but each year less than 100 students graduate as chemistry majors. More than 90% of those 1800 students major in other subjects relating to the biological sciences. I believe we should teach to that 90 % and material that exclusively relates to laboratory organic syntheses tends to complicate and confuse. My preference is that methods for laboratory organic syntheses (a topic I love) should be taught in upper level classes after chemistry that has parallels *in vivo* is covered at the sophomore level.

This workbook focuses on chemistry useful to students majoring in the biomedical sciences (including chemistry majors). Reactions exclusively for synthetic organic chemistry are *not* emphasized, though some are included because many instructors want it. Thus, mercuration, hydroboration, organometallic cross-couplings, alkene metathesis, and regioselective serial additions of electrophiles to benzene derivatives, and free radical halogenations are not included.

Fundamental Concepts

Like nearly all books for undergraduate chemistry, this one introduces hybridization early, but it also trains students to identify hybridization states of atoms in larger molecules relevant to medicine or biochemistry. Section 2 introduces minimalist molecular structure representations (*ie* usually not involving the symbols *C* or *H*), and leads students to realize zigzag conformations are favored *because of preferred conformations of acyclic hydrocarbons.* Thereafter, minimalist representations of organic molecules are used throughout.

Chemists in general tend to use various abbreviations for fragments and to represent functional groups in different ways; this makes learning organic chemistry particularly hard for the students. To help, section 3 of this book introduces functional groups. Effort that might have been spent on classical nomenclature is spent on introducing the ways functional groups are drawn, because it is more important to distinguish an ester and an amide than it is to be able to name 3-methylhexane and not use "4-methylhexane".

Section 5 of this book is completely devoted to electron flow. This is one of the most difficult skills to teach, but one of the most important to learn. Consequently, this section is followed by another one (6) on curly arrows applied to resonance structures.

Students who solve sections 1 – 6 without consulting the model answers will be in pole positions for the rest of the course; these sections are the most important in this two-book series. The rest of the content is more conventional and self-explanatory. There is one section on cycloadditions (16) particularly azide-alkyne reactions that often feature in biological chemistry, grouped with other cycloadditions that can have applications in biomedicinal chemistry.

Unlike most classical textbooks for sophomore organic, there is some discussion on fundamentals of fluorescence and to introduce a few common fluors (after UV in section 19). This is included because of the ubiquitous applications of fluorescent probes in the biological sciences. However, there is little material covered in Book 1 that would not be found in classical organic textbooks for US sophomore organic chemistry.

To Students

Philosophy

For sophomore organic chemistry, 40 – 50 hours of *focused, targeted* practice per semester may be enough to get a good grade. The catch is that it must be *focused* study *targeted* on the parts of the course that you do not already understand. *Focused* means no distractions (texts, emails, calls, TV, casual web browsing *etc*). *Targeted* is harder to define, but attempts to memorize particular sections of textbooks or lecture notes is boring, leads to loss of focus, and is therefore ineffective.

This *workbook* is intended to be *a guided approach to targeted study*. It is mostly organized by mechanisms, not by functional groups, because recognition of similarities in related key concepts makes them easier to learn. Throughout, this workbook avoids details that might seem important to remember, but are not. Not everything is covered from any particular sophomore organic chemistry text (*eg* the one your instructor may recommend) but, on the other hand, diligently working through the problems in this book will be helpful for *any* sophomore organic class taught from any standard textbook.

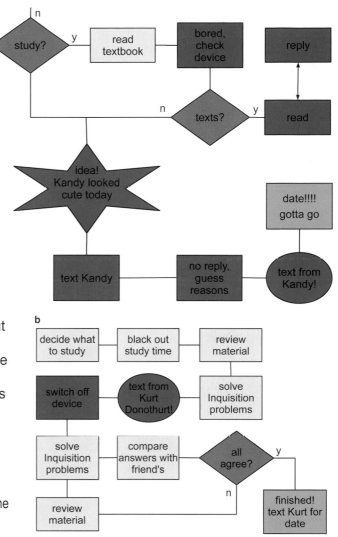

Figure 1. **a** Student Kurt's studies based on a conventional textbook are boring and untargeted, so he is open to distractions; but, **b** Kandy is focused and targeted because she is researching and reasoning answers herself, responding to questions in a *By Inquisition* book.

How To Use This Book

(i) Gain a basic understanding of the material.

(ii) Attempt the problems *without looking at the ideal answers provided on the website for this book*.

(iii) When unable to solve a problem, determine if it is searching for a fact or testing understanding of a key concept.

(iv) If a problem requires memorization of a fact, but that memory is not available, look up the answer in the text, from the web, anywhere *except the ideal answers provided on the website for this book*.

(v) If a problem requires application of a concept but the required understanding is not there yet, learn more about the concept, then try again *without looking at the ideal answers on the website for this book*.

(vi) Crosscheck your answers with friends, and discuss if necessary.

(vii) Finally, check the ideal solutions provided on the web if there is any uncertainty about the correct ones.

Understanding [as in (i)] can be gained by targeted web surfing, from a textbook, going to lectures, talking to friends or instructors, or watching appropriate videos from sources like YouTube. The best way to gain understanding is to do all these things.

Contents

in·qui·si·tion (ĭn′kwĭ-zĭsh′ən, ĭng′-) *n.*

1. The act of inquiring into a matter; an investigation. See Synonyms at **inquiry**.

2. *Law* An inquest.

3.

a. Inquisition A tribunal formerly held in the Roman Catholic Church and directed at the suppression of heresy.

b. An investigation that violates the privacy or rights of individuals, especially through rigorous or harsh interrogation.

c. A rigorous or severe questioning.

I'm <u>NOT</u> a textbook!

1   Hybridization: The Shape Of Things To Come

from chapter(s) _____ in the recommended text

A Introduction

Focus

Atoms and molecular fragments re-purpose their atomic orbitals to maximize bonding in molecules. They mix orbitals to create hybrid orbitals that enable atoms to combine to form molecules more effectively. Thus *hybridization states* of atoms in molecules determine the geometries of bonds to that atom in that molecule, and, conversely, geometries of bonds to a particular atom determine its hybridization state. This is fundamental to the process by which atoms assemble into molecules in favorable (energetically accessible or thermodynamically preferred) shapes. This section is focused on hybridization.

Reasons To Care

Shapes of molecules are intimately related to their reactivities. Mastery of a few simple concepts enables prediction of hybridization states of atoms in organic molecules, therefore the way bonds

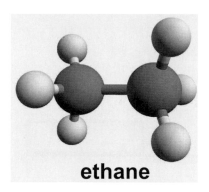

ethane

organize around those atoms, and orientations of other atoms and of electron lone pairs around them.

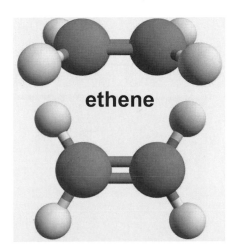

ethene

Collectively, shapes around atoms define the overall shape, or preferred shapes, of molecules. Reactivities of molecules are intimately related to their shapes, so the ability to predict shapes is a powerful tool.

Why is it, for instance, that ethane (C_2H_6) comprises of two carbon atoms that project bonds to each other and to hydrogen atoms in tetrahedral geometries? What is different about ethene (C_2H_4) that makes the carbon atom environment flat, and coplanar? These questions are clear from consideration of *hybridization states*.

Concepts From Prior Classes

electronic structures of elements • atomic orbitals • mixing atomic orbitals to give hybrids

Objective

Students who survive this initial *Inquisition* will be much stronger and able to face more demanding challenges. They fearlessly look at organic molecules, almost *any* organic molecule, point to any atom, and predict its hybridization state. Knowing the hybridization state about atoms affords the power to understand the shape of a molecule.

B Electron Counting

In Atoms

Electronic structures of neon, potassium, and silicon can be shown in the following way to emphasize their outermost electronic orbitals (*ie* levels 1, 2, 3, 4 *etc*):

$1s^2$ | $2s^2 2p^6$

neon

[Ar] or
$1s^2 2s^2 2p^6 3s^2 3p^6$ | $4s^1$

potassium

$1s^2 2s^2 2p^6$ | $3s^2 3p^2$

silicon

Refer to a periodic table, then write the electronic structures of the following elements in a similar way.

nitrogen

carbon

hydrogen

fluorine

bromine

chlorine

oxygen

sulfur

boron

In Molecules, and Valency

Favored electronic configurations have *2 / 8 / 16* electrons in the first shell, *2 / 8 / 16* in the second, and *2 / 8 / 16* in the third.

Covalent bonds are formed when atoms *share / completely donate or receive electrons* to form stable electronic shells; ionic bonds are formed when atoms *share / completely donate or receive electrons*.

Hydrogen atoms have the electronic structure $1s^1$. If an *H*-atom shares that electron with another hydrogen that also contributes 1*e*, then dihydrogen is formed, and the structure can be represented as H $1s^1 1s^1$ H. In that H_2 molecule each hydrogen atom has *2 / 8 / 16* first shell electrons.

One bond containing *1 / 2 / 3* electrons is formed in this sharing process, and the hydrogen atom is connected to one other so the *valency* of hydrogen in H_2 is *1 / 2 / 3*.

The electronic structure of *Ne / He / Ar* is $1s^2$ so a hydrogen atom achieves the structure of that most similar inert gas by forming H_2 and sharing electrons.

Indicate the number of hydrogen atoms the elements above must share with to achieve the filled outer shell electronic configurations of the corresponding inert gases.

C _____ N _____ O _____ F _____ Cl _____ Br _____ S _____

This number referred to above corresponds to "red electrons" (using the convention invented here) that hydrogen atoms bring into a covalent bond. Each hydrogen atom may only bring *1 / 2 / 3* electron(s) into a covalent bond, and the valency of hydrogen in common molecules is *1 / 2 / 3*.

Write the formulae of the compounds formed when one atom of the following elements combines with hydrogen to form a neutral molecule (no charges):

C _____ N _____ O _____ F _____ Cl _____ Br _____ S _____

Using the color scheme above, the second shell electronic structure of ammonia is:

$$N\ 2s^2 2p^1 2p^1 1s^1 1s^1 1s^1\ H_3$$

The blue and red electrons are shared in bonds, two per bond, so ammonia has two electrons that are not in bonds, *ie* a lone pair.

18

Write the structures of the following compounds in the same way as above. Remember this is self-study; if you have trouble with any of the questions, check the web or an organic chemistry textbook.

water electronic structure	bonds	lone pairs

hydrogen fluoride electronic structure	bonds	lone pairs

hydrogen bromide electronic structure	bonds	lone pairs

methane electronic structure	bonds	lone pairs

Borane is unusual because it only has six electrons, not eight, in its outer shell. The outer electronic shell is the third rather than second for the other examples, and a favored electron count for that is *2 / 8 / 16*.

borane electronic structure	bonds	lone pairs

hydrogen sulfide electronic structure	bonds	lone pairs

tetrahydrosilane electronic structure	bonds	lone pairs

phosphine electronic structure	bonds	lone pairs

The representations above are oversimplifications. Electrons are not colored, and information about the atomic origin of electrons *is / is not* lost once they are combined in a molecule. Further, the orbitals that contain them change to maximize bonding interactions in molecules.

c Mixing Atomic Orbitals To Maximize Overlap In Molecules

Combining *s*- and *p*-Orbitals

Terms like "*s*- and *p*-orbitals" refer to maximum probability surfaces for finding an electron in atoms, hence they are called *atomic / genius* orbitals.

An orbital is like a bookshelf; it defines where the content will go, and it is still there even if it does not contain anything. Similar probability surfaces in molecules are called molecular orbitals, and they tend to have *different / the same* shapes as atomic orbitals.

Label the following orbitals as *s*-, *p*-, or *d*-.

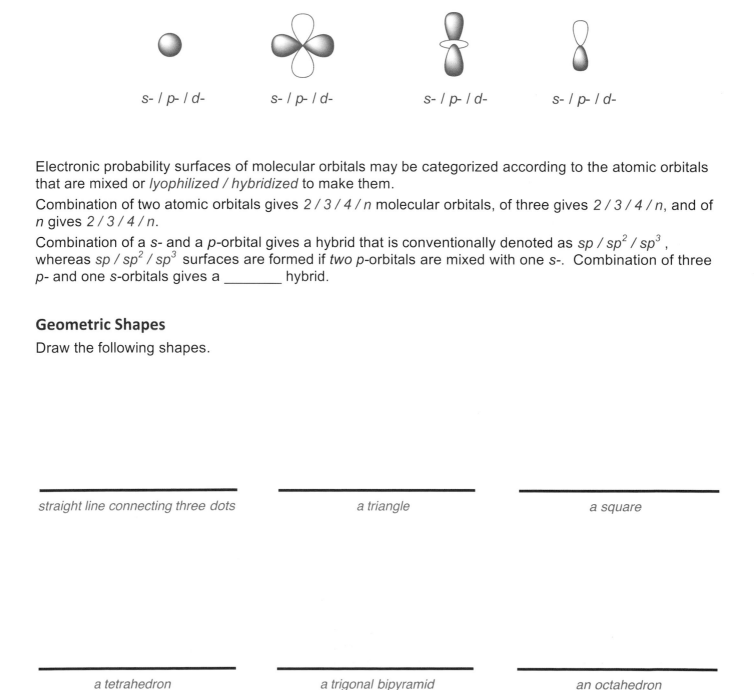

s- / p- / d-   *s- / p- / d-*   *s- / p- / d-*   *s- / p- / d-*

Electronic probability surfaces of molecular orbitals may be categorized according to the atomic orbitals that are mixed or *lyophilized / hybridized* to make them.

Combination of two atomic orbitals gives *2 / 3 / 4 / n* molecular orbitals, of three gives *2 / 3 / 4 / n*, and of *n* gives *2 / 3 / 4 / n*.

Combination of a *s*- and a *p*-orbital gives a hybrid that is conventionally denoted as $sp / sp^2 / sp^3$, whereas $sp / sp^2 / sp^3$ surfaces are formed if *two p*-orbitals are mixed with one *s*-. Combination of three *p*- and one *s*-orbitals gives a _____ hybrid.

Geometric Shapes

Draw the following shapes.

_____   _____   _____

straight line connecting three dots   *a triangle*   *a square*

_____   _____   _____

a tetrahedron   *a trigonal bipyramid*   *an octahedron*

Imagine a boy attached to two girls by pieces of string, one girl tied to each of his hands. These girls do not like each other, so the arrangement is most stable when they are as far apart as possible. Stability is best achieved by forming a line with the boy *near one end / in the middle.*

In that *linear* arrangement, the girl-boy-girl angle is *109° / 120° / 180° / 270°*; this is called the *ideal bond / triangular* angle.

A girl is equally attracted to three boys, who like her too but find each other repulsive. The most convenient place for her to be is at the same distance to the boys, but with them as far apart as possible. She may do this by placing herself in the middle of a *square / straight line / triangle / trigonal bipyramid / tetrahedron / octahedron* with the boys at the corners; the bond angle is then *109° / 120° / 180° / 270°.*

If a nucleus is surrounded by four bonds (which repel each other like jealous boyfriends) the most stable arrangement is with the point in the middle of a *square / straight line / triangle / trigonal bipyramid / tetrahedron / octahedron*, and then the bond angle is *109° / 120° / 180° / 270°.*

Shapes Of Molecules Based On Geometric Shapes

Combination of one *s-* and one *p-* atomic orbitals gives *0 / 1 / 2 / 3 / 4 sp*-hybrid orbitals.

Similarly, one *s-* and two *p*-orbitals give *0 / 1 / 2 / 3 / 4* hybrid orbitals, and *0 / 1 / 2 / 3 / 4* arise from one *s-* and three *p*-orbitals.

Draw hybrid orbitals on the following frameworks to indicate sp, sp^2, or sp^3. *Bold / dashed* lines mean "emerges from the plane of the paper" and *bold / dashed* lines indicate "projects behind the plane".

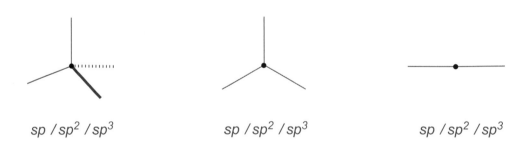

sp / sp^2 / sp^3   *sp / sp^2 / sp^3*   *sp / sp^2 / sp^3*

Joining the bonds termini in the diagrams gives geometric shapes; those same geometric shapes are used to describe molecular structures. The approximate geometric shape of a molecule is governed by the total number of atoms connected to it plus the number of outer shell non-bonding lone pairs. If a central atom has to accommodate three atoms and/or lone pairs, then a triangle will be formed and the central atom will be *sp / sp^2 / sp^3* hybridized.

A tetrahedron of *sp / sp^2 / sp^3* hybrids will be formed if *0 / 1 / 4 / 3* bonds and/or lone pairs are accommodated, and a linear arrangement of two peripheral groups is generated from two *sp / sp^2 / sp^3* hybrid orbitals.

Methane, CH$_4$ has four hydrogen atoms around the carbon, and after the carbon has shared one electron with each hydrogen atom, it has *1 / 2 / 3 / 0* lone pairs in the second electron shell, therefore it is *trigonal / tetrahedral / linear.*

Fluorine in HF is surrounded by one atom, with which it shares one electron, and it has *0 / 1 / 6 / 8 / 4* electrons that it did not share, *ie 0 / 1 / 4 / 3* lone pairs.

Totally, that fluoride has *0 / 1 / 4 / 3* entities (atoms + lone pairs) to place around itself. Viewing only atoms, the structure of hydrogen fluoride is just two atoms bonded to each other, H-F.

However, the geometry of atoms *plus lone pairs* around the fluorine in hydrogen fluoride is approximately *linear / triangular / tetrahedral*.

Similarly, in:

water, *oxygen* is surrounded by *0 / 1 / 2 / 3 / 4* objects (atoms + lone pairs) so the geometry around *O* in this molecule is *linear / triangular / tetrahedral / trigonal bipyramidal*

hydrogen chloride, *chlorine* is surrounded by *0 / 1 / 2 / 3 / 4* atoms + lone pairs so the geometry around *Cl* is *linear / triangular / tetrahedral / trigonal bipyramidal*

ammonia, *nitrogen* is surrounded by *0 / 1 / 2 / 3 / 4* atoms + lone pairs so the geometry around *N* is *linear / triangular / tetrahedral / trigonal bipyramidal* arrangement

hydrogen sulfide, *sulfur* is surrounded by *0 / 1 / 2 / 3 / 4* objects (atoms + lone pairs) so the geometry around *S* in this molecule places it at the center of a *linear / triangular / tetrahedral / trigonal bipyramidal* arrangement; and,

borane, *boron* is surrounded by *0 / 1 / 2 / 3 / 4* objects (atoms + lone pairs) so the geometry around *B* in this molecule places it at the center of a *linear / triangular / tetrahedral / trigonal bipyramidal* arrangement.

The electronic environment around:

C in methane is *linear / trigonal / tetrahedral* with a dihedral angle of *109° / 120° / 180° / 270°*

O in water is *linear / trigonal / tetrahedral* with a dihedral angle of *109° / 120° / 180° / 270°*

Br in hydrogen bromide is *linear / trigonal / tetrahedral* with a dihedral angle of *109° / 120° / 180° / 270°*

N in ammonia is *linear / trigonal / tetrahedral* with a dihedral angle of *109° / 120° / 180° / 270°*

S in H_2S is *linear / trigonal / tetrahedral* with a dihedral angle of *109° / 120° / 180° / 270°*

B in BH_3 is *linear / trigonal / tetrahedral* with a dihedral angle of *109° / 120° / 180° / 270°*

If an atom is connected to **n** objects (bonded atoms or lone pairs) it usually needs **n** hybrid orbitals, and must form them from **n** atomic orbitals (AOs). The s orbital is always the first atomic orbital used to hybridize the outer shell of electrons.

combination of a s and a p orbital gives a *sp / sp² / sp³* hybrid consisting of *2 / 3 / 4 / 5* MOs in a *linear / trigonal / tetrahedral* arrangement with a dihedral angle of *109° / 120° / 180° / 270°*

one s and two p orbitals can combine to give *2 / 3 / 4 / 5 sp / sp² / sp³* MOs, and these arrange in a *linear / trigonal / tetrahedral* arrangement with a dihedral angle of *109° / 120° / 180° / 270°*

one s and three p orbitals can combine to give *2 / 3 / 4 / 5 sp / sp² / sp³* MOs, and these arrange in a *linear / trigonal / tetrahedral* arrangement with a dihedral angle of *109° / 120° / 180° / 270°*

Draw the shapes of the following hybrid orbitals to depict their 3D geometries.

sp	*sp²*	*sp³*

Draw the structures of the following molecules in ways that depict their 3D geometries; show atoms, bonds, lone pairs, but not orbitals.

eg

H⸝⸝⸝ ⟋H
  ⟍O⟋
 ⟍ ⟍

water	*hydrogen fluoride*	*methane*

HBr	_BH_$_3$	_hydrogen sulfide_

_PH_$_3$	_SiH_$_4$	_CCl_$_4$

D Multiple Bonds

In methane, the _C_-atom has _0 / 7 / 8 / 9_ electrons in its second shell. In the methyl radical, $CH_3\bullet$, the _C_-atom shares _0 / 7 / 8 / 9_ electrons in its second shell; this _is /is not_ a particularly favorable arrangement, explaining why methyl radicals _are / are not_ relatively reactive.

Methyl radicals could be _sp / sp^2 / sp^3_ hybridized, with a single electron in one of the lobes, but an alternative is a flat, triangular CH_3 arrangement, with an unpaired electron in the _p_-orbital that was _not_ used to form the _sp^2_-hybrid. Draw both these possibilities by superimposing the orbitals on the following diagrams, filling in the hybrid orbitals and the unused _p_- if required, and circle the option to the hybridization state.

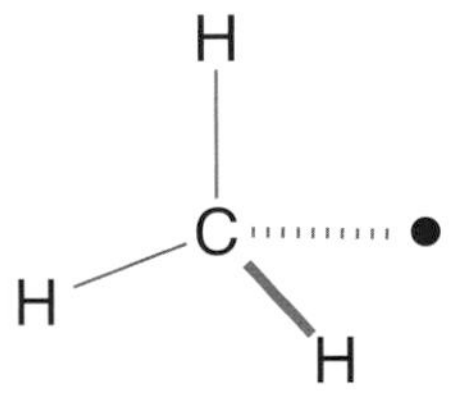

_sp / sp^2 / sp^3_ 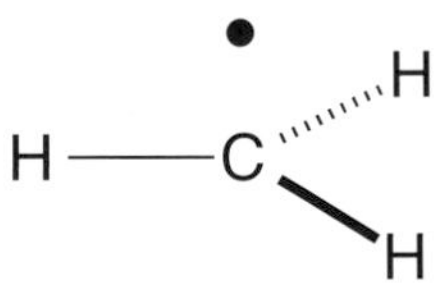   _sp / sp^2 / sp^3_

In fact, methyl radicals are not flat because there is nothing to compensate the extra electronic repulsion energy that would be involved if they were.

Represent ethene, H_2CCH_2, as σ-bonded *sp / sp² / sp³* hybridized *C*-atoms, each with an unpaired electron in an empty *p*-orbital; those *p*-orbitals parallel to maximize bonding interactions. Show this by superimposing the orbitals on the diagram below left, *ie* filling in the hybrid orbitals and the unused *p*-orbitals.

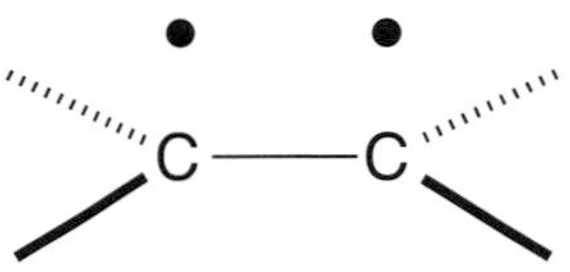

*ethene **before** mixing*
p-orbitals

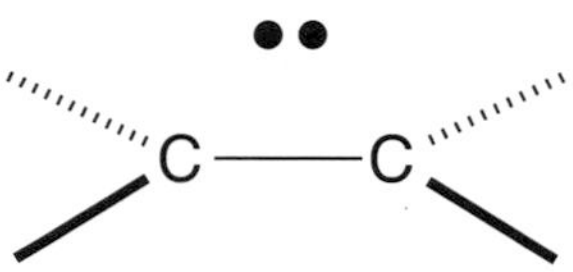

*ethene **after** mixing*
p-orbitals

Complete the diagram above on the right in the same way as on the left, but show the shape of the bonding probability surface formed when the two parallel *p*-orbitals mix, and which now contains the two electrons.

Bonds formed by combining *spⁿ*-hybrid orbitals (*n* = 1 – 3) are called *sigma, σ / pi, π / delta, δ*.

When two parallel *p*-orbitals mix then that is called a *sigma, σ / pi, π / delta, δ* bond.

Maximal overlap *is / is not* achieved between two *p*-orbitals when they are parallel.

Perpendicular *p*-orbitals *do / do not* interact.

The carbons in ethene *are* flat because their *sp²*-hybridization is stabilized by formation of a *σ / π / δ* bond.

When drawing organic structures, σ-bonds are represented by *0 / 1 / 2* line(s), and π-bonds are represented by *0 / 1 / 2* parallel line(s). Indicate the number of double bonds in the following structures.

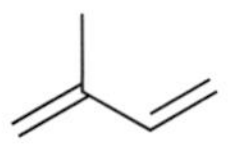

# ____	# ____	# ____	# ____	# ____	# ____
isoprene	*pyruvic acid*	*an imine*	*lactic acid*	*benzene*	*β-pinene*

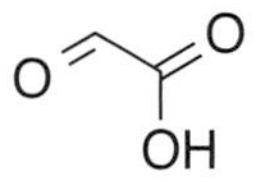

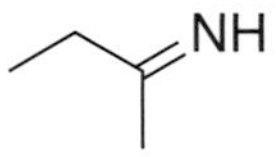

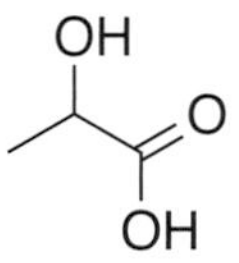

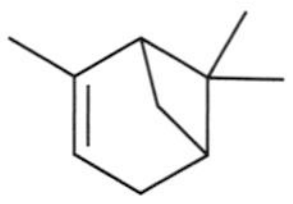

What dictates whether an electron will be used in a bond or in a lone pair? In bonding, atoms use combinations of atomic orbitals that may maximize overlap with peripheral atoms, while some other outer shell atomic orbitals may not be used usually because they *would / would not* contribute to the binding interaction.

Atoms in molecules *can / cannot* selectively hybridize some atomic orbitals and not others to gain extra stability by forming multiple bonds.

Carbene, CH_2, is a highly reactive species with *0 / 1 / 8 / 6* shared electrons in the *C*-second shell.

Carbenes can be sp^2-hybridized with one lobe of the hybrid containing *2e* from *C*, and with an unoccupied *p*-orbital; this is called the *singlet / triplet* state.

Alternatively, carbenes can be sp^2-hybridized with one electron in each of the hybrid lobes that does not point to a hydrogen; this is a *singlet / triplet* state.

Another possibility is a *sp*-hybridized carbon with an electron in the two remaining *p*-orbitals; here we call this an *unstable triplet* state.

Draw the three possibilities for hybridization in carbenes, by superimposing the hybrid and unused *p*-orbitals on the diagram below. Circle the correct identifying option in each case.

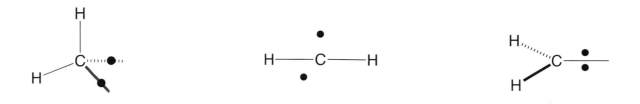

singlet / triplet / unstable triplet   *singlet / triplet / unstable triplet*   *singlet / triplet / unstable triplet*

Like two *unstable triplets* joined, ethyne, HCCH, has σ-bonded $sp / sp^2 / sp^3$ hybridized *C*-atoms. Before the *p*-orbitals are mixed, each with two unpaired electrons occupy an empty *p*-orbital. Show this by completing the diagram below on the left, filling in the hybrid orbitals and the unused *p*-orbitals.

*ethyne **before** mixing*
p-orbitals

*ethyne **after** mixing*
p-orbitals

Mixing the two parallel *p*-orbitals gives two σ / π / δ bonds surrounding the σ / π / δ bond that connects the two *C* atoms via head-on interaction of the *sp*-hybrid lobes; this type of interaction is called a *single* / *double* / *triple* bond.

Indicate the number of triple bonds for each of the following structures.

#____ *propyne*   #____ *1-butyne*   #____ *2-butyne*   #____ *butane*   #____ *acetonitrile*   #____ *1,3-butadiyne*

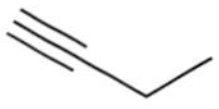

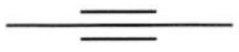

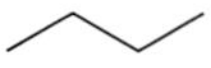

To approximate the structure of a molecule it *does* / *does not* matter if multiple or single bonds are used to link to any particular surrounding atoms; the prime consideration is the total number of atoms and lone pairs.

Indicate the hybridization state of the highlighted atoms in the following molecules; if they have two atoms or lone pairs around them they are *sp* / *sp^2* / *sp^3* hybridized, three *sp* / *sp^2* / *sp^3*, and four *sp* / *sp^2* / *sp^3*.

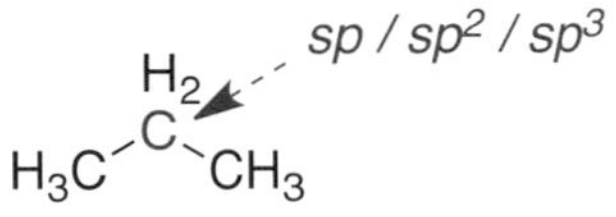

sp / *sp^2* / *sp^3*   *sp* / *sp^2* / *sp^3*

propane

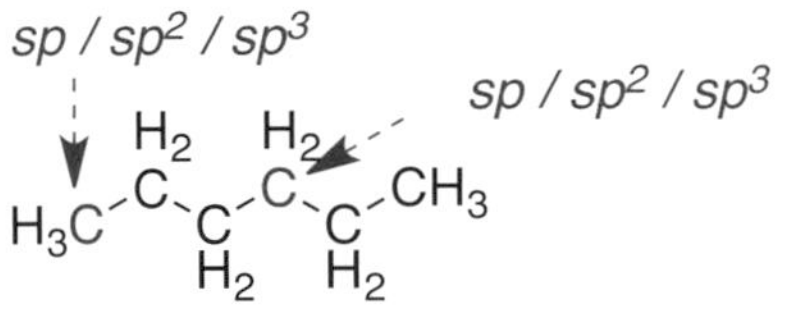

sp / *sp^2* / *sp^3*   *sp* / *sp^2* / *sp^3*

hexane

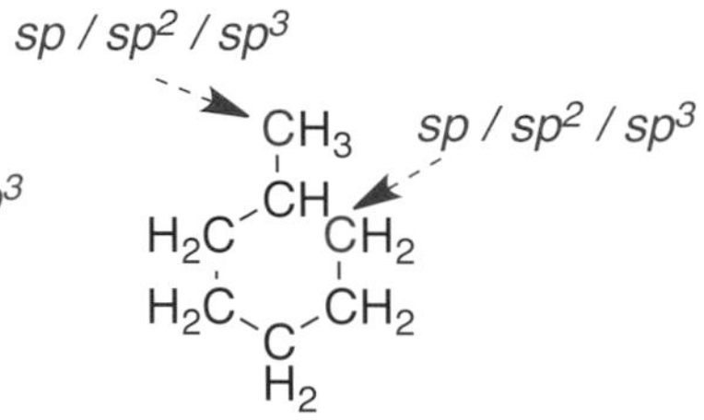

sp / *sp^2* / *sp^3*   *sp* / *sp^2* / *sp^3*

methylcyclohexane

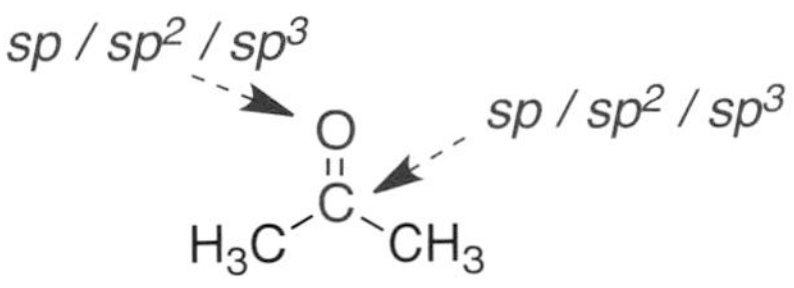

sp / *sp^2* / *sp^3*   *sp* / *sp^2* / *sp^3*

acetone

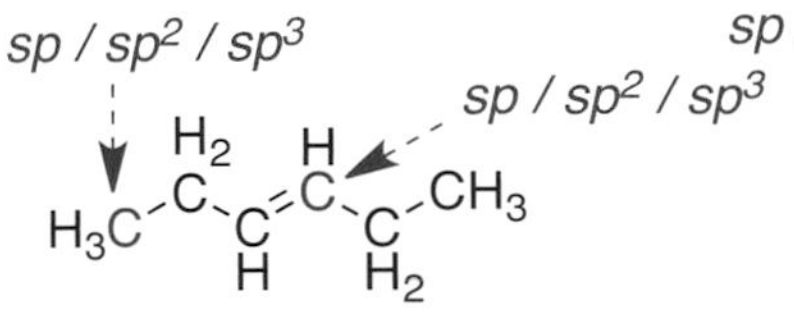

sp / *sp^2* / *sp^3*   *sp* / *sp^2* / *sp^3*

1-pentene

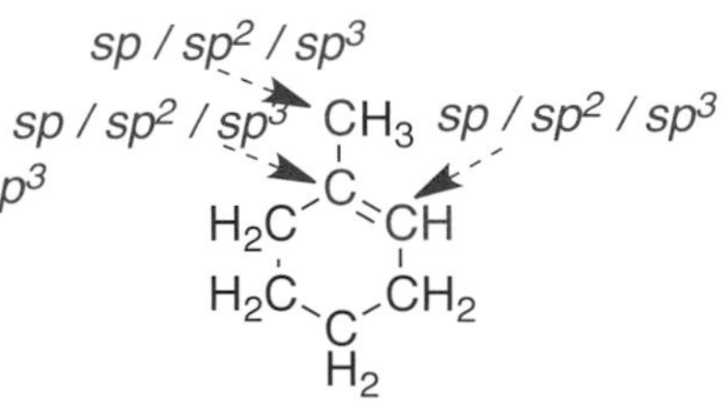

sp / *sp^2* / *sp^3*   *sp* / *sp^2* / *sp^3*   *sp* / *sp^2* / *sp^3*

1-methylcyclohexene

Indicate the hybridization states of the red atoms in the molecules below.

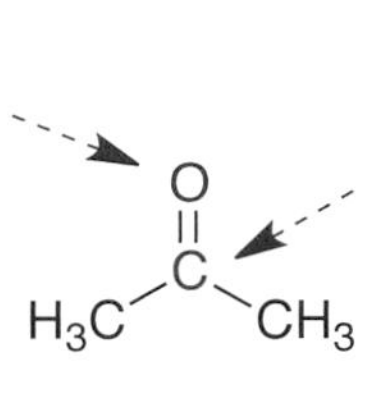

acetic acid

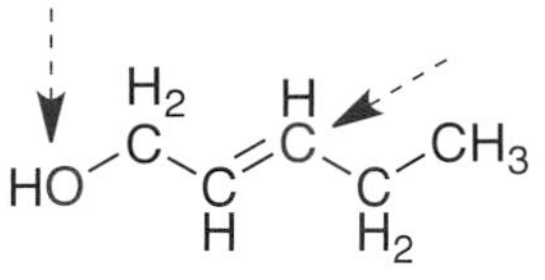

cis-1-hydroxy-2-butene

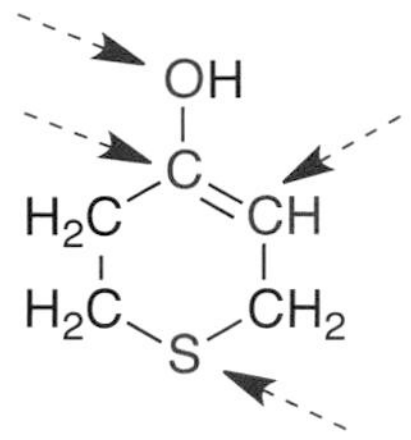

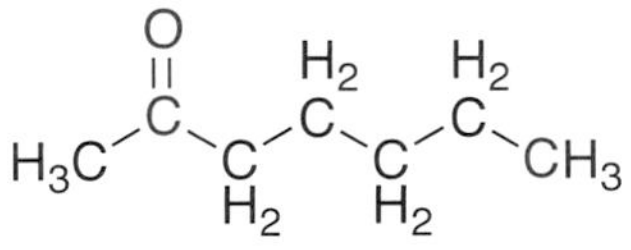

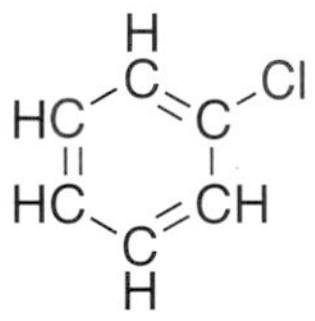

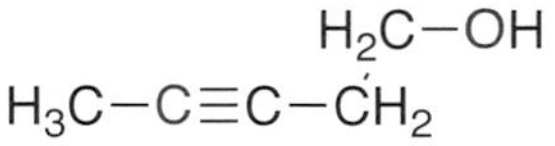

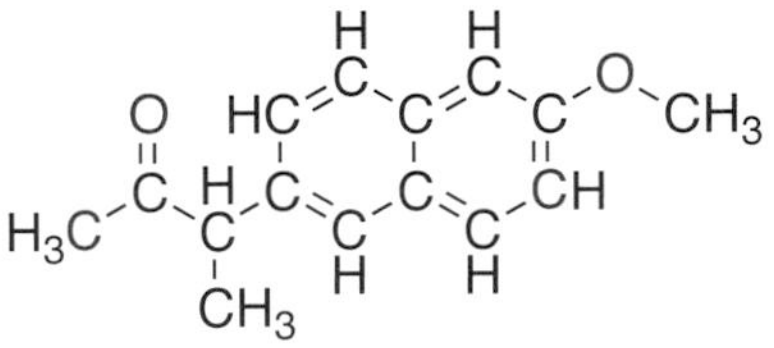

naproxen

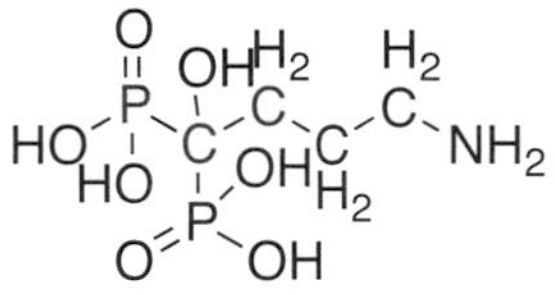

alendronate

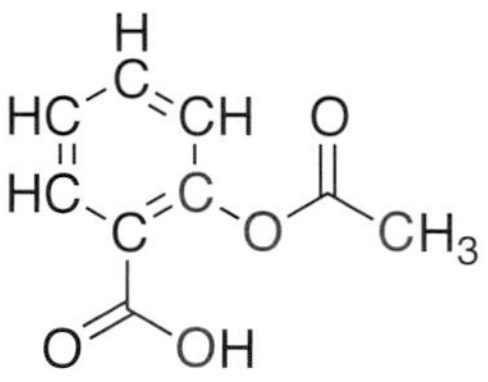

aspirin

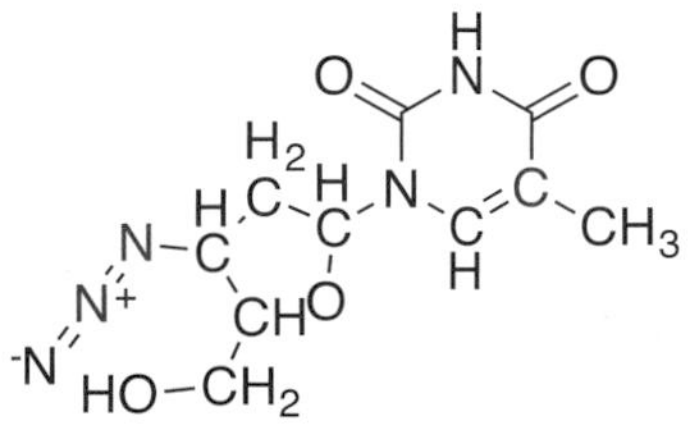

zidovudine (AZT)

2   Saturated Acyclic Hydrocarbons

from chapter(s) _____ in the recommended text

A   Introduction

Focus

Acyclic (non cyclic) hydrocarbons are quite unreactive; they do not undergo many reactions. Most molecules have a hydrocarbon skeleton, a core, that does not react unless adjoined to functional groups (more about them later), but it forms the basis for their preferred molecular shapes.

The focus here is not on the reactivity, names, or physical properties of acyclic hydrocarbons because these are facts that can be instantly understood from any textbook. Instead, this section is about preferred *molecular shapes* or *conformations* of acyclic hydrocarbons.

Reasons To Care

Some fundamental textbooks depict acyclic hydrocarbons in "road-kill" shapes, like the picture here of flattened hexane; this type of representation is simplistic and unrealistic. All the carbons in hexane, for instance, are sp^3 hybridized with tetrahedral geometries of about 109° between bonds originating from carbon.

hexane flattened

Better representations of hexane are as a zigzag conformer. These are more real since all the carbons have tetrahedral geometries. The question is *which* zigzag conformer, because there are lots. Just a few hexane conformers are shown to the left (solid bonds project out of the paper toward the reader, dashed bonds behind).

In fact, liquid acyclic hydrocarbons exist as many conformers, but the one most frequently encountered (*ie* most populated) is the linear zigzag form on the bottom left. The problems in this section are designed to reveal why that is so.

some hexane zig-zag conformers

A consequence of understanding the special significance of linear zigzag conformations of acyclic hydrocarbons is that *the carbon skeleton of any organic molecule*, can be simplified. Carbon chains can be drawn with zigzagging lines, the hydrogens do not need to be shown (the number and orientations is known from hybridization states), and the letter *C* is *not* used.

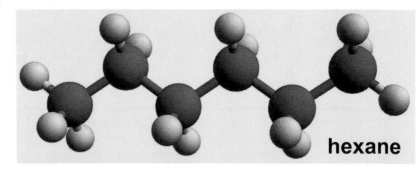
hexane

hexane

Concepts Involved

hybridization • interplay of shapes around atoms and the preferred shapes of molecules • drawing organic molecules in realistic conformations with the least clutter

Objective

To understand concise ways to draw organic structures that realistically represent their preferred molecular shapes.

B Conformations Of Acyclic Hydrocarbons

Acyclic hydrocarbons have near ideal sp^3 hybridization angles, but this only partially defines their preferred shapes. Favorable conformations of acyclic hydrocarbons are those that reduce destabilizing interactions between atoms and between bonds.

Ethane

Complete the following "Newman projections" for ethane by placing in the hydrogen atoms, and mark them *staggered* and *eclipsed*. Mark their relative energies (using the information from the question above).

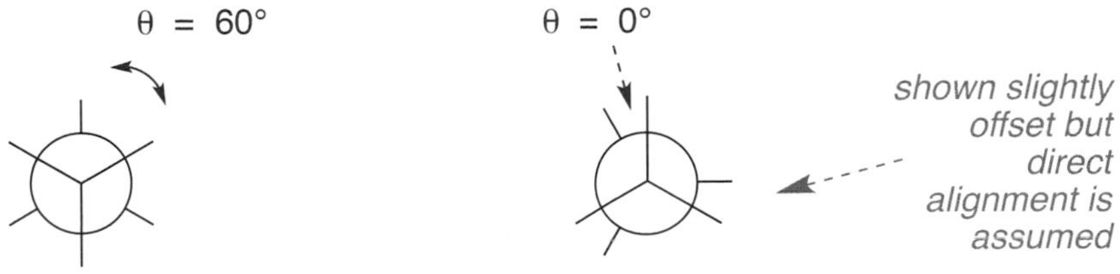

$\theta = 60°$

$\theta = 0°$

shown slightly offset but direct alignment is assumed

staggered / eclipsed

staggered / eclipsed

The diagrams below are different ways of representing *two* conformations of ethane. For each diagram below, show if the conformer is *staggered* or *eclipsed*.

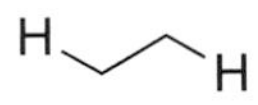

staggered / eclipsed

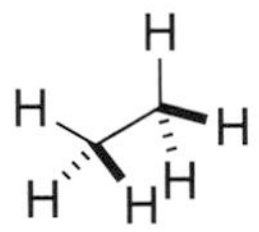

staggered / eclipsed

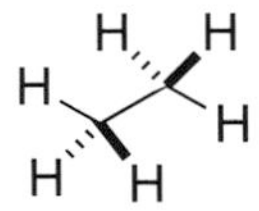

staggered / eclipsed

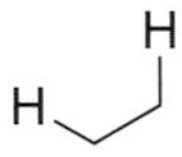

staggered / eclipsed

The *staggered / eclipsed* ethane conformer is more stable than the other by 12 kJ•mol^{-1}; complete the following diagram by rotating the *C*-atom in the front of the projection clockwise, and show how the energy fluctuates by putting crosses at 60° intervals. Finally, join the crosses with a sinusoidal line.

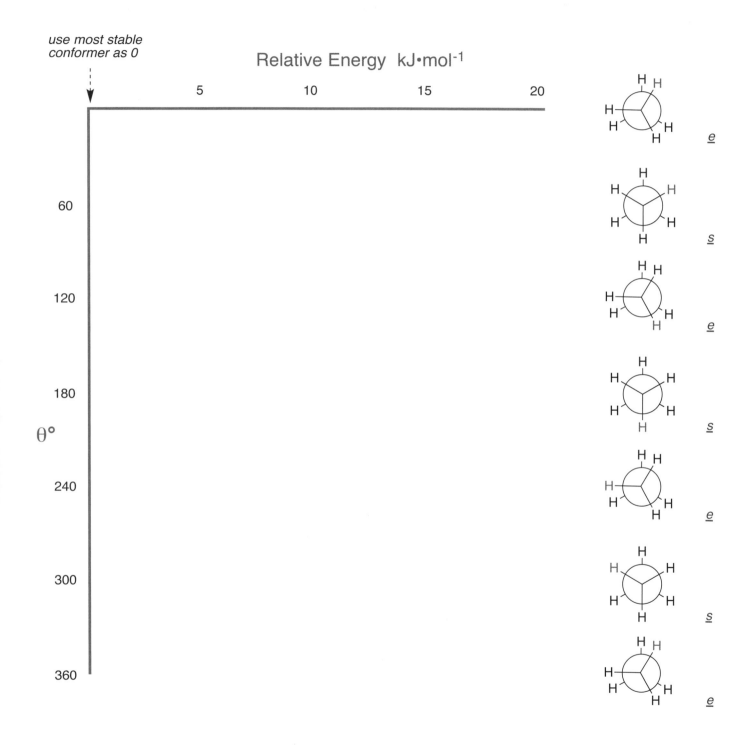

When bonds are eclipsed, repulsion between the electrons in those bonds is maximum; this is called *torsional / angle* strain.

Complete the following molecular orbital diagrams to indicate *stabilizing / destabilizing* interactions between filled orbitals in eclipsed conformations, and *stabilizing / destabilizing* interactions between empty and filled orbitals in staggered conformations. Note that if both the highest occupied molecular orbital (HOMO) and lowest unoccupied molecular orbital are filled, this is slightly *destabilizing / stabilizing*.

One filled s-orbital contributes *0 / 2 / 4 e* to a molecular orbital diagram like this, and an empty one donates *0 / 2 / 4 e*.

attractive / repulsive

σ

σ

torsional / angle strain

attractive / repulsive

σ^*

σ

add electrons to the diagrams below and indicate bond orders:

σ

σ

bond order = ____

σ

σ^*

bond order = ____

Propane

Complete the following Newman projections for propane, and mark them *staggered* and *eclipsed*.

$\theta = 60°$

$\theta = 0°$

shown slightly offset but direct alignment is assumed

staggered / eclipsed

staggered / eclipsed

One conformer in the above is more stable than the other by 14 kJ•mol^{-1}; complete the following diagram and mark the staggered states *s* and the eclipsed states *e*.

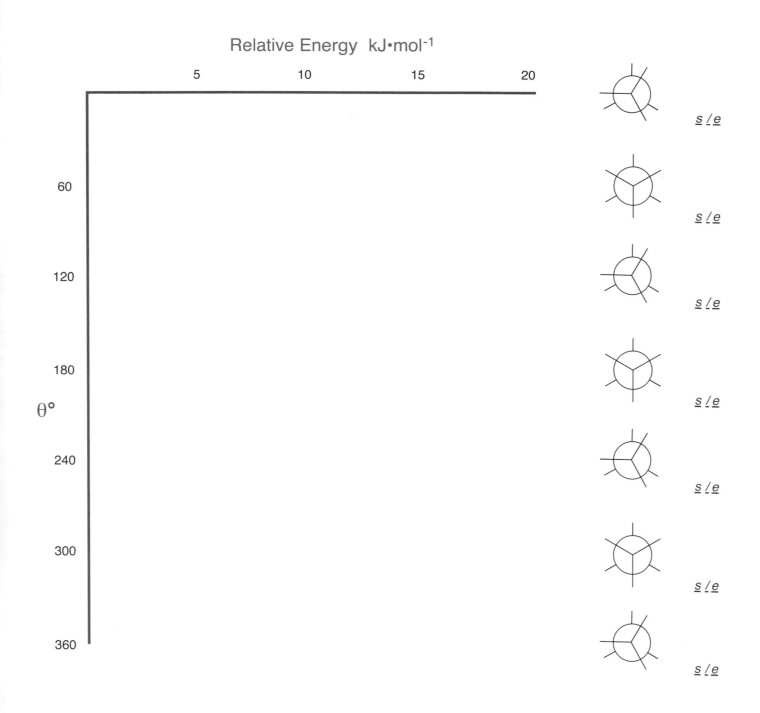

Circle the drawing below that best illustrates the most stable conformation of propane (*ie* with least eclipsing *C-H* and *C-C* bonds).

Butane

Classify the butane conformers below as *very high*, *high*, *low*, or *very low* energy states.

Circle the drawing below that best illustrates a stable conformation of butane.

Complete the following projections for butane, and write under them *fully eclipsed*, *partially eclipsed*, *gauche*, or *antiperiplanar* as appropriate; here these conformations are abbreviated to *fe*, *pe*, *g* and *a*.

_____   _____   _____   _____

Conformers in the above diagram have relative energies of about 20, 15, 4, and 0 kJ•mol⁻¹, respectively; complete the following diagram by rotating the front carbon clockwise, and mark them *fe*, *pe*, *g* or *a*.

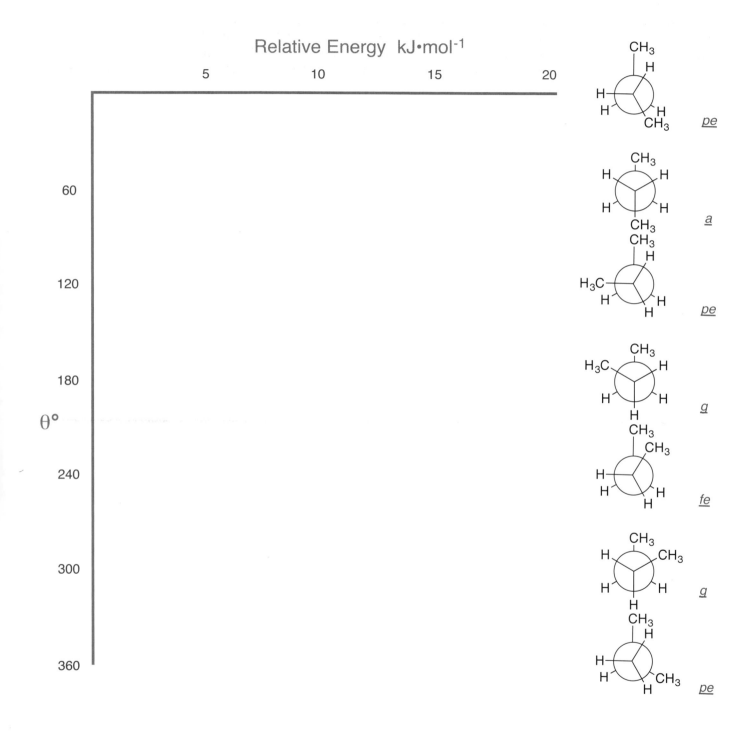

Art In Organic Chemistry

Draw organic compounds as simply as possible, in consistent and revealing orientations, but emphasize the important atoms. Show electron flow and movement of atoms, accurately and deliberately. Practitioners who do this can communicate in the language of organic chemistry, and, at the highest level, it becomes a form of art. Step 1 is to draw organic frameworks well.

In minimalist representations of organic molecules, carbon atoms are represented as apices, and hydrogen atoms on carbon are not shown at all unless there is some purpose. Neutral carbons in organic molecules have four bonds, any time a bond is not shown then it is understood hydrogen is attached. Consequently, organic chemists know how many hydrogen atoms are present on a carbon *without explicitly drawing them*. For instance, if there is one bond to an apex that {terminal point} represents CH_3 / CH_2 / CH, two bonds to an apex means it is a CH_3 / CH_2 / CH, and three bonds to a branch point represent CH_3 / CH_2 / CH. If there are four bonds to a central point, this means there are *1 / 2 / 3 / 4 / 0* hydrogen atoms on that carbon.

Represent the following molecules without using the symbols *C* or *H*. Draw the longest hydrocarbon chain in a horizontal "zig-zag" shape to keep the structures organized. It does not matter if the chains zigzag up then down or down then up.

propane	*pentane*	*nonane*

ethane	*butane*	*decane*

hexane   *heptane*   *octane*

$$H_3C-\underset{H_2}{C}-\underset{H_2}{C}-\underset{H_2}{C}-\underset{H_2}{C}-CH_3$$

$$H_3C-\underset{H_2}{C}-\underset{H_2}{C}-\underset{H_2}{C}-\underset{H_2}{C}-CH_3$$

$$H_3C-\underset{H_2}{C}-\underset{H_2}{C}-\underset{H_2}{C}-\underset{H_2}{C}-CH_3$$

When drawing *zig*-zag lines to represent non-cyclic (*acyclic*) hydrocarbons it is important to use angles of about 109° because these reflect stable orientations in which non-bonded interactions are minimized. More about this will be covered later, but the root of the explanation is that ideal bond (*H-C-H*) angles for sp³ hybridized carbons are *109° / 120° / 180°*.

Each of the carbon atoms in the above structures has *2 / 3 / 4* bonds to other atoms.

In undergraduate organic chemistry, carbon atoms in organic structures *usually / always* have this number of bonds *unless* they bear positive or negative charges, or support an unpaired electron (radical).

Organic *C*-atoms in common organic molecules *never / sometimes / always* have five or more atoms attached to them.

The hybridization state of the carbons in the above molecules is *sp / sp² / sp³ because* they have *2 / 3 / 4* atoms attached.

Carbon atoms that are sp³ hybridized have groups surrounding them at the corners of a *linear / trigonal / tetrahedral* shape. Dihedral angles in this arrangement are ideally about *109° / 120° / 180°* and good diagrams tend to convey those preferred angles.

Circle the representation of 2-methylpentane that most accurately depicts its shape.

Draw the following compounds as linear *zigzag* representations that most accurately reflect the true geometry around the carbon atoms (you might call them 3D formulae).

2,2-dimethylpentane   *2,2-dimethylpropane*   *2,2-dimethylbutane*

$$H_3C-\underset{\underset{CH_3}{|}}{\overset{\overset{CH_3}{|}}{C}}-CH_3$$

$$CH_3CH_2C(CH_3)_2CH_3$$

Draw the following alkanes without using the letters *C* or *H*.

37

_____

octane

_____

heptane

_____

2-methylhexane

_____

methylpropane

_____

2-methylbutane

_____

2,7-dimethylnonane

_____

3-methylpentane

_____

2-chlorohexane

_____

3-fluoroheptane

_____

2,3-dimethylpentane

_____

3-bromohexane

_____

1-iododecanane

_____

$CH_3CH_2CH_2CH_2CH_3$

_____

$CH_3CH_2CHClCH_2CH_3$

_____

$BrCH_2CH(CH_3)CHClCH_2CH_3$

For emphasis, any hydrogen atom can be shown, but good diagrams express the geometry about the carbon realistically. Circle the best representation of 3-methylpentane from those shown below.

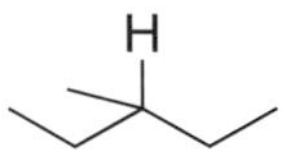

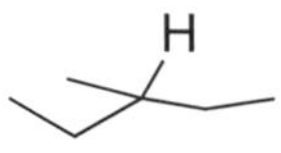

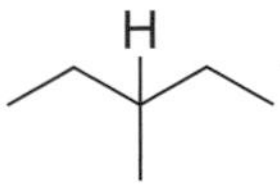

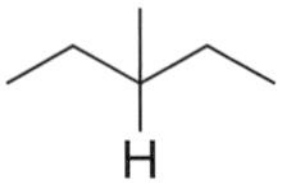

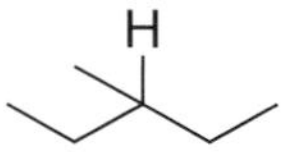

Draw the following molecules in conventional representations, with realistic bond orientations and the longest hydrocarbon chains horizontal.

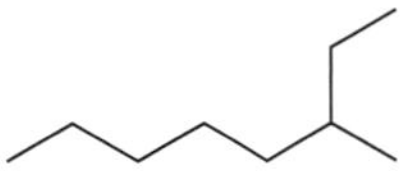

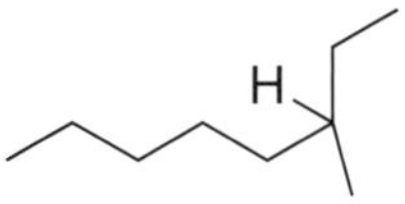

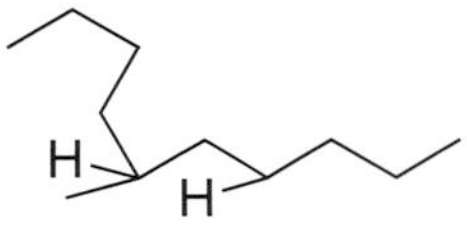

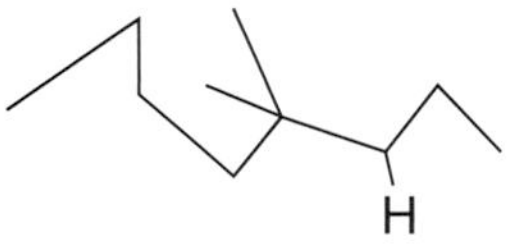

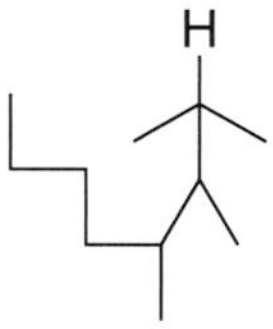

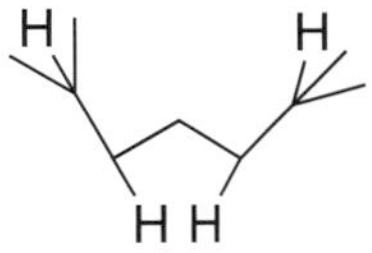

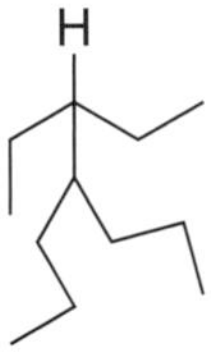

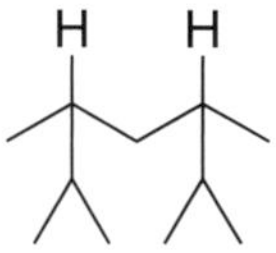

Three Dimensional Diagrams Of Organic Molecules

Sometimes additional conventions are used when it is necessary to show a molecule in three dimensions. Generally, dashed lines are used to represent projection behind the paper, and solid ones show orientation towards the reader. Whoever drew the molecules below wanted to emphasize particular hydrogen orientations, but failed to do this realistically, except in one case. Circle the diagram that most accurately reflects the true geometry around C^2.

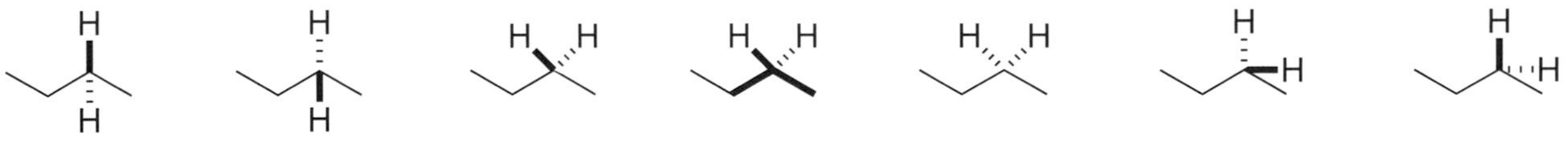

An alternative way to represent 3D on paper is to use wedge-shaped bonds *with the thin end of the wedge at the carbon in the plane*. All of the following diagrams of 3-methylhexane are fine, except one has an improperly drawn wedge bond; circle that one.

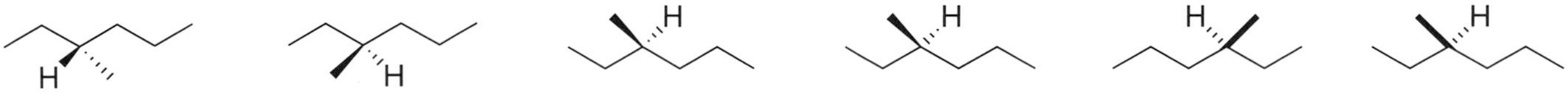

Questions in this book use solid and dashed bonds that are not and are not tapered: either convention is correct. This lack of consistency reflects what is in the chemistry literature.

Re-draw the following molecules, but show .....

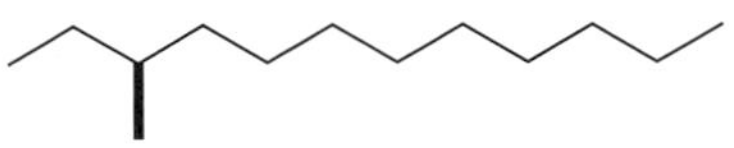

.... the C³ hydrogen 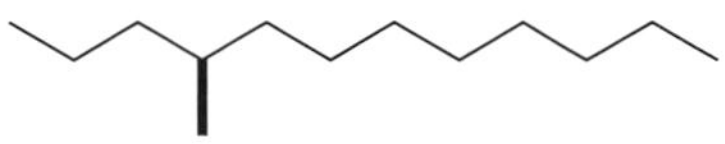   _.... both hydrogens on C³_   _.... the H on unique C_

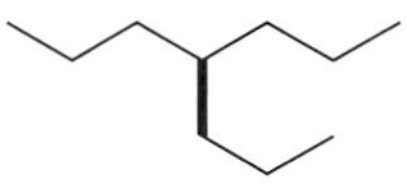

Alkyl Fragments

A carbon connected to three hydrogens is called a *methyl / methylene / methine*. *Methylene* fragments (of molecules) are those that have $CH_3 / CH_2 / CH / C$ connected to anything. *Methine* is the name given to $CH_3 / CH_2 / CH / C$ fragments. CH_3 connected to anything is called a *methyl / methylene / methine*. A quaternary C has $4 / 3 / 2 / 1 / 0$ hydrogen atoms attached. Label every carbon in the following molecules methyl, methylene, methine, or quaternary carbon.

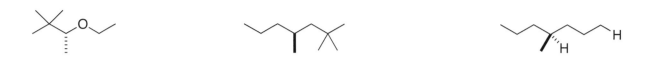

If one hydrogen from methane is removed and replaced with something else, *ie added / substituted*, then the product contains a methyl group. This can be represented as CH_3, Me, CH_3CH_2 (circle all correct).

If a hydrogen atom of ethane is substituted with something else, then the product contains an ethyl group. This can be represented as CH_3, Me, CH_3CH_2, Et (circle all correct).

An ethyl group *can / cannot* be isolated and put in a bottle; it *is / is not* a discrete compound, but it *is / is not* a molecular fragment.

A jagged line drawn perpendicularly across a bond means the fragment that *is / is not* attached to something else.

Propane contains *1, 2, 3, 4, 5* types of hydrogen atoms insofar as replacing them gives *the same / different* outcomes. Replacement of a hydrogen at the end of the chain gives a *normal / abnormal / iso-* propyl group that can be represented as CH_3, ^iPr, $(CH_3)_2CH$, Et, $MeCH_2CH_2$, $EtCH_2$, ^nPr (circle all correct). Conversely, removal of a proton at C^2 gives a(n) *normal / abnormal / iso-* propyl group that can be represented as CH_3, ^iPr, $(CH_3)_2CH$, Et, $MeCH_2CH_2$, $EtCH_2$, ^nPr (circle all correct). Complete the following diagram without using the letters C and H, but using jagged lines in the same way as above.

ethane   ethyl

propane	*n-propyl*	*butane*	*n-butyl*

Butane contains *1, 2, 3, 4, 5* types of hydrogen atoms that can be replaced to give different fragments.

Replacement of a hydrogen at the end of a butyl chain gives a *normal / abnormal / iso- / sec-* butyl group that can be represented as $CH_3CH_2CHCH_3$, $^iPrCH_2$, Me_3C, $(CH_3)_2CH$, CH_2, $MeCH_2CH_2CH_2$, $EtCH_2$, $^nPrCH_2$, $CH_3CH_2CH_2CH_2$ (circle all correct).

Substitution of a hydrogen at C^2 of butane gives a(n) *n- / sec- / iso- / tert-* butyl group that can be represented as $CH_3CH_2CHCH_3$, $^iPrCH_2$, Me_3C, $(CH_3)_2CH$, CH_2, $MeCH_2CH_2CH_2$, $EtCH_2$, $^nPrCH_2$, $CH_3CH_2CH_2CH_2$ (circle all correct).

2-Methylpropane is an *isomer / aunty* of butane: it has _____ chemically inequivalent hydrogen atoms. Replacement of a methyl hydrogen in 2-methylpropane gives an isomer of a ^nBu group, *ie* a ^iBu / ^tBu / Et group.

Replacement of the methine hydrogen 2-methylpropane creates a fragment with a *tertiary* carbon attached to something, *ie* ^nBu / ^iBu / ^tBu.

Complete the following diagrams of fragments, without using the letters *C* and *H* but with jagged lines to show where they are attached to other things.

n-butyl	*tert-butyl*	*sec-butyl*	*iso-butyl*

Use abbreviations (*eg* Me, Et, ^{n}Pr, ^{i}Pr, ^{n}Bu, ^{s}Bu, ^{i}Bu, ^{t}Bu) to represent the following alkyl halides (compounds with an alkyl fragment attached to a halogen).

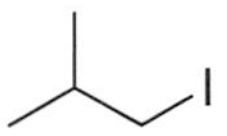

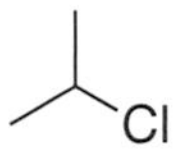

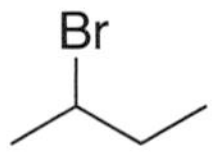

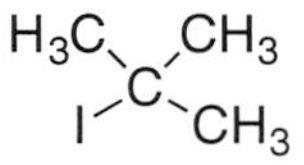

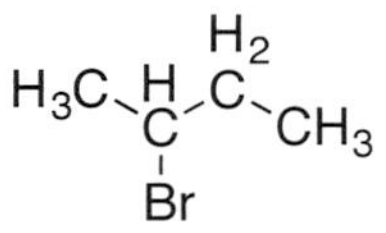

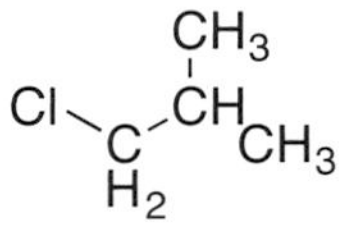

Alcohols are organic compounds that contain hydroxyl (*OH*) groups attached to carbon atoms that are not bonded to any other heteroatom. Draw expanded forms of the following alcohols as zigzag representations, with the longest carbon chain horizontal, and without using *C* and *H* (except in *OH*).

^{t}BuOH	^{n}BuOH	^{i}PrOH	^{s}BuOH	EtOH

Ethers are comprised of oxygen atoms attached to two carbon atoms that are not bonded to any other heteroatom. Draw expanded forms of the following ethers with their longest carbon chains horizontal, and without using C and H. Oxygen atoms in ethers are sp^3 hybridized, so the chain zigzags around that atom as if it was a CH_2, at about 109°.

^{t}BuOMe	EtOEt	^{i}PrO^{i}Pr	^{t}BuO^{i}Pr	MeOMe
	an anesthetic			

Amines have NH_2, NH, or N attached to carbon atoms that are not bonded to any other heteroatom. Draw expanded forms of the following amines as zigzag representations, with the longest carbon chain horizontal, and without using C and H except on N.

^{t}BuNHMe	Et$_3$N	^{i}PrNH$_2$	^{t}BuNMeEt	MeNH$_2$

Thioethers are just like ethers except they feature a sp^3-hybridized S instead of a sp^3-O. Draw expanded forms of the following thioethers as zigzag representations, with the longest carbon chain horizontal, and without using C and H.

^{s}BuSMe	EtS^{t}Bu	^{i}PrSEt	^{i}BuSMe	Me$_2$S

Draw expanded forms of the following compounds as zigzag representations, with the longest carbon chain horizontal, and without using *C* and *H*, *and* label each one alcohol, amine, ether, or thioether.

————	————	————	————
HO^nPr	MeS^nBu	^iPrNHEt	$^iBuNMe_2$
- - - - - - - - - - -	- - - - - - - - - - -	- - - - - - - - - - -	- - - - - - - - - - -

name functional groups as alcohol, amine, ether, or thioether on the dashed lines

C Conclusion

Draw the following linear hydrocarbons in their most stable conformations without using the symbols *H*, *C*, or abbreviations like *Me*. These *are / are not* zigzag conformations.

————	————	————	————
pentane	*hexane*	*heptane*	*decane*

The most stable conformation of linear hydrocarbons *can / cannot* be represented as lines that zigzag about a horizontal axis.

3   Fragments And Functional Groups

from chapter(s) _____ in the recommended text

A   Introduction

Focus

Not all molecular fragments are functional groups, but all functional groups are molecular fragments. Functional groups have characteristic reactivities that are general for many organic molecules. Chemistry textbooks tend to be arranged according to functional groups (chapters on alkanes, alkenes, alkynes, *etc*) because functional groups *are* important. Please determine if your textbook is arranged like this. This section is about drawing common molecular fragments including functional groups.

Reasons To Care

In nomenclature, being able to draw a compound from its name is usually enough. *It is much more important to be able to name functional groups and recognize other molecular fragments.* If you think this is easy, consider this: all the structures below represent benzyl ethanoate.

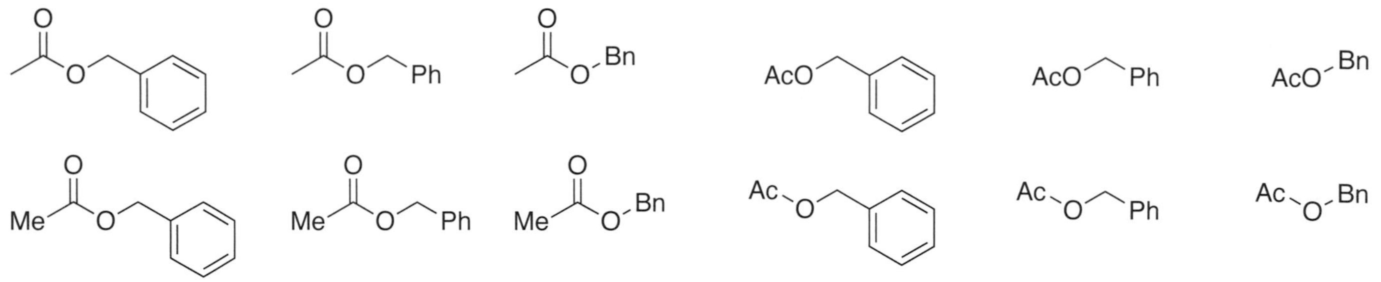

CH_3COOCH_2Ph $CH_3CO_2CH_2Ph$ $CH_3C(O)OCH_2Ph$ CH_3COOBn CH_3CO_2Bn $CH_3C(O)OBn$

$MeCOOCH_2Ph$ $MeCO_2CH_2Ph$ $MeC(O)OCH_2Ph$ $MeCOOBn$ $MeCO_2Bn$ $MeC(O)OBn$

$CH_3COOCH_2C_6H_5$ $CH_3CO_2CH_2C_6H_5$ $CH_3C(O)OCH_2C_6H_5$ $CH_3COOCH_2C_6H_5$ $CH_3CO_2CH_2C_6H_5$

$CH_3C(O)OCH_2C_6H_5$ $AcOCH_2Ph$ $AcOBn$ *etc* ......

Being unable to name compounds accurately is often not that restrictive, but correctly interpreting molecular drawings, *eg* as an ester with the intended substituents, is usually vital. The problem is that there are a few ways to draw each functional group, and several widely used abbreviations for fragments that simply must be learned; chemists frequently draw the same molecule in different ways, and different chemists tend to favor different abbreviations; this is challenging for students.

Concepts Involved

interpreting drawings of organic molecules, especially ones drawn in cryptic ways, via consideration of element valencies to predict atomic connectivities • collection of atoms into functional groups • common abbreviations for molecular fragments

Objective

Question the subject until *he / she* cannot avoid recognizing most common functional groups and fragments, and understand the ways molecules might be drawn.

B Fragments

Name the following groups: phenyl, *n*-propyl, *i*-propyl, benzyl, acyl, methoxy, allyl, vinyl, amide or carboxamide, cyano or nitrile, ester or carboxyalkyl, hydroxyl, amine, carbonyl chloride or acid chloride, carboxyl *etc.* The suffix "group" means this is a *molecular fragment / complete compound* connected to something else and *can / cannot* be isolated.

Throughout, a jagged line means a bond where the group on the other side is unspecified. However, jagged lines are not always shown in organic chemistry.

_____   _____   _____   _____
name of fragment

_____   _____   _____   _____

_____   _____   _____   _____

_____   _____   _____   _____

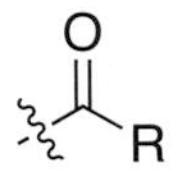

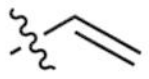

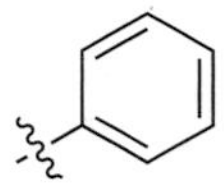

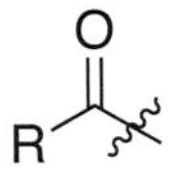

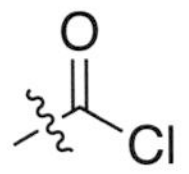

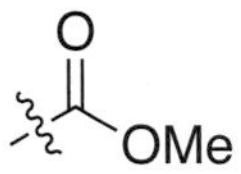

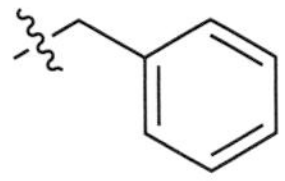

R

COMe

R

Cl

OMe

-CO$_2$Et

Ac

Bn

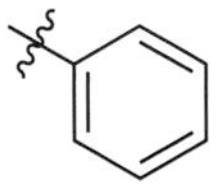

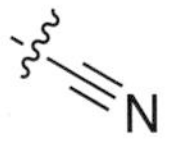

-CO$_2$Et

Ac

Bn

N

CH$_2$C$_6$H$_6$

Ph

-COMe

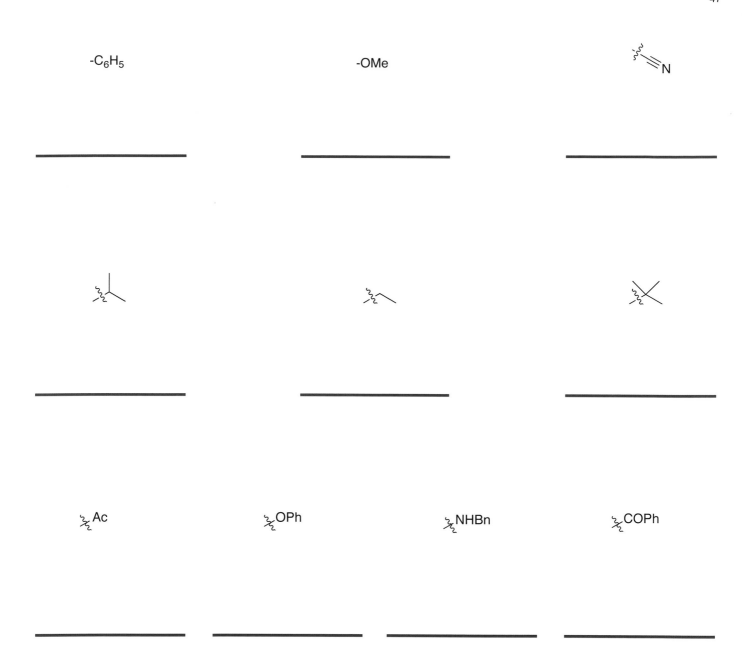

-C₆H₅

-OMe

_____   _____   _____

_____   _____   _____

Ac

OPh

NHBn

COPh

_____   _____   _____

Carbon atoms that are adjacent to functional groups are often referred to as α-, β-, γ- *etc.*, and this also applies to protons attached to those carbons. Label appropriate carbons in the following molecules as α-, β-, γ- , δ.

In Greek, . ω means *first / last*.

C Expanded Forms Of Functional Groups

Identify the functional group in these molecules from the following possibilities: alkene, alkyne, arene, alcohol, ether, monophosphate, diphosphate, amine, amide, lactam, imine, nitrile, thiol, sulfide, disulfide, sulfoxide, aldehyde, ketone, carboxylic acid, ester, thioester, acid chloride, carboxylic acid anhydride. Some of these functional groups may appear twice.

49

D Abbreviated Forms Of Functional Groups

Redraw the following molecules in completely expanded form using zigzag representations, *and* name the functional group that each one contains.

EtCOEt

name of functional group

EtCO(SMe)

name of functional group

$EtCO_2Me$

name of functional group

EtCOH

name of functional group

$MeCO_2COMe$

name of functional group

$EtOP(O)(OH)OP(O)(OH)_2$

name of functional group

$NCCH_2CH_2CN$

name of functional group

$(CH_3)_2CHCOCl$

name of functional group

$HCONMe_2$

name of functional group

MeCOOCOMe

name of functional group

$CH_3CH_2CO_2H$

name of functional group

$(CH_3)_2CHCH(CH_2CH_3)_2$

name of functional group

$C_6H_5CH_2CH_3$

name of functional group

$CH_3CH_2OCH_2CH_3$

name of functional group

$CH_3S_2CH_2C(CH_3)_3$

name of functional group

$CH_3CH_2CNHCH_3$

name of functional group

Me$_2$SO

HCO$_2$Et

CH$_3$CH$_2$C(CH$_3$)$_2$CN

CH$_3$CH$_2$C(CN)$_2$CH$_3$

name of functional group

name of functional group

name of functional group

name of functional group

^{i}PrNHMe

^{t}BuCONHEt

(CH$_3$)$_2$CHCN

CH$_3$CH$_2$COH

name of functional group

name of functional group

name of functional group

name of functional group

EtNH$_2$

EtCONH$_2$

EtCOOMe

CH$_3$CH$_2$COH

name of functional group

name of functional group

name of functional group

name of functional group

C$_6$H$_5$OH

^{s}BuOCOOMe

^{n}BuOCONHEt

CH$_3$HNCONHCH$_2$CH$_3$

name of functional group
phenol

name of functional group
carbonate

name of functional group
carbamate

name of functional group
urea

Redraw the following compounds showing the missing functional group in expanded form (check your answers against the name using Wiki). Recall, solid lines indicate a bond coming towards the reader, dashed lines indicate one going away.

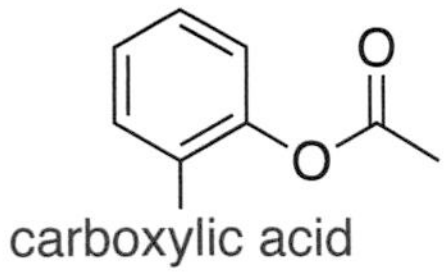

carboxylic acid

carboxylic acid

alcohol

alcohol

_____   _____   _____   _____

aspirin 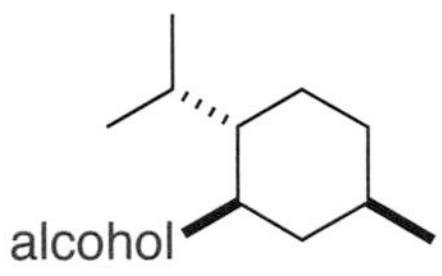   *menthol* 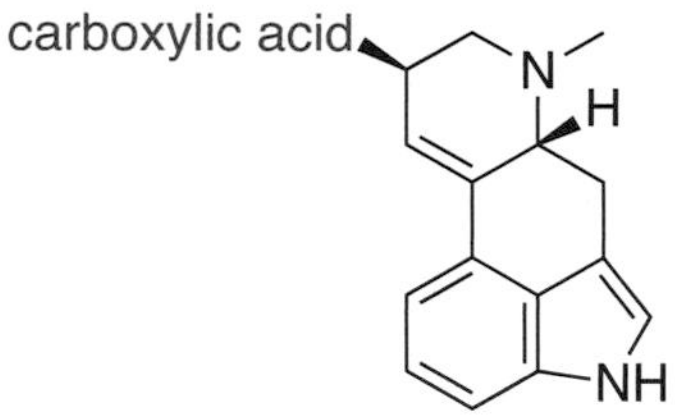   *lysergic acid (LSD)* 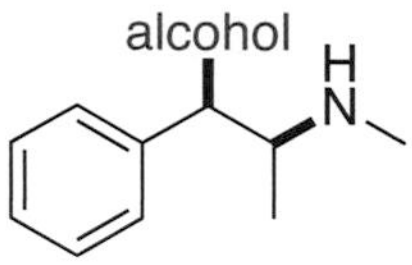   *ephedrine*

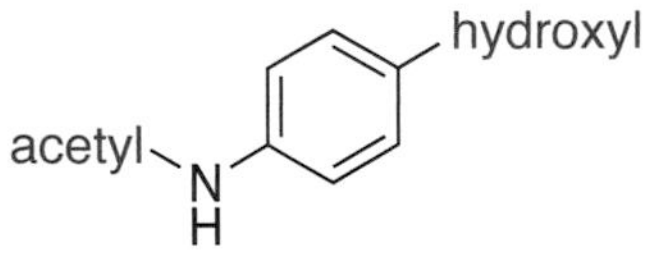

hydroxyl

acetyl

ethyl   phenyl

dimethylamino

amino

_____   _____   _____

acetaminophen (tylenol) 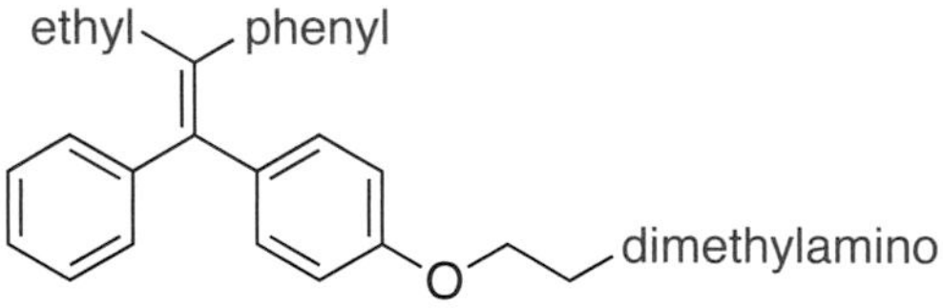   *tamoxifen* 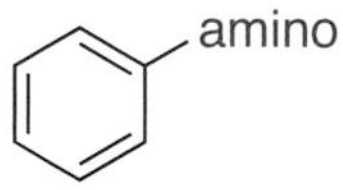   *aniline*

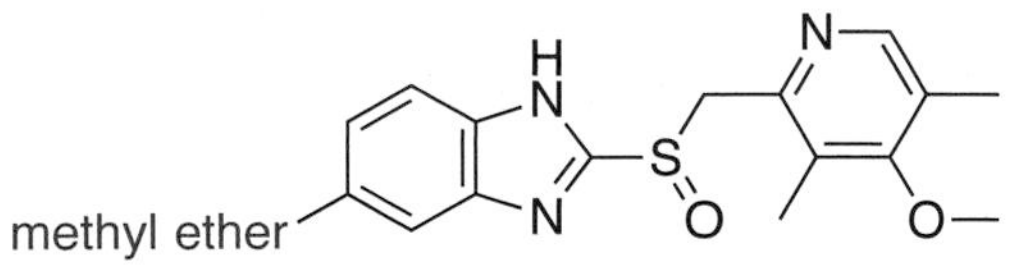

methyl ether

carboxyl

azide

omeprazol

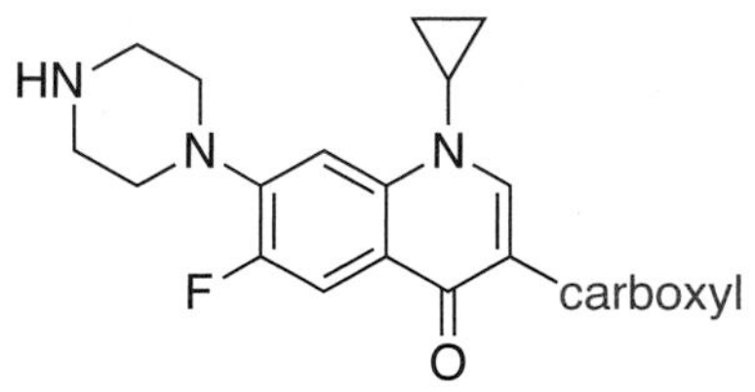

ciprofloxacin "cipro"

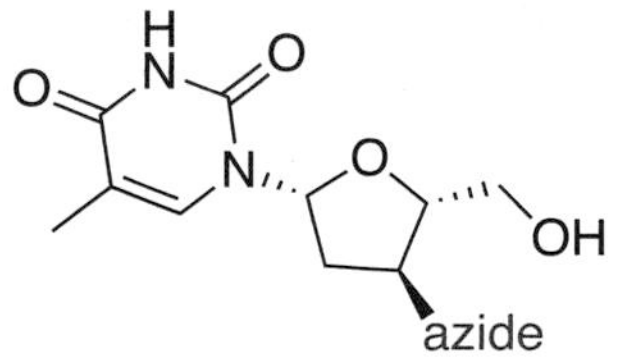

azidothymidine

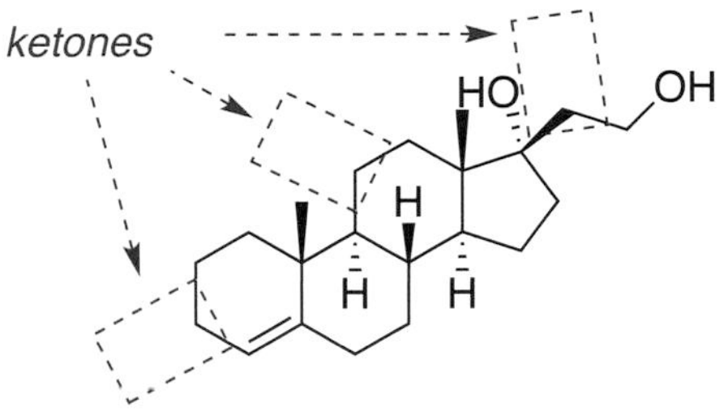

ketones

HO

OH

cortisone

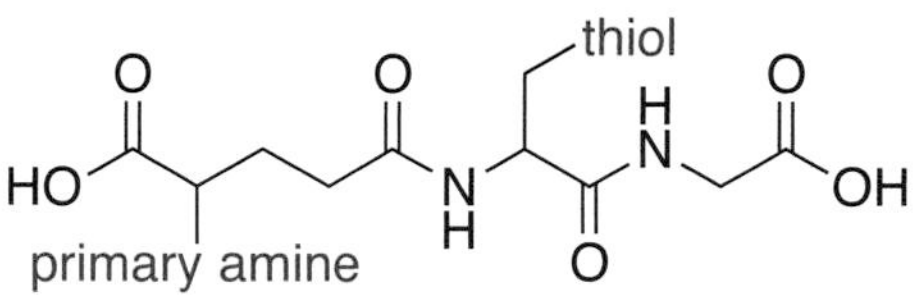

thiol

HO

primary amine

glutathione

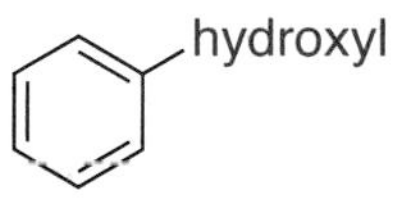

hydroxyl

phenol

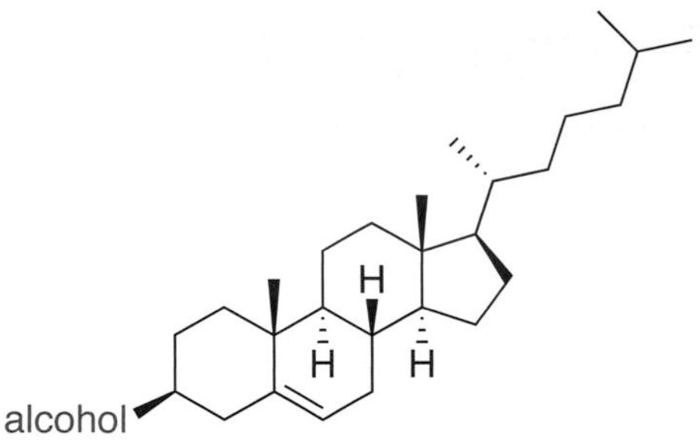

alcohol
H
H
H

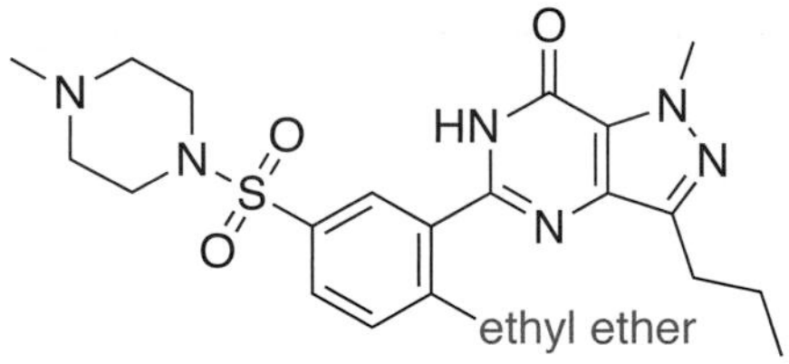

N
N
S
O
O
HN
O
N
N
N
ethyl ether

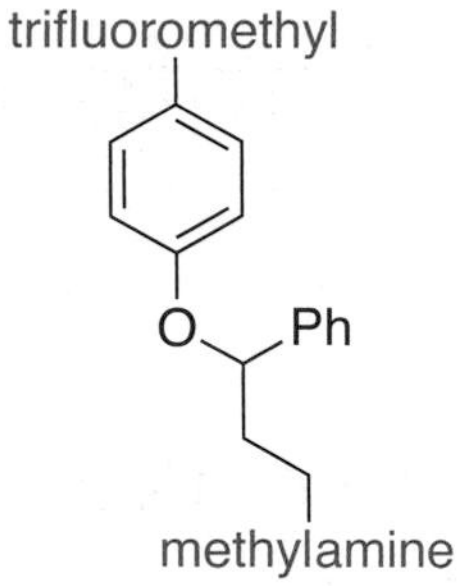

trifluoromethyl
O
Ph
methylamine

cholesterol

viagra

prozac

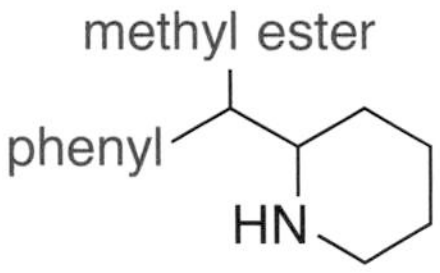

methyl ester
phenyl
HN

My chemistry instructor might like me to take methylphenidate (other name: _________) to improve my *weight lifting / attention / social skills*.

methylphenidate

4 Conformations Of Cyclic Hydrocarbons

from chapter(s) _____ in the recommended text

A Introduction

Focus
Cyclic hydrocarbons tend to be more rigid than acyclic ones. Cyclohexane and cyclohexene conformations are governed by trends that are both logical and almost universally applicable; the focus of this section is on those structures.

Reasons To Care
Some cyclic 6-membered rings can flip between well-defined conformations, while others are constrained by substituents to exist mainly in one conformation. Many molecules of interest in biology, biochemistry, and pharmaceutical chemistry have cyclohexane or cyclohexene rings. Being able to predict the preferred 3D conformation around this ring is a powerful tool for understanding how these types of molecules react under various conditions, and interact with receptors, *eg* ones in biological systems.

Concepts Involved
ideal valence bond and torsional angles • interplay of substituent orientations and preferred conformations in cyclohexanes, fused cyclohexanes (decalins, including steroids), and in cyclohexenes

Objective
After this part of the *Inquisition,* survivors will know how to look at molecules like those below and recognize at least some features of their preferred 3D structure or structures.

oseltamivir *menthol* *limonene* *myo-inositol*

cholesterol *cholic acid* *testosterone*

B Angle Strain

Assign the angles within the following geometric shapes as 90°, >120°, >>120°, ~109°, 60°, 120° by writing one of those values on each of the lines provided.

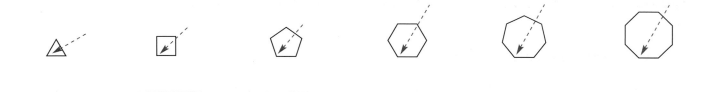

_____   _____   _____   _____   _____   _____

Ideal bond angle for sp³ hybrid orbitals is around *90°, 109°, 120°, 123°*.

When constraints cause deviation from ideal bond angles the molecule has *angle / bond / steric* strain.

If they were flat, the following cyclic hydrocarbons would have C-C-C bond angles that would be compressed relative to the ideal value for sp³ hybridization: *cyclopropane / cyclobutane / cyclopentane / cyclohexane / cycloheptane / cyclooctane.*

Conversely, the following compounds would have internal angles that would be stretched wider than the ideal value for sp³ hybridization *if they were flat*: *cyclopropane / cyclobutane / cyclopentane / cyclohexane / cycloheptane / cyclooctane.*

In this series, the cyclic hydrocarbons with the most compressed and expanded angles are: *cyclopropane / cyclobutane / cyclopentane / cyclohexane / cycloheptane / cyclooctane.*

C Torsional Strain

Circle the angles shown in the diagrams below that are torsional angles, and put a rectangle around the word "angle" if it is a bond angle (or, more specifically, valence bond angle).

Valence bond angles involve *2 / 3 / 4* atoms, whereas torsional angles involve *2 / 3 / 4*.

Torsional strain primarily involves interactions between *e⁻ in bonds / sterically large groups* and is *minimized / maximized* as the torsional angle approaches 180°.

Eclipsed conformations involve high *angle / torsional* strain.

D Cyclohexanes

Unsubstituted Cyclohexane

If cyclopentane and cyclohexane existed in flat conformations, the first, cyclopentane would have *more / less* angle strain because the internal angle is *closer to / further from* the ideal sp^3 angle.

The most stable conformers of cyclopentane and cyclohexane are *not* flat due to *bond angle / torsional* strain.

To draw a cyclohexane chair conformer:

(i)   draw two parallel diagonal lines (like in a parallelogram) to represent the *C–C* bonds that are in the plane of the paper;

(ii) starting from one end of each of the lines, draw a second pair of parallel lines (another set of parallel *C–C* bonds); and,

(iii) draw the remaining two bonds to close the ring.

Show this process by highlighting two bonds at a time on the following diagram.
Overwrite on this diagram to follow the process outlined above.

Following the steps above, draw a cyclohexane chair conformer starting with the two parallel lines below.

Express the *ring flip* equilibrium between the two chair representations by completing the following diagram. The two conformers have *different / exactly the same* energies.

To represent a cyclohexane half-chair accurately:

(i)   draw three end-to-end horizontal bonds;

(ii)   draw any pair of the other *C – C* bonds that are also *parallel*; and,

(iii) draw the remaining *parallel* bonds. Show this process by highlighting two bonds at a time on the following diagram.

Overwrite on the following diagram as outlined above.

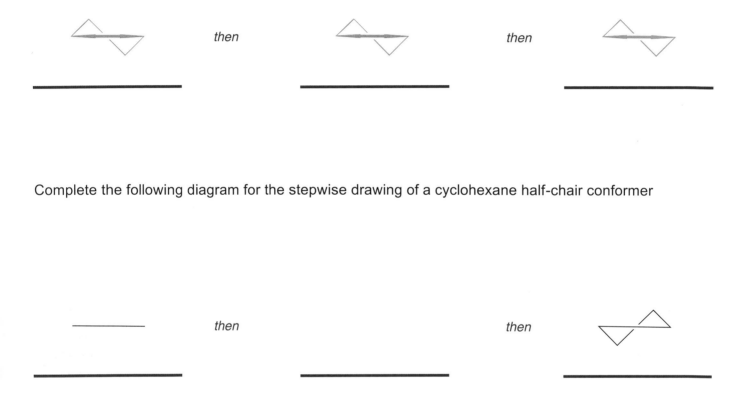

Complete the following diagram for the stepwise drawing of a cyclohexane half-chair conformer

Cyclohexene has one double bond in a cyclohexane ring. Draw a half-chair diagram of cyclohexene with a double bond at the front.

Flipping between chairs involves half-chair transition states and twist-boat intermediates as follows (arrows here denote the direction for flipping bonds, *not* electron flow):

43 kJ•mol⁻¹

21 kJ•mol⁻¹

0 kJ•mol⁻¹

Complete the following energy diagram by first placing crosses to represent the energy of each cyclohexane conformer (from the previous graphic), then join these crosses in a flowing waveform to show how the energy changes on progressing from one conformer to another.

0   10   20   30   40 kJ•mol⁻¹

Boat conformers *must be / are not necessarily* intermediates in flipping of one chair form to another, as depicted in the following diagram. Circle the two boat conformers.

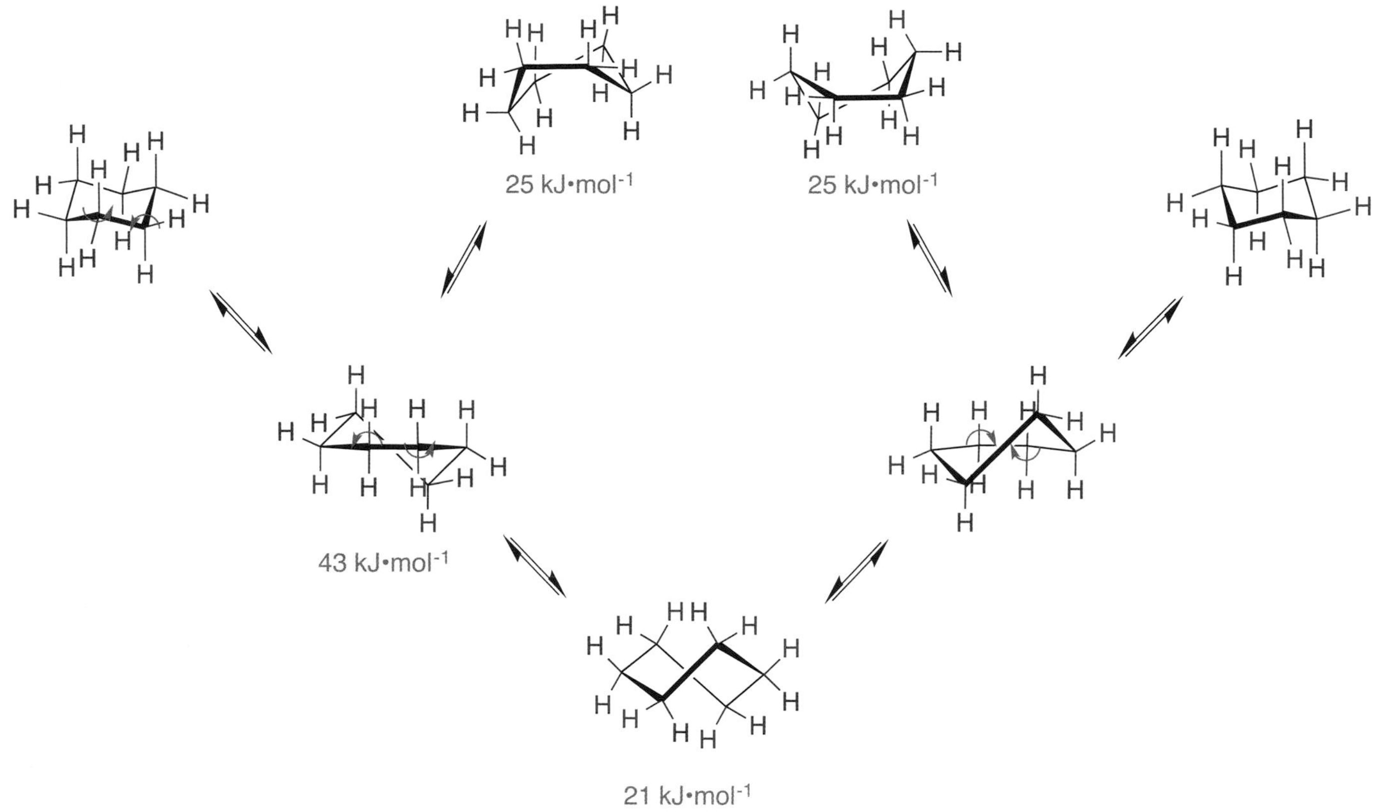

25 kJ·mol^{-1}

25 kJ·mol^{-1}

43 kJ·mol^{-1}

21 kJ·mol^{-1}

The discussion above illustrates energy surfaces that describe interconversion of two chair conformers are *one / two / three*-dimensional.

Complete the following double Newman projections for the chair and boat conformations of cyclohexane, viewing along the bonds $C^a - C^b$.

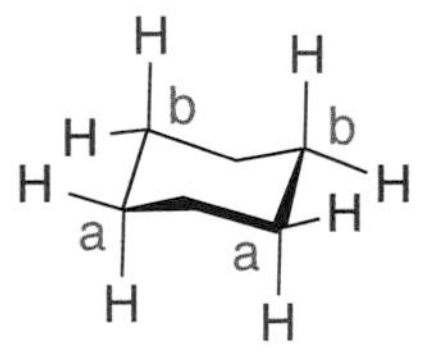

chair

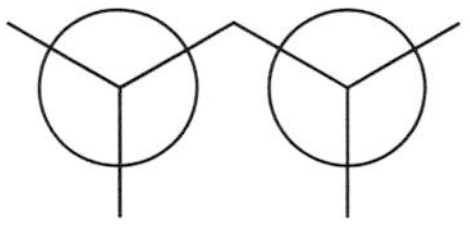

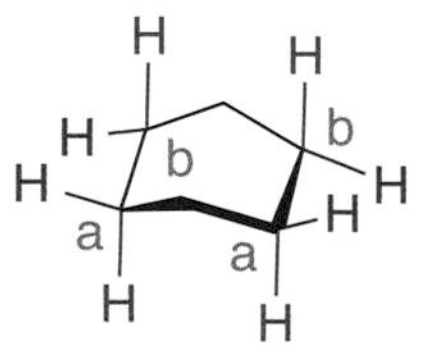

boat

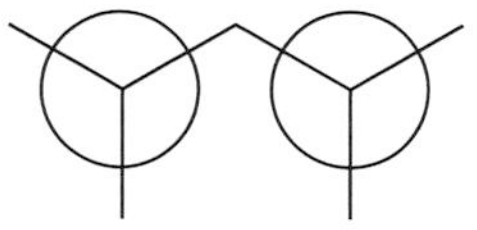

In the chair conformer of cyclohexane, the bonds around $C^a - C^b$ are aligned like the *synperiplanar / gauche / antiperiplanar* conformation of butane, whereas in the boat form they are like the *synperiplanar / gauche / antiperiplanar* conformer.

Monosubstituted Cyclohexanes

Show the chair structure that results from ring-flipping methylcyclohexane on the diagram below. Also complete the double Newman projections for the two conformers viewing along the *Ca* – *Cb* bonds, and indicate their relative stabilities.

more / *less* stable   *more* / *less* stable

The conformer where the methyl group is axial has *0 / 1 / 2* gauche interaction(s), whereas there are *0 / 1 / 2* similar interactions when the methyl group is equatorial.

Complete the following conformers of methylcyclohexane, ethylcyclohexane, *iso*-propylcyclohexane, and *tert*-butylcyclohexane so that the substituents are axial and aligned in a way that best minimizes 1,3-diaxial interactions. Do not use abbreviations for these substituents and show, for instance, how the methyl group of the ethyl substituent is oriented.

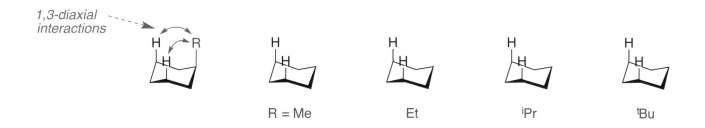

1,3-diaxial interactions

R = Me   Et   ᶦPr   ᵗBu

The axial conformer of *tert*-butylcyclohexane is much less stable than the other members of this series because _____

_____.

Destabilization of a *tert*-butyl group in cyclohexane axial positions is so much that a single ᵗBu-substituent on a cyclohexane biases the equilibrium so much that only the *equatorial / axial* conformer is observed.

At room temperature in solution, NMR *does / does not* give distinct peaks for the monosubstituted cyclohexane conformers, corresponding to equatorial and axial forms.

Proton NMR at room temperature cannot differentiate molecular forms that equilibrate faster than about *10 / 100 / 1,000 / 10,000* times per second.

Methoxycyclohexane is more stable as the conformer with an axial methoxy group than might be expected because $C - C$ bonds, $C - O$ bonds have *higher / lower* σ- and σ*-orbitals than $C - C$ bonds. Complete the following diagrams to illustrate the effects this has on the destabilizing σ-to-σ, and the stabilizing σ-to-σ* interaction; do this feeding electrons into the molecular orbitals. Note the σ*-orbital for the $C - O$ bond is lower than that of the $C - C$, and therefore closer to the filled σ-orbitals.

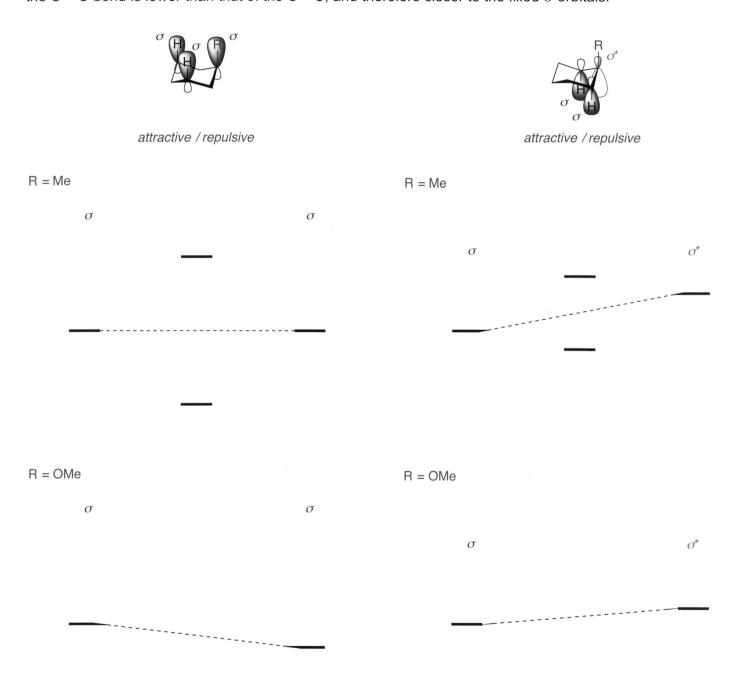

attractive / repulsive   *attractive / repulsive*

1,2-Interactions of the σ-to-σ* orbitals involve *more / less* overlap than the corresponding σ-to-σ 1,3-interactions, and, based on the orbital energy levels, the 1,2-interaction for the σ-to-σ* is *more / less* R = Me than it is for R = OMe.

The axial conformer of methoxycyclohexane is significantly more stable than ethylcyclohexane because

_____

_____.

Disubstituted Cyclohexanes

Complete the following diagrams to show ring flipping of the following compounds, and indicate the number of 1,3-diaxial interactions involving the indicated substituent.

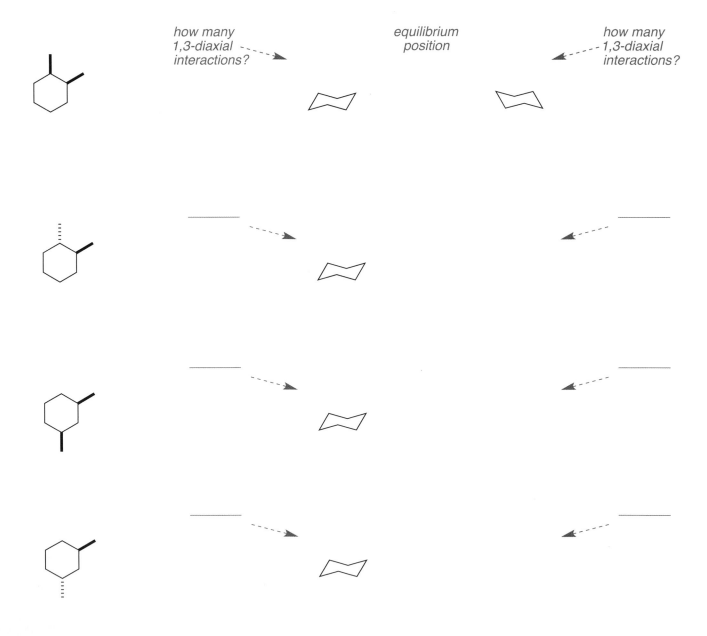

Some of the following disubstituted cyclohexanes are handed (chiral), and it is important to draw the *same* enantiomer (hand) as indicated on the left.

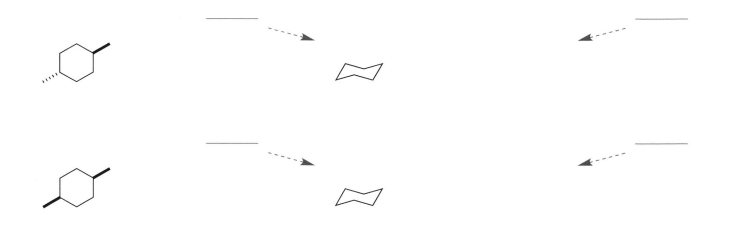

Decalins

Decalins feature two cyclohexane rings sharing *an atom / a bond*; look up the structure in Wiki.
Complete the following diagrams for *trans*-decalin, and for *cis*-decalin indicating how it can flip.

complete here ⤶   *complete here* ⤷

_____   _____   _____

trans-decalin   *cis-decalin*   *cis-decalin*

Research molecular structures of steroids on the web, then circle each of the following structures that have a steroid framework.

Put a cross underneath each of the structures above that may undergo ring-flip at one of the cyclohexane rings (if any can).

Cyclohexenes

Circle each of the structures below that accurately depict a low energy conformation of a cyclohexene. If a *tert*-butyl substituent encounters 1,3-diaxial interactions, or if the bond angle to it is inappropriate, then the conformer cannot be very stable.

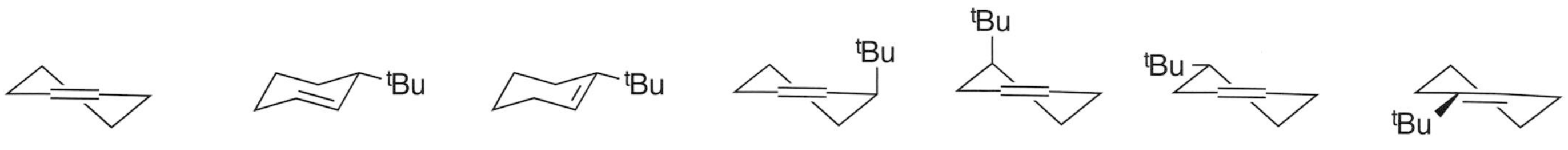

There are problems with the conformational equilibria below. In some cases the site of substitution shown is inconsistent. In other cases there are carbon atoms with four different substituents that can have mirror image forms, and the writer has mistakenly changed the *configuration*, *ie* changed from one mirror image to another, and not "flipped" the half-chair. Draw corrected versions assuming the first conformer on the left is correct throughout.

E Other Rings

Draw cyclobutane and cyclopentane in butterfly and envelope conformations.

cyclobutane   _cyclopentane_

In solution these molecules _do / do not_ rapidly interchange (on the NMR time-scale) between other butterfly and envelope conformations.

Three membered rings in cyclopropanes are _rigid and flat / flexible and twisted._

Cyclopropane substituents are _eclipsed / staggered_ relative to each other.

5   Curly Arrows And Electron Flow

A Introduction

Focus

Chemical reactivity is driven by movement of electrons from sites where there is excessive negative charge, towards places where nuclei are less shielded. This is easy to see when the origin has one more electron than the nucleus it is associated with, *ie* a negative charge, and the destination is positively charged because it has one less. However, either the origin or destination, or both, can be neutral.

Organic chemists have a language to show movement of electrons, and a major part of this involves full-headed curly arrows drawn from the origin to the destination (and *never* the other way around!). Drawing these arrows accurately is the focus of this section.

Reasons To Care

All organic chemistry involving reactivity uses curly arrows. Instructors test understanding of how to push arrows, and immediately recognize shot-in-the-dark efforts to sling arrows on target. After hybridization and the ability to draw conformationally realistic structures, ability to express electron flow with curly arrows is *the* most important concept in undergraduate organic chemistry.

Concepts Involved

Some generalities:

- when drawing an arrow, start by putting your pen on the area of highest electron density, then think where to push;
- push arrows towards points of low electron density (positive charges or positively polarized bonds);
- the furthest an arrow can move is from a bond, through the atom in the bond, to another bond to this atom;
- if more than one arrow is required, think of balanced dominos in a line, the first one to fall knocks over the next, *etc*;
- arrows move electrons, movement of charges is incidental;
- the overall charge of all the starting materials equals the net charge of all the products; and,
- pushing arrows logically is like speaking a language clearly, what is being said is not necessarily true, but a thought is communicated effectively.

Objective

To eliminate evil sloppy, inaccurate arrows, leaving only those that strike targets in the name of electron flow; like these do .....

$$A{-}B \longrightarrow A^+ + B^- \qquad A{-}B \longrightarrow A^- + B^+ \qquad A{=}B \longrightarrow {}^+A{-}B^- \qquad A{=}B \longrightarrow {}^-A{-}B^+$$

$$A{-}B \quad C^+ \longrightarrow A^+ + B{-}C \qquad A{=}B \quad C^- \longrightarrow {}^-A{-}B{-}C \qquad {}^+A{=}B \quad C^- \longrightarrow A{-}B{-}C$$

B Electron Flow

Movement of a pair of electrons is illustrated using a *fishhook / full* arrow.

The arrow begins where the electrons *are / are going to*, ie at a site of relatively *high / low* electron density.

Arrows depicting flow of electrons *always / never* begin with a positively charged atom.

Affecting Only One Bond

Complete the following *heterolytic / homolytic* bond fission reactions, carefully drawing a curly arrow to depict the electron flow.

H–H $\longrightarrow$ _____ + _____   I–I $\longrightarrow$ _____ + _____

Cl–Cl $\longrightarrow$ _____ + _____   D–D $\longrightarrow$ _____ + _____

H_3C–CH_3 $\longrightarrow$ _____ + _____ $\longrightarrow$ _____

Everything ever said in grammatically correct, clear, precise English *is / need not be* absolutely true; it is *possible / impossible* to tell lies in impeccable English.

Arrows are the language of organic chemistry; if the arrows are accurate that *does / does not* mean the movement of electrons expressed will occur.

In any balanced organic equation, if a neutral molecule undergoes *heterolytic* fission then the number of cations formed *must not / must* equal the number of anions.

One full arrow represents movement of *1 / 2 e*; this *always / sometimes* severs the link between the two atoms.

Complete these diagrams to illustrate heterolytic fission of the multiple bonds indicated.

O=O   ⟶   HN=NH ⟶

_____   _____

H_2C=CH_2 ⟶

_____

HC≡CH ⟶   N≡N ⟶

_____   _____

Complete diagram **a** to show heterolytic bond cleavage as depicted by the curly arrow. Similarly, complete diagram **b** to show the electrons moving *in the opposite way*.

a   **b**

X–Y ⟶   +   X–Y ⟶   +

_____   _____

If, in fact, pathway **a** is more favorable, then this implies X is *more / less* electronegative than Y.
If Y were more electronegative than X then electrons would tend to move *away from / towards* Y.

71

Show both possible heterolytic fission pathways, and indicate if they are more or less favorable.

pathway 1   *pathway 2*

H−Cl ⟶   +   H−Cl ⟶   +

——————————   ——————————
more / less favorable   *more / less* favorable

I−Cl ⟶   +   I−Cl ⟶   +

——————————   ——————————
more / less favorable   *more / less* favorable

Me₂N−Cl ⟶   +   Me₂N−Cl ⟶   +

——————————   ——————————
more / less favorable   *more / less* favorable

HN=CH ⟶   HN=CH ⟶

——————————   ——————————
more / less favorable   *more / less* favorable

N≡CMe ⟶   N≡CMe ⟶

——————————   ——————————
more / less favorable   *more / less* favorable

$H_2C=O \longrightarrow$

_____

more / less favorable

$H_2C=O \longrightarrow$

_____

more / less favorable

Affecting Two Bonds

Complete the following reactions; in one atom X acts as an electron donor, and in the other it acts as an electron acceptor.

a

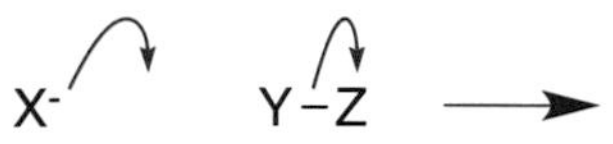

$X^- \quad Y{-}Z \longrightarrow \qquad +$

_____

b

$Z^- \quad Y{-}X \longrightarrow \qquad +$

_____

Pathway **a** tends to be *favored / disfavored* if X is more electronegative than Z.

Show both possible pathways for the reactions below (showing a complete set of accurate arrows throughout), and predict if they are more or less favorable.

pathway 1

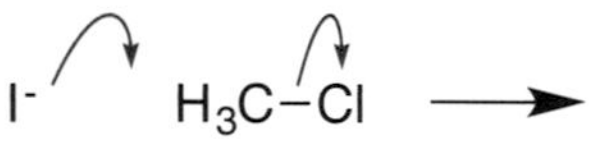

$I^- \quad H_3C{-}Cl \longrightarrow \qquad +$

_____

more / less favorable

pathway 2

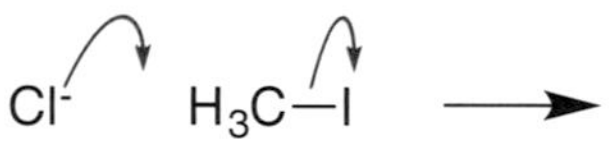

$Cl^- \quad H_3C{-}I \longrightarrow \qquad +$

_____

more / less favorable

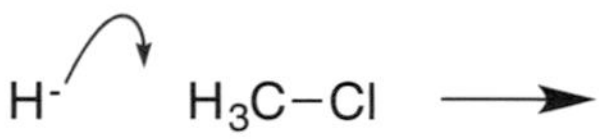

$H^- \quad H_3C{-}Cl \longrightarrow \qquad +$

_____

more / less favorable

$Cl^- \quad H_3C{-}H \longrightarrow \qquad +$

_____

more / less favorable

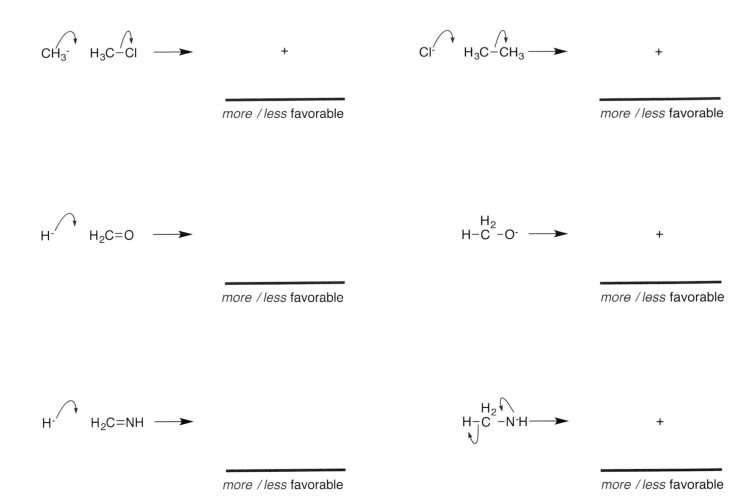

CH_3^- H_3C-Cl $\longrightarrow$ +

_____
more / less favorable

Cl^- H_3C-CH_3 $\longrightarrow$ +

_____
more / less favorable

H^- $H_2C=O$ $\longrightarrow$

_____
more / less favorable

$H-C^{H_2}-O^-$ $\longrightarrow$ +

_____
more / less favorable

H^- $H_2C=NH$ $\longrightarrow$

_____
more / less favorable

$H-C^{H_2}-N\cdot H$ $\longrightarrow$ +

_____
more / less favorable

Affecting Four Bonds

Complete the following two reactions, one in which atom X acts as an electron donor, and another in which it acts as an electron acceptor.

a

X^- H Y $\longrightarrow$ + +

_____   _____   _____

b

Y^- H X $\longrightarrow$ + +

_____   _____   _____

Pathway **a** tends to be *favored / disfavored* if X is more basic than Y.

74

Representations Of Charged Hydrocarbon Scaffolds

A difference between chemists and plumbers is the way they pronounce *"p-shell / unionized"*.

A negative charge on a *C*-atom means a lone pair of electrons is present; that electron pair counts as one *group* when assessing hybridization state.

A sp^3 hybridized carbon has four groups around it. Abstracting a proton replaces a hydrogen atom (one group) with a lone pair. Consequently, when a proton is abstracted from a sp^3 hybridized carbon the resulting anion is *sp / sp^2 / sp^3* hybridized.

When a proton is abstracted from a sp^2 hybridized carbon the electrons move *towards C* and the resulting anion is *sp / sp^2 / sp^3* hybridized.

sp / sp^2 / sp^3-Hybridized carbanions are formed from sp hybridized carbons.

Complete the following diagrams, show the lone pair on the carbanion *C*-atom in each case, and indicate the hybridization state of that carbon (throughout, B⁻ is a suitable anionic base).

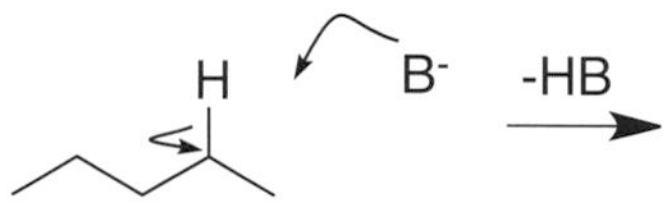

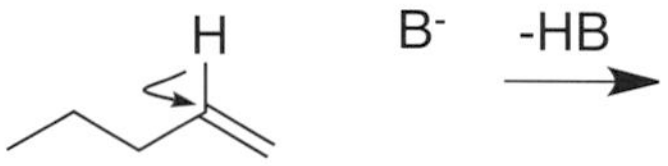

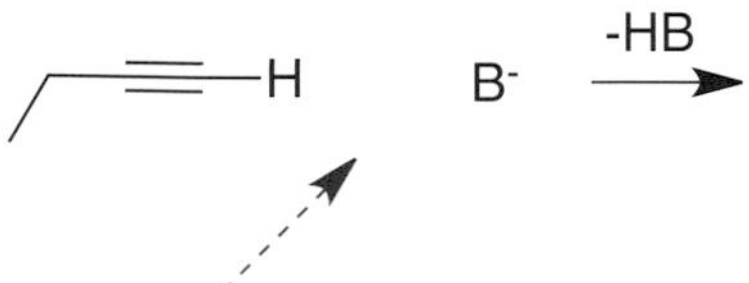

put in arrows

Positively charged *C*-atoms have empty orbitals on that atom. Thus when a leaving entity dissociates from a *C*-atom with the lone pair of electrons that was in the bond, then there is one group *less* around the carbon. That leaving group is very rarely a hydride; cleavage of C-X bonds is more likely to form carbocations and *halide* (*eg* H⁻ is far less stable, less able to act as a leaving group, than Cl⁻).

A sp^3-hybridized carbon has _____ groups around it. Abstracting an anionic surrounding group (a "leaving group") causes rehybridization to sp^2 and an empty p-orbital. Generally, carbocations formed from sp^3 hybridized atoms tend to be *sp / sp^2 / sp^3* hybridized.

Complete the following diagrams, show the empty orbital on the carbocation C-atom in each case, and indicate the hybridization state of that carbon (throughout, A^+ is a suitable Lewis acid).

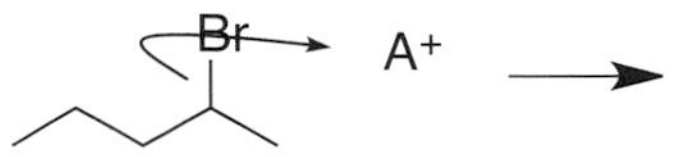

A^+ ⟶

A^+ ⟶

_____   _____

Draw the following carbocations and carbanions as line diagrams without using the letter C. Indicate the geometry about the charged carbon.

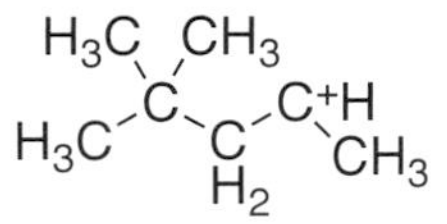

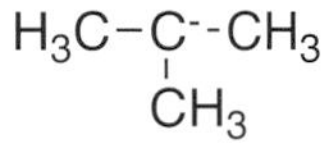

_____   _____   _____

$H_3C-\overset{\cdot\cdot}{\underset{CH_3}{C}}-CH_3$ $C^-H_2CH_2SC(Me)_2CH_3$

_____   _____   _____

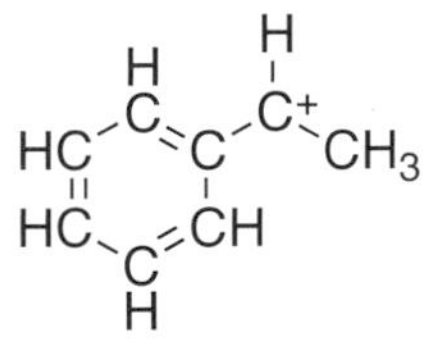

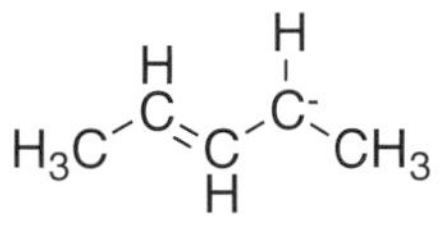

                   $^tBuSeCH_2^-$

Carbocations of the type C^+R_3 tend to be sp / sp^2 / sp^3 hybridized, and carbanions C^-R_3 are sp / sp^2 / sp^3 hybridized. Explain why this is so by considering the number of electrons around carbon in C^+H_3 and in C^-H_3.

_____

_____

_____

Convert the following line diagrams to ones that show all the *C*- and *H*-atoms.

C Heteroatoms, Lone Pairs, And Moving Electrons

Indicate the hybridization state of every *heteroatom* (non-carbon atoms) in these molecules by writing 1, 2, or 3 near each one to correspond to sp, sp^2, and sp^3. Show the lone pairs on the heteroatoms.

When a lone pair on a heteroatom X becomes protonated the lone pair is replaced by a bond to hydrogen. There *is / is not* a change in the number of groups around the heteroatom so protonation of sp^3 hybridized heteroatoms gives *sp / sp^2 / sp^3* hybridized protonated heteroatoms.

Similarly, sp^2 hybridized heteroatoms become *sp / sp^2 / sp^3* hybridized protonated heteroatoms, and sp hybridized heteroatoms become *sp / sp^2 / sp^3* hybridized protonated heteroatoms.

Conversely, there *can / cannot* be a change in hybridization state when electrons shift to atoms without protonation.

Complete the following diagrams and indicate the hybridization state of the charged atoms that are produced.

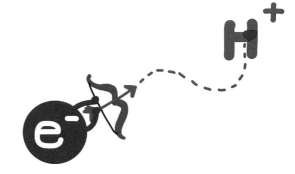

_____   _____

_____   _____

put in missing arrows

_____   _____

_____   _____

When drawing reaction mechanisms, it is *usually / never* advisable to put the pen on the electron density and push towards the electron deficient center.

People who do not know chemistry might write the following descriptions of electron flow. Interpret what they really mean by completing the diagram on the right using accurate curly arrows.

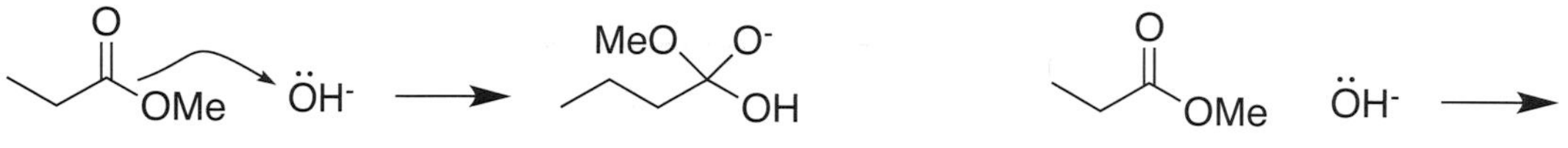

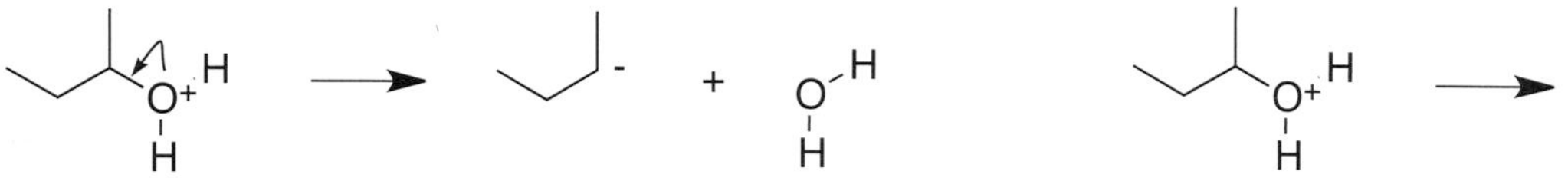

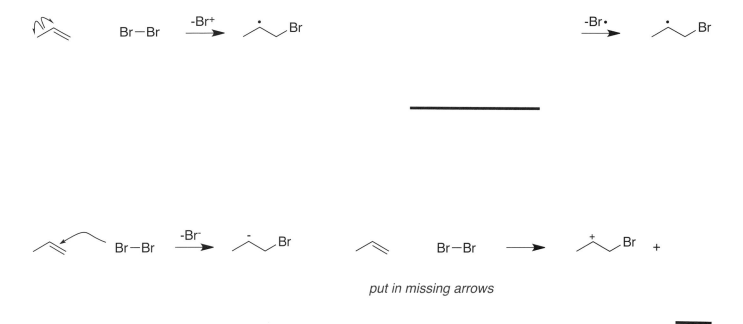

put in missing arrows

This section closes with a couple of reactions that, curiously, do not appear to be driven by charge (they are, but the charges are partial and in the frontier molecular orbitals).

should be

show all arrows

6 Acids And Bases

from chapter(s) _____ in the recommended text

A Introduction

Focus

This section describes how to calibrate acidity and basicity in organic compounds, organic acid-base equilibria, how to predict where organic molecules might be protonated, and Lewis acids.

Reasons To Care

Imagine we would like a nucleophilic organic compound NuH to combine with an electrophilic one, EX, but they do not react, even when heated.

$$NuH \; + \; EX \; \longrightarrow \; \textit{no reaction}$$

There are two classical tactics to deal with this common "road-block". The first is to deprotonate (remove a proton from) NuH so it becomes a more electron-rich, therefore more reactive, entity Nu⁻. Another approach is to protonate the electrophile so that it becomes EX^+H and potentially more attractive to NuH; if NuH does combine with EX^+H then a proton is usually lost, regenerating the acid.

basic conditions:

$$NuH \; + \; base^- \;\; \xrightarrow{\text{-baseH}} \;\; Nu^-$$

$$Nu^- \; + \; EX \;\; \xrightarrow{\text{-X}^-} \;\; Nu{-}E$$
more nucleophilic than NuH

acidic conditions:

$$EX \; + \; H^+ \;\; \longrightarrow \;\; EX^+H$$

$$NuH \; + \; EX^+H \;\; \xrightarrow{\text{-H}^+} \;\; Nu{-}EXH$$
more electrophilic than EX

Choosing a suitable base or acid for these reactions is pivotal. If the base is too reactive it may have undesirable effects on the substrates, or combine with the medium used to dissolve that compound. Conversely, if it is not reactive enough, it will not deprotonate NuH. Similarly, really strong acids decompose many organic compounds, but we need one strong enough to do the job. Consideration of acidity and basicity scales helps make informed choices.

Concepts Involved

equilibrium constants extended to organic acids and bases • common interactions of organic compounds with acids and bases

Objective

To appreciate that acid-base equilibria influence reactivity of organic compounds, and how pH can be manipulated to achieve a desired result.

B Log Scales To Measure Proton Dissociation From Organic Molecules

Equilibria That Generate Protons

A hundred thousand fans are watching a football game, and it is so cold everyone brought hats, but not everyone wears them at any given moment.   At equilibrium, the number of people who get hot and take off their hats equals the number that put them on because they are cold.

people wearing hats $\rightleftharpoons$ people without hats + hats not worn $\quad or \quad$ PH $\rightleftharpoons$ P + H

On that day, the *number* of hats not worn at any moment is a *constant / variable*, because an equilibrium has been reached.

When comparing different games played under the same conditions, there may be 90,000 - 110,000 fans, the number of hats worn at equilibrium in *different* games will be *constant / variable*, therefore it *is / is not* a good parameter to gauge the tendency to remove hats in the stadium under these conditions.

Statistically, the *ratio* of *people wearing hats* to *people not wearing hats will / will not* change significantly if there are in fact 90,000 or 110,000 in the stadium, provided the conditions are the same.

To relate this ratio to the number of hats not worn we may define the *equilibrium constant*, K, where:

$$K = \frac{[\text{people not wearing hats}]\,[\text{hats not worn}]}{[\text{people wearing hats}]}$$

This *is / is not* effectively the same as the statement:

$$[\text{hats not worn}] = \frac{K\,[\text{people wearing hats}]}{[\text{people not wearing hats}]} \quad or \quad [H] = \frac{K\,[PH]}{[P]}$$

In organic chemistry, concentrations of protons in acid base equilibria *may / may not* be related to the equilibrium constant for dissociation of a proton by the following:

$$HA \rightleftharpoons H^+ + A^- \qquad [H^+] = \frac{K\,[HA]}{[A^-]}$$

A certain fraction (sometimes infinitesimally small) of the molecules will be dissociated to generate protons for *all / some* organic compounds that contains hydrogen.

Weak acids dissociate to give a *large / small* fraction of protons relative to the total number of molecules involved.

If the fraction of protons relative to the number of non-dissociated molecules in a sample is high then that compound is a *weak / strong* acid and the equilibrium constant is *high / low*.

When methane, CH_4, dissociates a proton then the K value is 10^{-60}. Methane is therefore a *weak / strong* acid. The equilibrium constant for generation of protons (K_a; *a* denoting *acid*) represents dissociation of the molecules into protons.

$$CH_4 \; \rightleftharpoons \; CH_3^- \; + \; H^+ \qquad and \qquad [H^+] = \frac{K_a \, [CH_4]}{[CH_3^-]}$$

Dissociation of acetic acid has a K_a value of 1.75×10^{-5}; that compound is therefore a significantly *stronger / weaker* acid than methane.

$$[H^+] = \frac{K_a \, [CH_3CO_2H]}{[CH_3CO_2^-]}$$

*acetic acid
or ethanoic acid*

*acetate
or ethanoate*

Trifluoroacetic acid CF_3CO_2H has a K_a of 0.59. Put a circle around the strongest acid, and a square around the weakest acid in the following series:

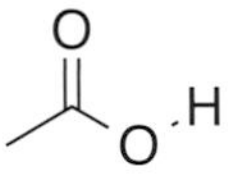

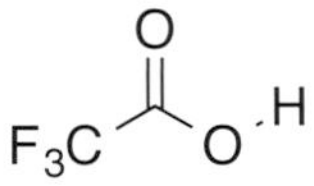

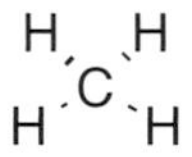

When methane dissociates, the number of moles of CH_3^- *does / does not* equal the concentration of protons, *ie* $[H^+]$. If the K_a for methane is 10^{-60} then in a sample of 10^{60} molecules, the number of molecules dissociated into protons and methyl anions is, on average (circle the correct answer):

$$10^{60} \qquad 10^6 \qquad 10 \qquad 1 \qquad 10^{-6} \qquad 10^{-60}$$

Rank the following acids by putting "1" under the most acidic, "2" under the second most acidic, *etc.*.

| 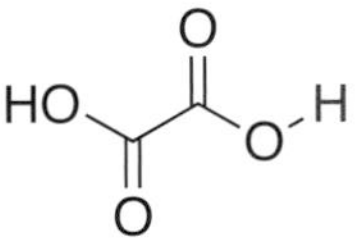 $K_a = 5.4 \times 10^{-2}$ | 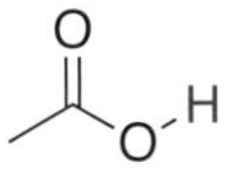 1.8×10^{-5} | 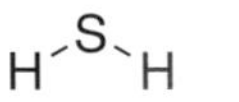 1.1×10^{-7} | 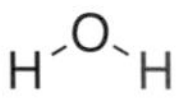 1.0×10^{-14} | 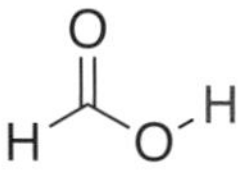 1.8×10^{-4} | 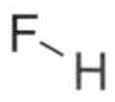 6.6×10^{-4} |

Compared with these compounds, a substance with a K_a of 1 would be a *weak / strong* acid.

For each of the following compounds, show the equilibrium that leads to dissociation of the highlighted proton, and an equation that defines [H$^+$] in terms of the constant, K$_a$, for that molecule.

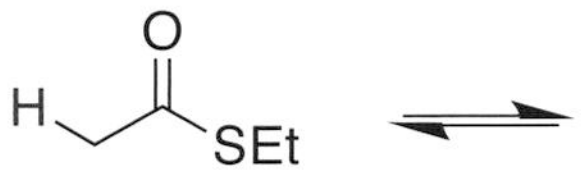

+   H$^+$ *and*   [H$^+$] = _____

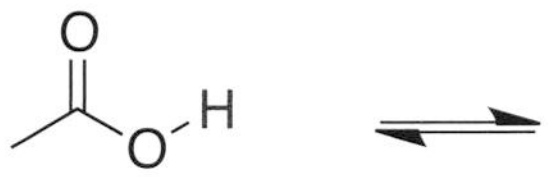

_____

+   H$^+$ *and*   [H$^+$] = _____

_____

H———H   ⇌

+   H$^+$ *and*   [H$^+$] = _____

_____

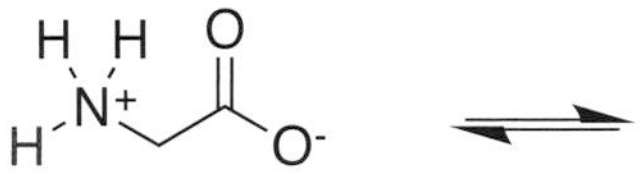

+   H$^+$ *and*   [H$^+$] = _____

_____

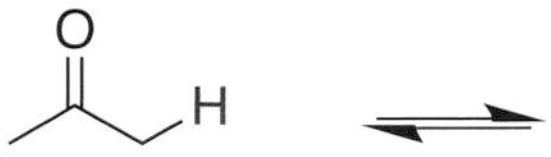

+   H$^+$ *and*   [H$^+$] = _____

_____

Simplifying The Scale: pKa

Differences in K_a values are crucial to chemical reactivity. However, differences in K_a's are so huge that it is easy to lose perspective of the numbers involved. For instance, in the above discussion, did you appreciate that to find one dissociated methane (K_a 10^{-60}; MM 16), it would probably be necessary to sift through 10^{37} moles, *ie* 16 x 10^{37} grams of methane? That is a lot of gas.

For another example, $MeCO_2H$ is ten times less ionized than HCO_2H and this leads to some significantly different reactivities. However, HCO_2H is ~10^{56} times more easily ionized than methane; these compounds have completely different chemical reactivity profiles.

When these differences are expressed on a log scale the log figures numerically are *less / more* than the absolute differences. Calculate the log (*ie* log to base 10) of the following K_a values (one example is given on the left):

| K_a = 5.4 x 10⁻² | 1.8 x 10⁻⁵ | 1.1 x 10⁻⁷ | 1.0 x 10⁻¹⁴ | 1.8 x 10⁻⁴ | 6.6 x 10⁻⁴ |

$logK_a$ = -1.27   _____   _____   _____   _____   _____

$-logK_a$ = 1.27   _____   _____   _____   _____   _____

Indicate on the diagram above the values for $-logK_a$; this is called the *pK_a / nK_a / mK_a* value.

Most organic molecules have K_a values less than one, meaning *only a small amount / a lot* of the compound is ionized. An advantage of using negative logs of K_a values is they are *positive / negative* for most organic compounds.

Strong acids have *larger / smaller* K_a values than weak acids, *more / less* negative $logK_a$ values, and *smaller / larger* pK_a values.

Rank the following acids by putting "1" under the most acidic, "2" under the second most acidic, *etc*..

| lactic acid | oxalic acid | ascorbic acid | citric acid |
| pK_a = 3.86 | 4.19 | 4.10 | 3.08 |

_____   _____   _____   _____

A difference of one pK_a unit means that it is *1 / 10 / 1000* times easier to dissociate a proton from one compound compared with the other.

A difference of 10 pK_a units means that it is *10 / 1000 / 10,000,000,000* times easier to dissociate a proton from one compound compared with the other.

Rank the following acids by putting "1" under the most acidic, "2" under the second most acidic, *etc.*.

NH_4^+	NH_3	H_3O^+	H_2O
ammonium	*ammonia*	*hydroxonium*	*water*
$pK_a = 9.2$	38	-1.7	15.7
_____	_____	_____	_____

The pK_a differences shown above mean it is about 10^{29} times *more / less* likely that an ammonium ion will dissociate into ammonia and a proton, than ammonia is to dissociate into a proton and the NH_2^- anion.

Similarly, it is about 10^{17} times *more / less* likely that water will dissociate into hydroxide and a proton, than hydroxonium is to dissociate into a proton and the water.

c Acid-Base Equilibria

Based on the pK_a values given above, the following equilibrium favors the *starting materials / products* because the hydroxonium ion is about 10^{10} times more likely to dissociate a proton than ammonium is.

NH_4^+	+	H_2O	$\rightleftharpoons$	NH_3	+	H_3O^+
acid		*base*		*base*		*acid*

Any acid-base equilibrium is likely to favor the side with the *weakest / strongest* acid because this is least likely to give up a proton.

Weak acids have *higher / lower* pK_a values than stronger acids.

Identify the roles of each compound, acid or base, in the following equilibria.

EtO^-	+	H_2O	$\rightleftharpoons$	$EtOH$	+	OH^-
acid / base		*acid / base*		*acid / base*		*acid / base*

$MeOH$	+	Me_3NH^+	$\rightleftharpoons$	$MeOH_2^+$	+	Me_3N
acid / base		*acid / base*		*acid / base*		*acid / base*

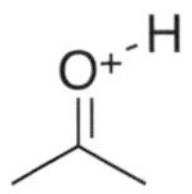

⟂O⁺-H	+	H_2O	$\rightleftharpoons$	⟂O	+	H_3O^+
acid / base		*acid / base*		*acid / base*		*acid / base*

acid / base   acid / base   acid / base   acid / base

It *is / is not* possible for the same compound to be an acid in some reactions and a base in others.

Identify the roles of each compound, acid or base, in the following equilibria *and* draw in curly arrows to express electron flow in the forward direction.

acid / base   acid / base   acid / base   acid / base

acid / base   acid / base   acid / base   acid / base

acid / base   acid / base   acid / base   acid / base

acid / base   acid / base   acid / base   acid / base

A base formed by deprotonating an acid can be called its *conjugate base / conjugate acid*.

Conjugate acid is the name given to the substance formed by *protonating a base / deprotonating an acid*.

Ammonium, NH_4^+, is the conjugate *acid / base* of ammonia.

Hydroxonium is the conjugate *acid / base* of water.

Find a table of pK_a values in your textbook or on the web, and use it to predict if the following acid-base equilibria favor starting materials or products. Do this by comparing the pK_a values of the acids on either side of the equilibria, and therefore ranking them as weaker or stronger acid. Finding this type of data, and using these tables (however they are presented) is a necessary skill.

stronger / weaker   *stronger / weaker*

favors *starting materials / products*

stronger / weaker   *stronger / weaker*

favors *starting materials / products*

stronger / weaker   *stronger / weaker*

favors *starting materials / products*

stronger / weaker   *stronger / weaker*

favors *starting materials / products*

88

NH

H_2N NH_2 + H_3O^+ ⇌ H_2N N^+H_2 NH_2 + H_2O

guanidine   *stronger / weaker*

favors *starting materials / products*

H + $^-$ ⇌ $^-$ + H

stronger / weaker   *stronger / weaker*

favors *starting materials / products*

H
N + $^-$ ⇌ N$^-$ + H

stronger / weaker   *stronger / weaker*

favors *starting materials / products*

H
N + $^-$ ⇌ N$^-$ + H

stronger / weaker   *stronger / weaker*

favors *starting materials / products*

H + NEt_3 ⇌ $^-$ + HN^+Et_3

stronger / weaker   *stronger / weaker*

favors *starting materials / products*

D Predicting Relative pK$_a$ Values

Predict relative, qualitative acidities of the following pairs of acids from the information given, and rationalize those observations as indicated. Show arrows to depict the electron flow that results in loss of a proton in each case.

Ethanoic acid is a *stronger / weaker* acid than trifluoroethanoic acid.

Trifluoroethanoate is more stable than ethanoate because it is relatively stabilized by *resonance / electronegativity* effects.

1,1,1,3,3,3-Hexafluoropropan-2-ol has a *higher / lower* pK$_a$ than propan-2-ol therefore it is a *stronger / weaker* acid.

The alkoxide from 1,1,1,3,3,3-hexafluoropropan-2-ol is *less / more* stable than that from propan-2-ol because of *resonance / electronegativity* effects.

Allyl anions are *more / less* stable than propyl anions due to *resonance / electronegativity* effects, hence propene is a *stronger / weaker* acid than propane.

The enolate from ethanal is *more / less* stable than allyl anions due to *resonance / electronegativity* effects, so ethanal has a *higher / lower* pK$_a$ than propene.

less / more stable

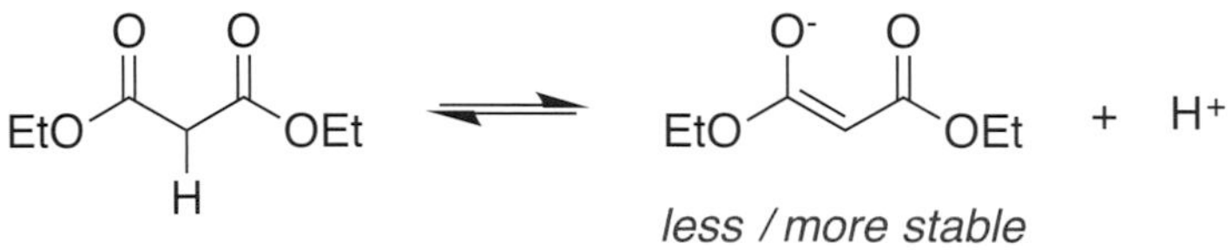

less / more stable

Dimethyl succinate has a *higher / lower* pK$_a$ than diethyl malonate, mainly due to *resonance / electronegativity* effects.

E Predicting Sites Of Protonation

Each of the following molecules has at least two obvious sites for protonation, but only one of them can be stabilized by resonance. Draw arrows to show the protonation at the most favorable site of these molecules, and the resonance structures that stabilize those particular protonated forms.

| *protonated form* | *protonated form* |

| *protonated form* | *protonated form* |

+ H⁺ ⇌   ↔

protonated form   *protonated form*

+ H⁺ ⇌   ↔

protonated form   *protonated form*

SMe + H⁺ ⇌   ↔

protonated form   *protonated form*

+ H⁺ ⇌   ↔

protonated form   *protonated form*

Me$_2$N

+ H$^+$ ⇌ ⟷

_____ _____
protonated form *protonated form*

Me$_2$N

+ H$^+$ ⇌ ⟷

_____ _____
protonated form *protonated form*

The following molecule is 1-methyl-1,2,3-triazole; it is likely to be protonated selectively at N^2 / N^3 / both. Explain your reasoning.

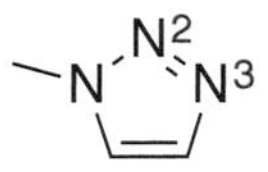

explanation:

_____
_____
_____ .

F Lewis Acids And Bases

All acids *do / do not* feature protons.

Lewis acids have a low-lying HOMO to accept electron density, *eg an empty p-orbital / a non-bonded electron pair*.

Lewis *acids / bases* tend to complex with molecules that have a non-bonded electron pair (a *lone pair of electrons*).

Boranes tend to be good Lewis *acids / bases* because they have *6 / 8 / 10* electrons in their valence shell and *an empty / a filled* p-orbital.

Protons *can / cannot* fit the definition of a Lewis acid.

Protons *do / do not* fit the definition of Brönsted Acids.

Circle those of the following compounds that are Lewis acids, and surround the Lewis bases with a box. Some of the compounds shown are neither Lewis acids nor bases, and others may be both.

BF_3

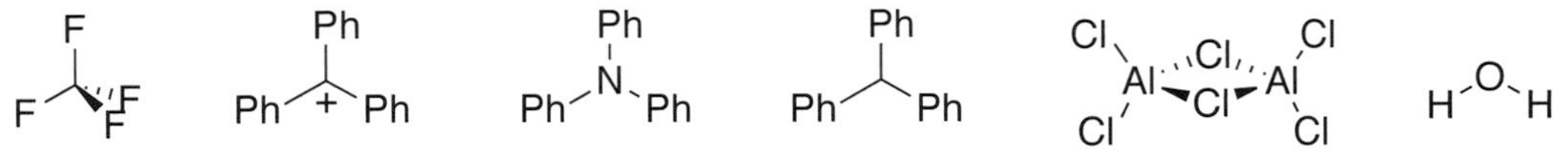

(dimer can dissociate)

H^+ NH_3

Draw the products of the following acid base equilibria including the three dimensional shape of the products, and show curly arrows to represent electron flow that occurs as the reaction moves in the forward direction.

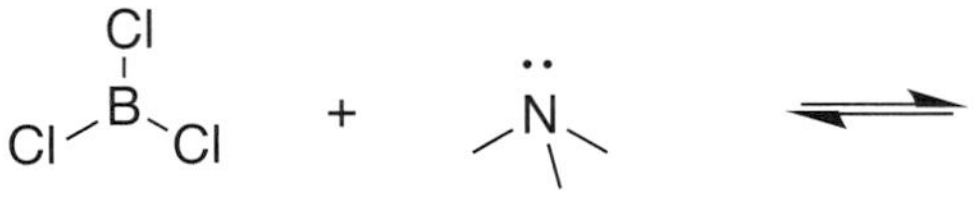

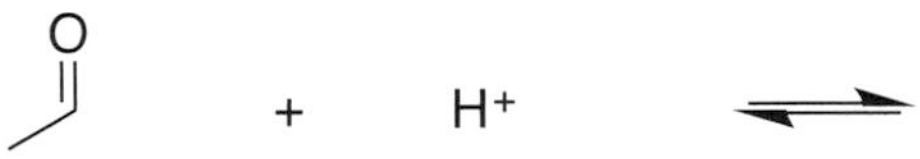

$+$ H^+

$+$ BF_3

In this last example, instead of drawing the geometry of the product, indicate if the two phosphorus atoms are sp / sp^2 / sp^3 hybridized.

7 Resonance: Practicing Curly Arrows

from chapter(s) _____ in the recommended text

A Introduction

Focus

Organic ions having more electrons than protons (anions), or more protons than electrons (cations) are most stable when the excess charge can be spread out, delocalized, across atoms; in fact, the more atoms involved the better. Delocalization of this kind can be expressed using curly arrows. Arrows can describe how electron density may flow back and forth between electronegative atoms, or towards positive charges effectively moving them around.

This section is about recognizing when resonance can occur, and using curly arrows to describe it when it does.

Reasons To Care

Resonance can explain differences in stabilities, acid-base strengths, and sites of reactivity.

Concepts Involved

hybridization • drawing structures • functional groups • curly arrows and electron flow • organic acids and bases

Objective

Application of curly arrows to resonance is not difficult, but it is empowering. This section illustrates how a few arrows to describe electron delocalization can explain some important concepts in organic chemistry.

B Resonance

Resonance is movement of electrons across an atomic framework. Electrons move *much faster than / much slower than / at about the same speed as* atoms in a molecule undergoing conformational changes.

The correct symbol to represent equilibrating resonance structures is (circle one):

It is *absolutely wrong / sometimes fine / optional* to use the other descriptors shown above.

To describe resonance, curly arrows are used to depict movement of *electrons / negative charges / positive charges / atoms*.

C Resonance Stabilized Anions

Hopping Across Atoms In Search Of Electronegativity

Draw curly arrows to describe the electron flow in the following resonance stabilized anions.

For allenes and some similar molecules, a bold dot may be used to differentiate two double bonds in series (1,2-dienes) from a long alkene double bond. Circle the allene anion above.

Electron flow *does / does not* allow the negative charge in the allyl anion to reside on C^2. The same *is / is not* true for the methyl allyl and 2-butynyl anions shown above.

Draw curly arrows and the missing resonance structures in the following diagram.

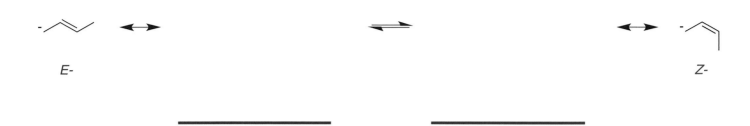

E-   Z-

_____   _____

It *is / is not* possible for Z-butenyl anions to equilibrate to their more stable *E*-isomers via equilibrating conformations.

It is *possible / impossible* for a molecule to have more than one resonance structure.
Complete the following diagrams by drawing in curly arrows and missing resonance structures.

_____   _____

_____   _____

Draw all the stable resonance forms of the following anion with curly arrows to depict electron flow.

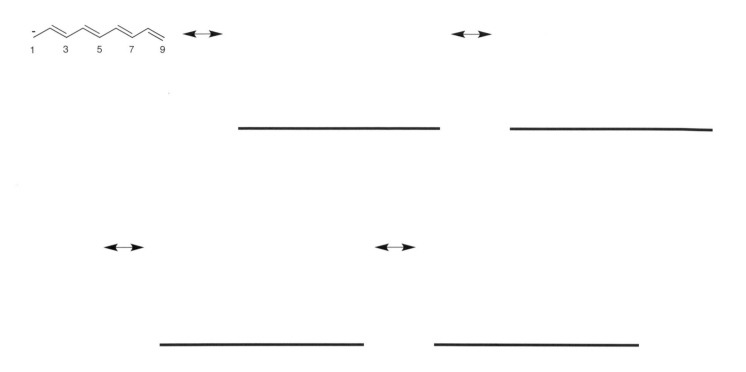

It *is / is not* possible for the negative charge on the nonatetraenyl anion to reside on the 1,3,5,7,9-carbon atoms. The negative charge in that anion *sometimes / never / always* can be found on C^2, C^4, C^6, and C^8, thus it *does / does not* appear that the negative charge hops between alternate carbon atoms.

An anion for which several stable resonance structures can be drawn is likely to be *more / less* stable than a similar one that has less resonance structures.

Circle the most stable anions in the following two sets.

Anions that have several resonance structures are said to be *delocalized / resonance stabilized / harder* relative to ones that do not.

The allyl anion is *more / less* stable than the pentadienyl anion, due to resonance.

Among the following, there are two pairs that are resonance forms of the same anion. Put circles around one pair, and boxes around the other.

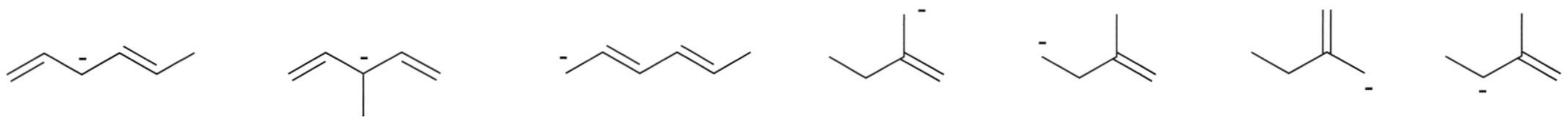

It *is / is not* possible for the negative charge to hop between atoms other than carbon.

Draw curly arrows and the missing resonance structures to show how the *E*- and *Z*-enolates shown below can equilibrate.

E-enolate   Z-enolate

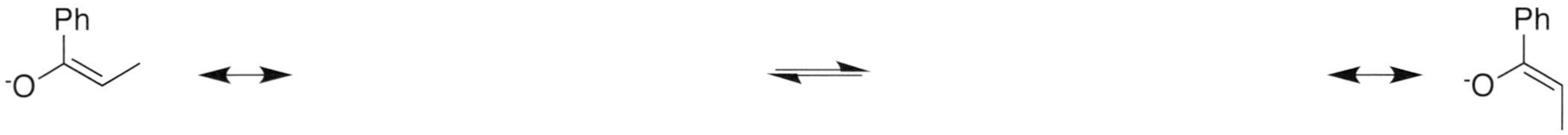

E-enolate   Z-enolate

SMe

Z-enolate

E-enolate

When resonance structures involve negative charges, the dominant one is that which has the charge on the most *electropositive / electronegative* atom.

Draw resonance structures of the following anions, and if one is more stable than the other, circle that dominant form.

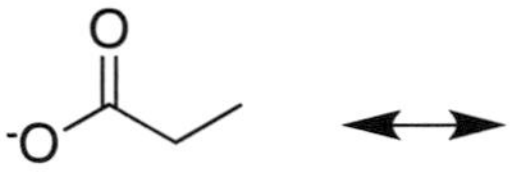

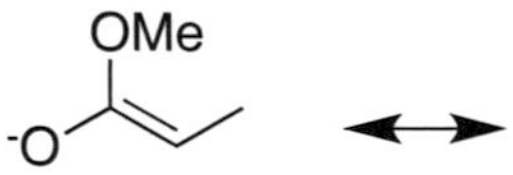

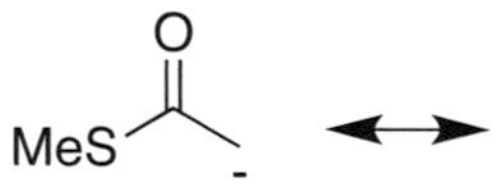

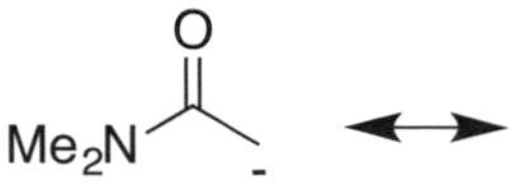

_____

_____

_____

_____

_____

_____

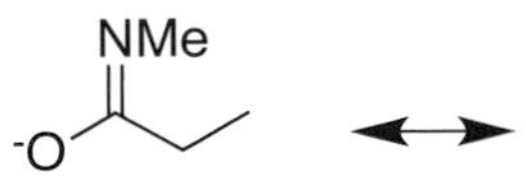

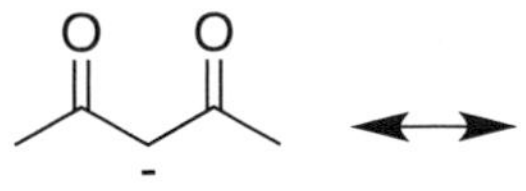

Put circles around those of the following anions that can be resonance stabilized.

Cl⁻ AcO⁻ BnO⁻ MeO⁻ ⁻N=N⁺:N⁻ NO₂⁻

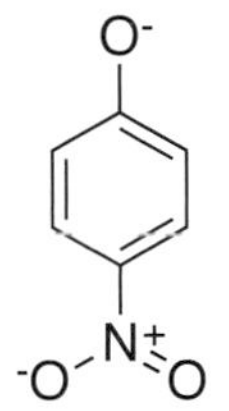

4-nitrophenolate

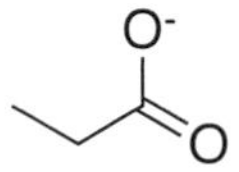

azide
anion

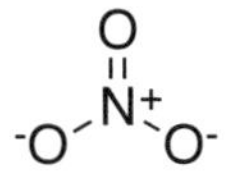

Circle those of the following parameters that significantly contribute to the stability of resonance structures.

-ve charge localized on   many contributing   highly localized   electron   -ve charge localized on
electronegative atom   resonance forms   charge   delocalization   electropositive atom

How Resonance Stabilization Of Anions Influences Acidity

The following equilibrium favors *product / starting material* if the anion A⁻ is resonance stabilized, relative to an equilibrium involving a very similar anion that is not.

$$HA \rightleftharpoons H^+ + A^-$$

Higher concentrations of protons correspond to *high / low* pK_a and pH values for the acid HA.

Rank the pK$_a$ values of the following sets of acids based on resonance delocalization considerations. Do this by writing *1* below the most acidic and *3* below the least.

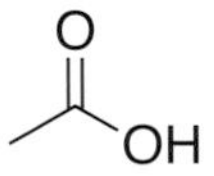

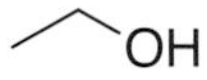

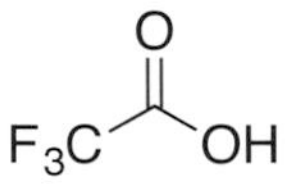

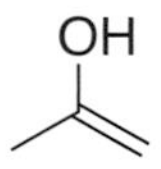

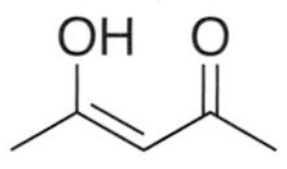

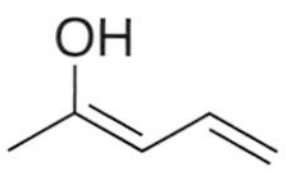

____   ____   ____   ____   ____   ____

Draw all the significant resonance forms of the phenolate anions shown below with curly arrows to show the electron flow.

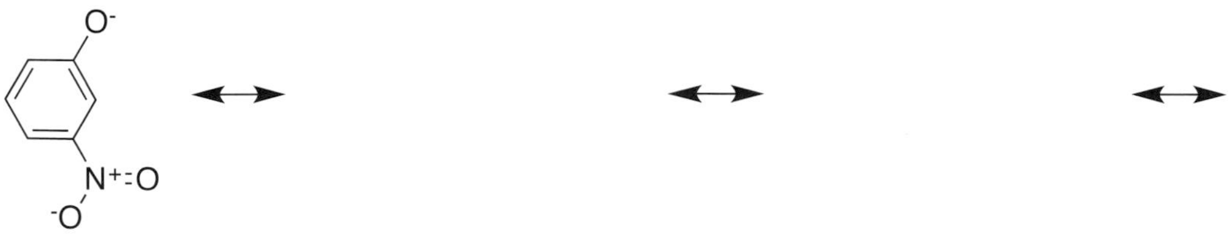

_____   _____   _____

_____   _____   _____

For 3-nitrophenolate (above), it *is / is not* possible for both the *O*-atoms of the nitro group to be negatively charged in the same resonance form.

Draw all the significant resonance forms of 2-methyl-4-nitrophenolate anion, and curly arrows to show the electron flow.

For 4-nitrophenolates (*eg* above), it *is / is not* possible for both the *O*-atoms of the nitro group to be negatively charged in the same resonance form.

For 2-nitrophenolates (not shown), it *is / is not* possible for both the *O*-atoms of the nitro group to be negatively charged in the same resonance form. 2-Nitrophenolates and 4-nitrophenolates tend to be *more / less* stable than their 3-isomers.

Rank the pK$_a$ values of the following sets of acids based on resonance delocalization considerations. Do this by writing *1* below the most acidic and *3* below the least.

Complete the following resonance profiles for the nitrite, nitrate, and hydrogen carbonate anions with curly arrows to show the electron flow.

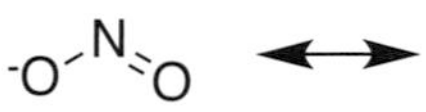

nitrite

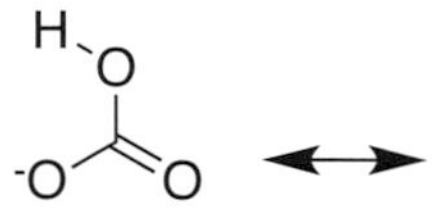

hydrogen
carbonate

nitrate

Based on resonance considerations, nitric acid should be a *stronger / weaker* acid than nitrous and carbonic acid.

pK_a values for nitrous, nitric, and carbonic acids are approximately 3.25, -1.35 and 6.35 so the strongest acid in the series is HNO_2 / HNO_3 / H_2CO_3.

D Resonance Stabilized Cations

Curly arrows most realistically represent flow of electrons *towards / away from* positive charges and rarely the reverse.

Complete the following diagrams by drawing in curly arrows and missing resonance structures.

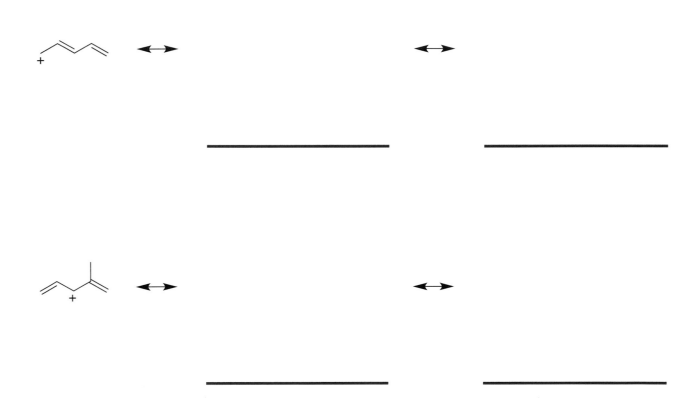

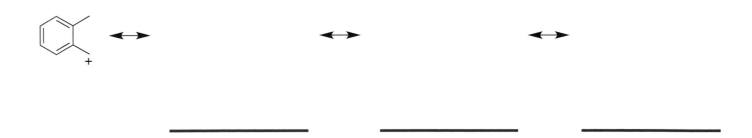

Draw all the stable resonance forms of the following cation with curly arrows to depict electron flow.

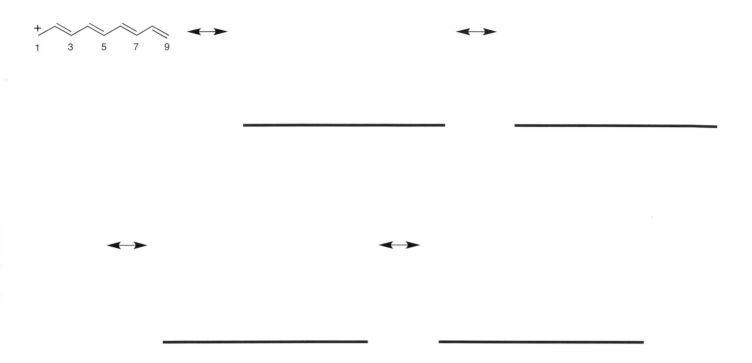

Positive charge in the nonatetraenyl cation *can / cannot* reside on the 1,3,5,7,9-carbon atoms and it is *sometimes / never / always* found on C^2, C^4, C^6, and C^8; consequently, it *does / does not* appear to hop between alternate carbon atoms.

A cation for which several stable resonance structures can be drawn is likely to be *more / less* stable than a similar one that has less resonance structures.

Circle the most stable cations in the following two sets.

Cations that have several resonance structures are said to be *more delocalized / harder* than ones that do not.

The allyl cation is *more / less* stable than the pentadienyl cation, due to resonance.

Among the following, there are two pairs that are resonance forms of the same cation. Put circles around one pair, and boxes around the other.

It *is / is not* possible for the positive charge to hop between atoms other than carbon.

When resonance structures have positive charges on different atoms, the dominant one is that which has the charge on the most *electropositive / electronegative* atom.

Cations with a positive charge on carbon, *ie carbanions / carbocations*, tend to be *more / less* stable when the carbon is more substituted with other carbons.

A carbocation that has one substituent is called *primary (1°) / secondary (2°) / tertiary (3°)*.

It *is / is not* possible to make a quaternary carbocation.

Draw resonance structures of the following cations, and if one is more stable than the other, circle that dominant form.

Elimination of water from histidinol in the biosynthesis of the amino acid histidine may involve resonance stabilization of a cationic intermediate. Show curly arrows to describe movement of electrons from the imidazole *NH* that shifts the positive charge into that nitrogen, and draw the resonance structure produced.

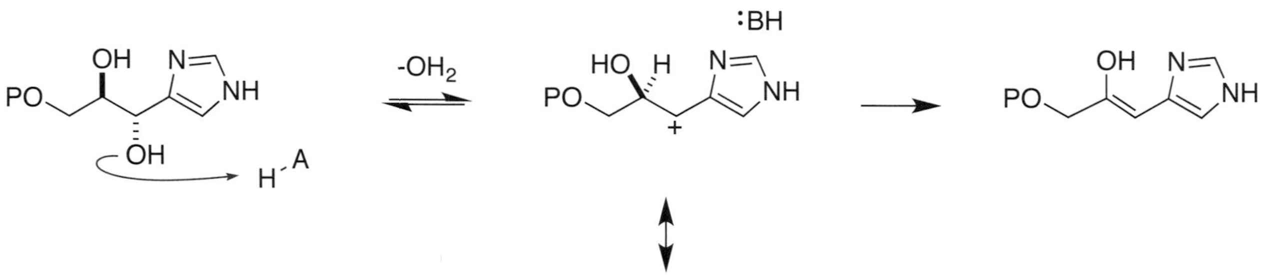

mediated by histidinol dehydrogenase

E Resonance In Neutral Molecules

Even though it is possible to draw charge separated resonance structures of neutral molecules, these tend to be significantly *more / less* stable than the corresponding neutral representations. Complete the following diagrams with curly arrows to relate these charge separated resonance structures to neutral forms.

There are two pairs of charge separated resonance structures among the following. Draw a circle around the most stable representation, and surround the least with a rectangle, for each pair.

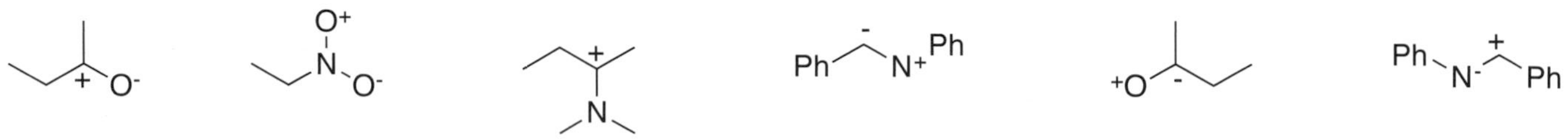

Some molecules that have a net neutral charge can only be represented as *zwitterions / counter ions*. Draw resonance structures of the following 1,3-dipolar molecules, and relate them with curly arrows.

$H_2C=N^+\!:N^-$ ⟷

diazomethane

$O=O^+\!-O^-$ ⟷

ozone

_____

_____

$N=N^+\!:N^-$ ⟷

methyl azide

$N\equiv N^+ O^-$ ⟷

nitrous oxide

_____

_____

F Resonance Stabilizes Some Conformations

Draw resonance forms of the following compounds, and indicate which one has the most stable "charge-separated" state.

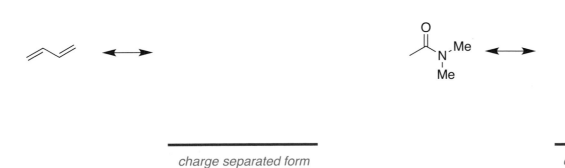

_____

charge separated form
more / less stable

_____

charge separated form
more / less stable

Match the rotations about the bonds illustrated in the following compounds with the energy barrier values shown, using the resonance structures above as a guide.

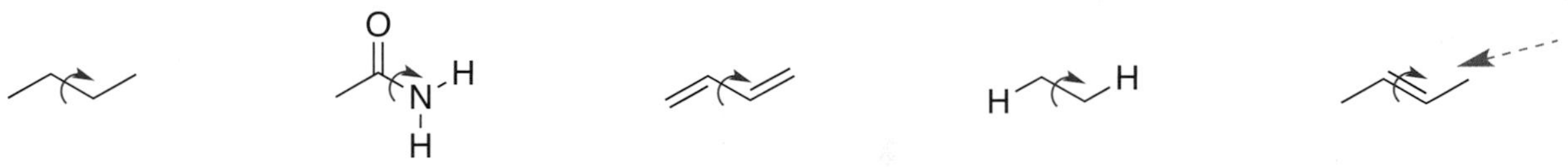

write numbers to indicate approximate maximum energy barriers

choices are: 260, 80, 20, 14, 12 kJ•mol⁻¹

8   Stereochemistry

from chapter(s) _____ in the recommended text

A   Introduction

Focus

Many molecules are handed (chiral). This section covers the essential concepts behind molecular chirality including priority rules to describe the handedness of molecules, properties of molecules that are of one handedness (enantiomers), that have two or more hands (diastereomers and epimers), and molecules that can easily become handed (prochirality including *Re*- and *Si*-nomenclature).

Reasons To Care

A large proportion of molecules can exist as handed forms, enantiomers. Chiral molecules like this include most major types of biomolecules, specifically DNA, RNA, carbohydrates, peptides, and proteins. Different stereoisomers (handed forms) of chiral pharmaceuticals do not have the same pharmacological profiles.

There has to be a set of priority rules to enable chemists to classify right or left-handed asymmetry when it occurs, and communicate the exact situation to others. These priority rules can be applied to enantiomers of handed molecules containing one, two, or multiple sites of asymmetry.

Priority rules can also be used to describe the face selectivity of approach of a reagent towards flat molecules that become chiral when the reagent adds (*ie* prochiral molecules).

Concepts Involved

how four different groups attached to a carbon cause it to be chiral • configurations • combinations of chiral centers • preferential approach of a reagent to one face of flat "prochiral" molecule favors generation of one stereoisomer • prochiral molecules (ones that become chiral via addition of one non-identical substituent)

Objective

Chirality is ubiquitous in life, on a macro- and molecular-scale. This section asks questions that make this apparent. People answering considering these questions carefully for the first time will see the world differently afterwards.

112

B Priority Rules

Substituents Without Multiple Bonds

According to the priority rules for determining stereochemistry, at the first point of difference, the atom with *higher / lower* atomic mass takes priority.

Circle the substituent from the following list that has the highest priority, and put a square around the one that has the lowest.

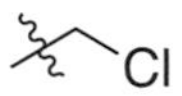

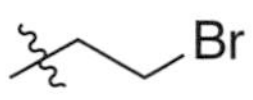

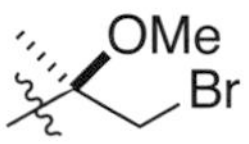

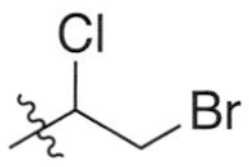

Cl   NMe₂   Cl   Br   OMe Br   Cl Br   Li

Substituents Connected To Multiple Bonds

Describe the problem assigning the priorities of the following substituents.

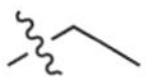

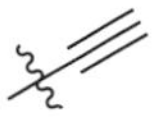

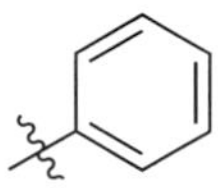

The problem is: _____ .

Priorities of substituents containing a multiple bond are determined by "splitting" them as in the example below; the priority is then determined at the first point of difference. Expand the other multiple bonds below in the same way.

eg   *is equivalent to*   H C H / C C

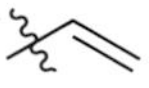

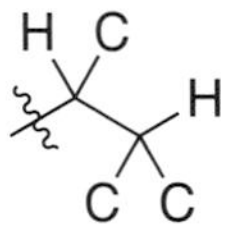

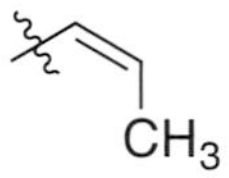

is equivalent to   CH₃

_____

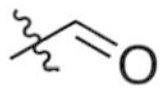

is equivalent to O

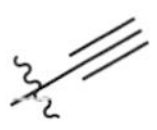

is equivalent to

_____   _____

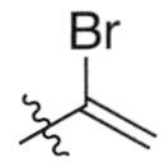

is equivalent to

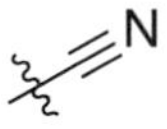

_____

is equivalent to

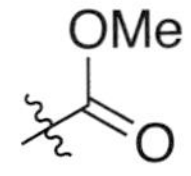

_____

is equivalent to

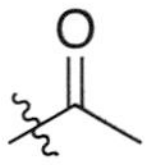

_____

is equivalent to

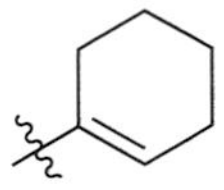

_____

is equivalent to

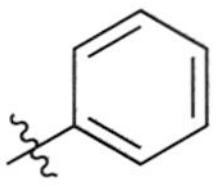

_____

is equivalent to

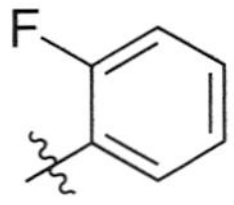

_____

is equivalent to

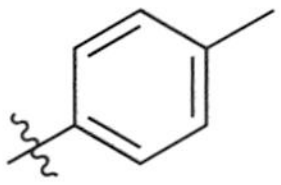

_____

is equivalent to

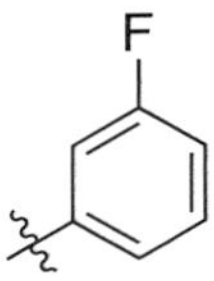

_____

is equivalent to

_____

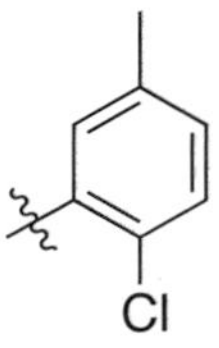

is equivalent to

_____

Circle the molecular fragment of highest priority in the following sets.

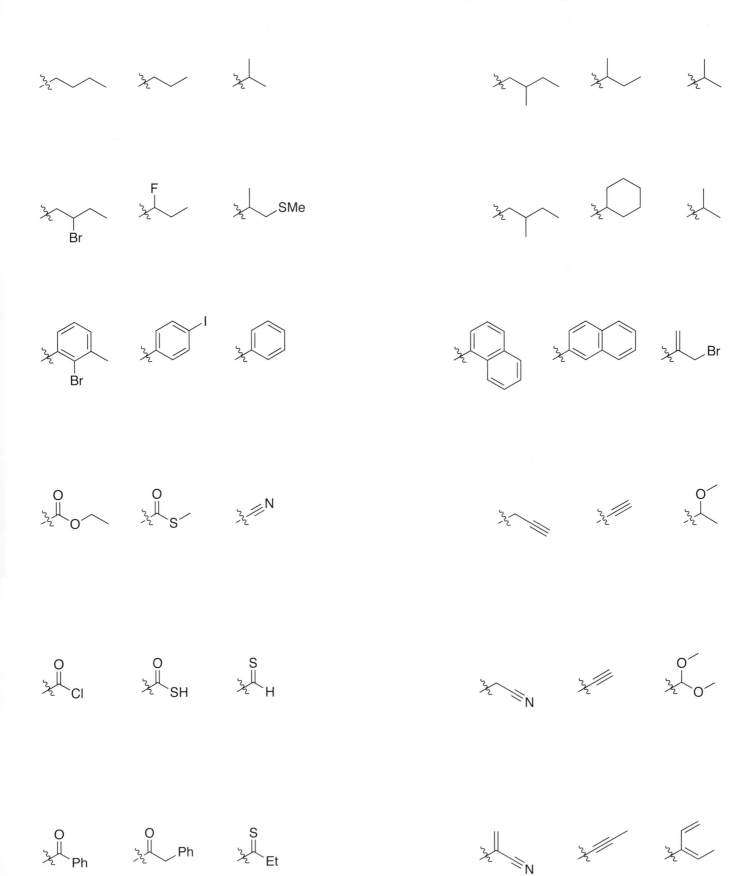

C Classifying Alkene Geometries

For alkenes, the terms *cis / trans* mean the same as / are different to *E / Z*.

Classify the following alkenes as *E*- or *Z*-, or circle *na* if this type of isomerism does not apply.

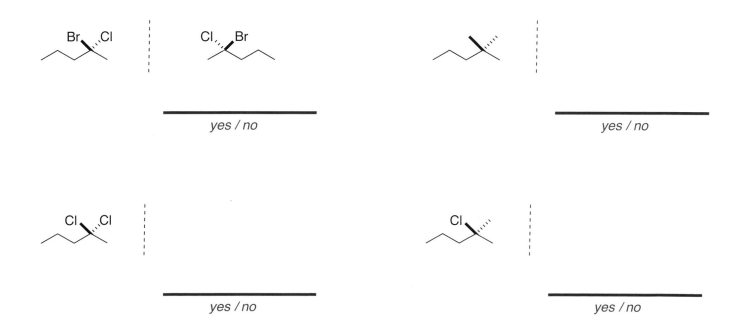

E- / *Z*- / na   *E*- / *Z*- / na   *E*- / *Z*- / na   *E*- / *Z*- / na   *E*- / *Z*- / na   *E*- / *Z*- / na   *E*- / *Z*- / na

E- / *Z*- / na   *E*- / *Z*- / na   *E*- / *Z*- / na   *E*- / *Z*- / na   *E*- / *Z*- / na   *E*- / *Z*- / na

D Chiral Centers

Draw images of the following molecules, as they appear in a mirror (represented by the dotted line), and indicate if that representation can be superimposed on the first one.

yes / no   *yes / no*

yes / no   *yes / no*

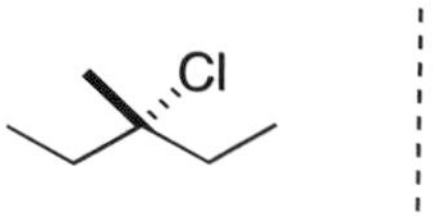

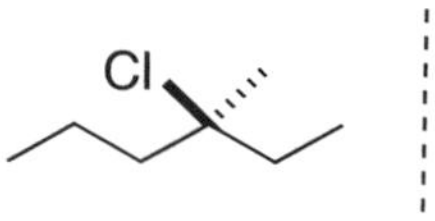

yes / no

yes / no

In molecules like those shown above, non-superimposable mirror images *do / do not* require that there be four different groups on a carbon atom.

Mirror images of organic molecules are called *diastereomers / enantiomers*, *only if / regardless of whether* they are superimposable or not.

Which of the following are enantiomers? To avoid mistakes, you may draw alternative conformations in potential mirror image poses.

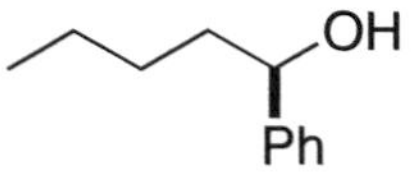 and 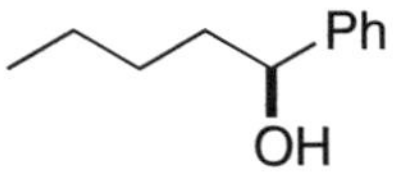 *is the same as* 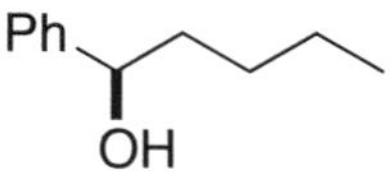 and 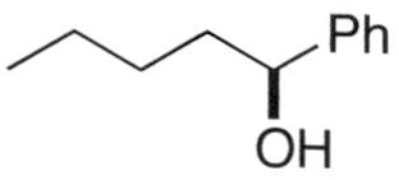

yes / no

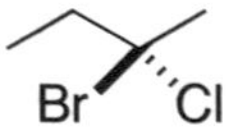 and 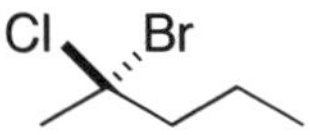

yes / no

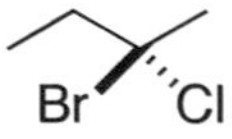 and 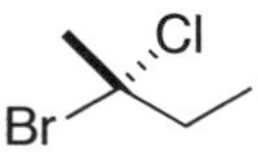

yes / no

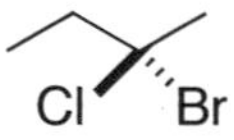 and 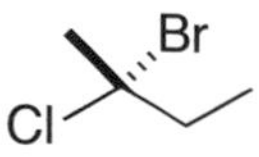

yes / no

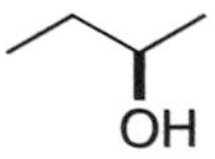 and 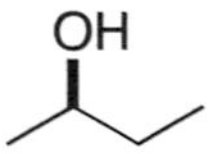

yes / no

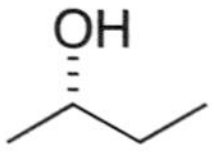 and 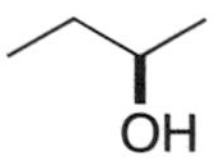

yes / no

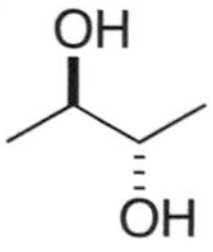 and 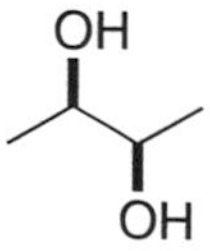

yes / no

yes / no   yes / no   yes / no

yes / no   yes / no   yes / no

Assign *R*- and *S*-configurations on every chiral center in the following molecules. Assigning chirality like this *can / cannot* establish if molecules are mirror images.

R / S   *R / S*   *R / S*   *R / S*   *R / S*   *R / S*

R / S   *R / S*

R / S   *R / S*   *R / S*   *R / S*   *R / S*   *R / S*

If a compound has *R*-stereochemistry, its enantiomer is always *R- / S-*.

If a compound has two chiral centers of *R,R*-stereochemistry, its enantiomer is always *R,R- / S,S- / S,R- / S,S*.

A diastereomer (not an enantiomer) of a compound that has *R,S-* stereochemistry can have a *S,S- / S,R-* configuration.

Pure enantiomers *do / do not* rotate plane-polarized light in equal but opposite amounts. This parameter, called the *optical rotation / plane rotation*, is constant if the conditions of measurement are the same, but otherwise depends on (circle those that apply): *compound concentration / temperature / wavelength of the light / solvent*.

E Combinations Of Chiral Centers

Meso-compounds *have / do not have* a plane of symmetry, and they *do / do not* rotate plane polarized light.

The following statement is *true / false*: in *meso* compounds the rotation caused by one chiral center is exactly canceled by an equal and opposite rotation from the other one.

Draw *meso*-isomers of the following optically active stereoisomers.

tartaric acid

Draw a diastereomer of the following compounds that is not an enantiomer.

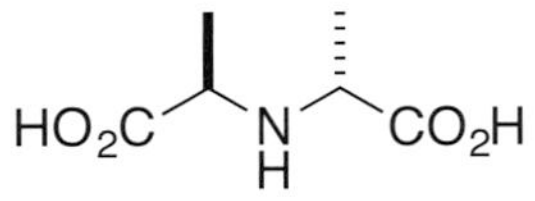

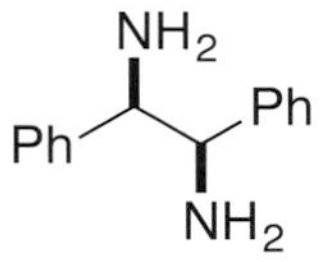

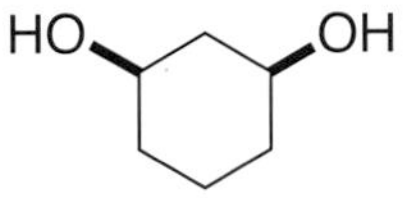

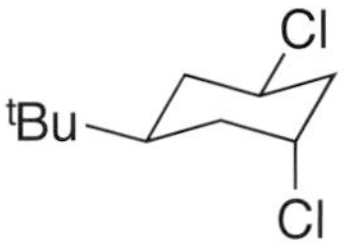

_____

_____

_____

_____

Draw all the possible stereoisomers of the following compounds.

_____ _____ _____

_____ _____ _____

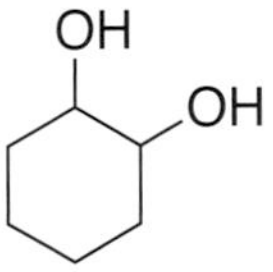

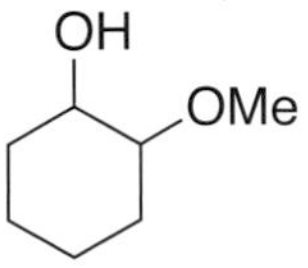

F Prochirality

Prochiral compounds *do / do not* necessarily rotate the plane of polarized light.

"Some prochiral compounds can be converted to chiral ones by *substituting* a group at the prochiral center" *true / false*.

Circle a carbon in the following molecules that is prochiral.

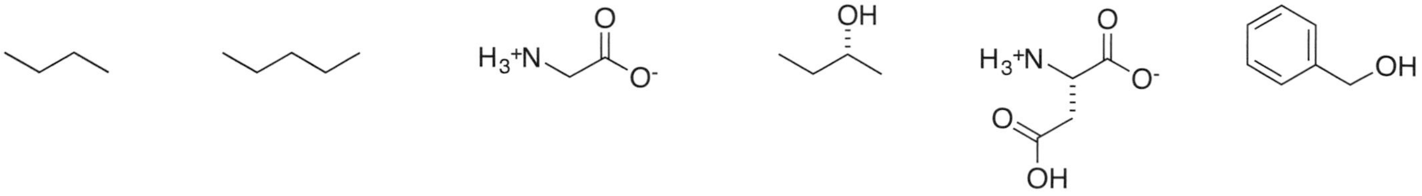

Circle a hydrogen in the following molecules that can be substituted by chlorine to give a *R*-enantiomer at a newly created chiral center. Choose only from the *H*-atoms shown.

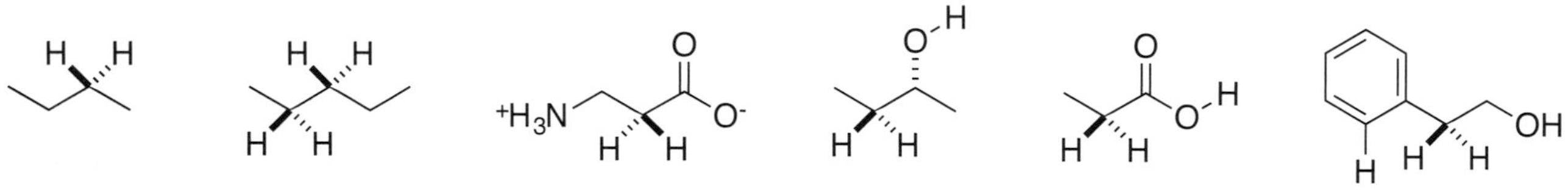

The hydrogen atoms circled in the diagram above are all *pro-S / pro-R / some pro-R and some pro-S*.

Circle a *methyl* group in the following molecules that can be substituted by a hydroxyl group (OH) to give a *S*-configuration at a new chiral center (if the substitution creates a new chiral center). Choose only from the methyl groups represented by "Me".

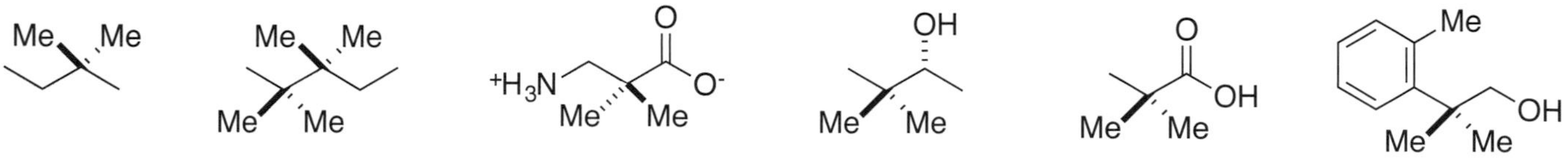

Methyl groups circled in the diagram above are all *pro-S / pro-R / some pro-R and some pro-S*.

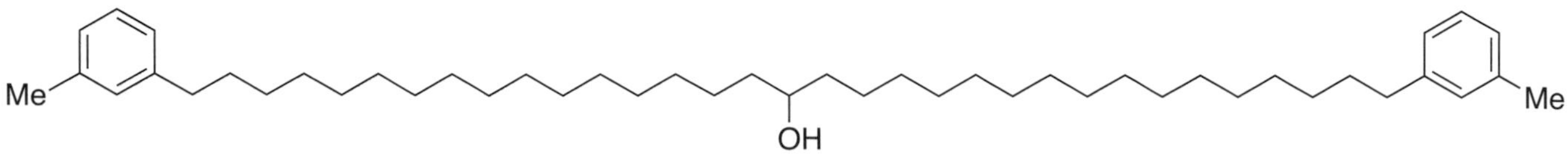

The two methyl groups in the molecule above *are / are not* prochiral.

Show the products of *syn*-addition of *H-OH* to the top face (above the paper) of the following alkenes.

H-OH

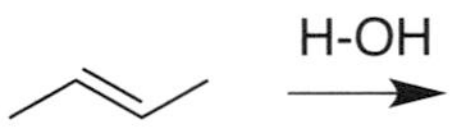

H-OH

_____

_____

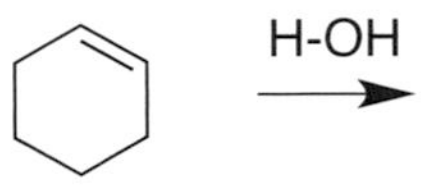

Show the possible products of *syn*-addition of *H-OH* to the top face of the following alkenes. In each case there are two possible products, but only one is chiral; show only that one.

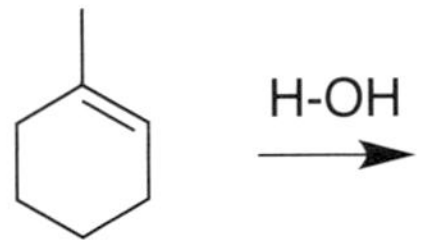

H-OH

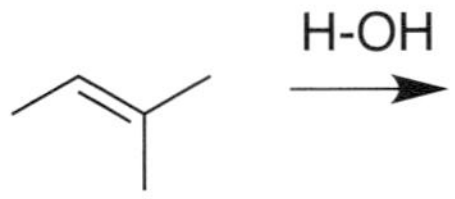

H-OH

_____

_____

"Some prochiral compounds can be converted to chiral ones by *adding* a group to the prochiral center" *true / false*.

When viewed from your orientation (looking down on the paper), the priority of the groups attached to the highlighted carbon in the following compounds are *all Re- / all Si / a mixture of Re- and Si-*.

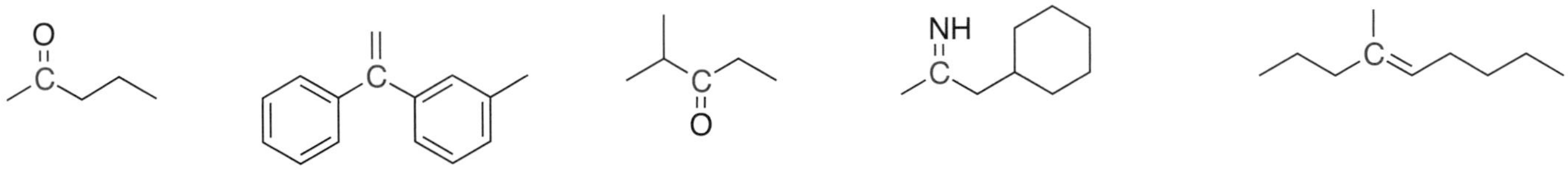

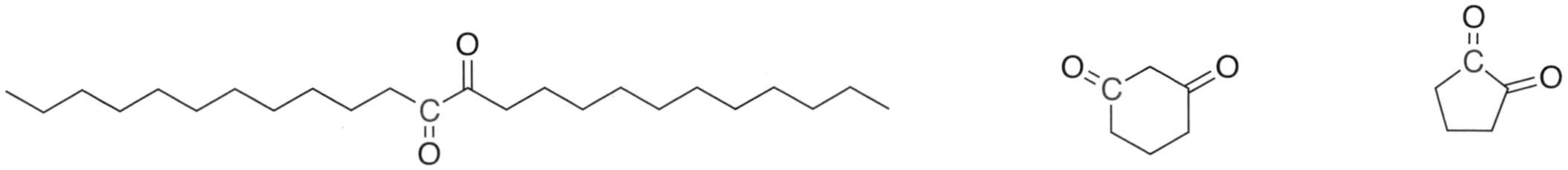

When viewed from the opposite orientation (looking up from below the paper), the priority of the groups attached to the highlighted carbon in the following compounds are *all Re- / all Si- / a mixture of Re- and Si-*.

An enzyme is found to be capable of adding hydrogen to the *pro-S* face of the following alkenes; draw the products.

Another enzyme delivers hydrogen to the *Re*-face of the following substrates. Draw the products. The last two examples involve *two* hydrogen addition reactions.

Reactions from the *Re*-face *sometimes / always / never* give the *R*-chiral centers, while reactions from the *Si*-face *sometimes / always / never* give the *S*-chiral centers.

9 S$_N$1 Displacement At sp^3 Centers

from chapter(s) _____ in the recommended text

A Introduction

Focus

Many reactions can be described in the following way, "A group dissociated from a molecule and left behind an organic cation, then that cation reacted with something else." Collectively, those reactions are called S$_N$1 processes.

Reasons To Care

There are a lot of complex molecules in Nature and man-made ones that interact with living systems. How do these come into existence? Some of them occur in Nature, they may quite literally grow on or in trees, for instance. Fine, but how did they get into the tree, or anywhere else? The answer is that complex organic molecules are built, "synthesized", from simpler building blocks. Who does the synthesis? Every living organism synthesizes organic molecules within their body, and chemists make them outside their body too.

Building molecules involves transforming one into another. One of the simplest possible ways by which this happens is:

- a suitable starting molecule has a fragment that can leave;

- that fragment is induced to leave thus forming an organic cation; then,

- the leaving group is replaced with something else.

taxol

"Well...How did I get here?"
Byrne, Frantz, Weymouth, Harrison, Eno and George

vinblastine

"Synthesis."
Burgess

S$_N$1 reactions like this occur in one flask, via processes wherein the leaving group departs in a step distinctly that precedes its replacement with a nucleophile.

Concepts Involved

hybridization • cation stabilities • kinetics as a tool to understand reaction mechanisms • how understanding mechanisms can help chemists make molecules

Objective

Much of chemistry involves: (i) understanding how a reaction has occurred; and/or, (ii) making a reaction give a desired product and not others. A huge number of different reactions occur via S$_N$1 pathways, and part of this *Inquisition* is to make sure the people recognize and apply them.

B Types Of Nucleophilic Substitutions

Negatively Charged Nucleophiles

Complete and balance the following equations.

N_3^- + MeI =   2 AcO⁻ + Cl⎓⎓Cl =

⎓⎓Cl + ⁻S⎓ =   BnBr + I⁻ =

Neutral Nucleophiles

Nucleophiles in nucleophilic substitution reactions can be neutral with no protons to conveniently lose after the process. Complete the following equations.

Et_3N + MeI =   2 ⎓Te⎓ + Cl⎓⎓Cl =

⎓⎓Cl + S⎓ =   BnBr + PPh_3 =

Nucleophiles in nucleophilic substitution reactions can be neutral and have protons that are conveniently lost. Complete the following equations.

Et_2NH + 1 MeI =   Ph⎓SH + Cl⎓⎓ =

Ph⎓Cl + HO⎓ = Me_3O^+ + I⁻ =

Charges On Leaving Groups

Leaving groups in nucleophilic substitution reactions can be anionic, as above. Complete the following equations.

$$\text{Cyclopentyl-Cl} + \quad {}^-N=N^+=N^- \quad =$$

$$MeI + NaSCN =$$

$$\text{(2-bromopentane)} + \quad NC^- =$$

$$^tBuCl + LiI =$$

Leaving groups can also be neutral. Complete the following equations.

$$\text{(pentyl-}N^+Ph_3) + \quad NC^- =$$

$$\text{(bicyclic } N^+\text{—Ph)} + LiI =$$

$$LiO\text{—}\diagup\diagdown\text{—}S^+\text{—}Cl^- \quad = \qquad\qquad + \qquad\qquad +$$

(intramolecular)

$$Ph_3P^+Me \; Cl^- \quad + \quad NaSEt \qquad\qquad = \qquad\qquad + \qquad\qquad +$$

c S_N1

Introduction Into The Key Steps

Substitution describes reactions in which one group *replaces another / adds to a molecule.*

S_N1 stands for substitution by a nucleophile *in one step / with first order kinetics.*

Show the carbocations and anions that are formed in the following processes.

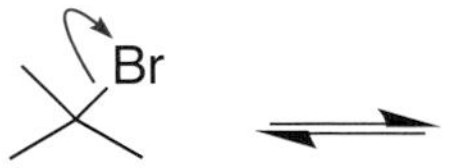

carbocation and bromide

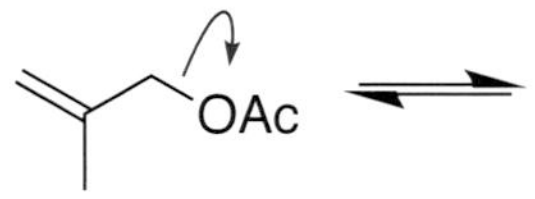

mesylate

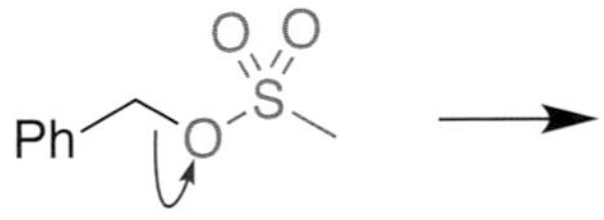

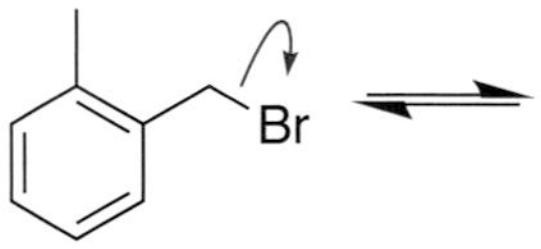

benzyl carbocation and ⁻OMs

In a S_N1 reaction, formation of a carbocation *is / is not* the rate limiting step.

Draw curly arrows to represent the following dissociation processes, and show the carbocations and anions that are formed.

tosylate

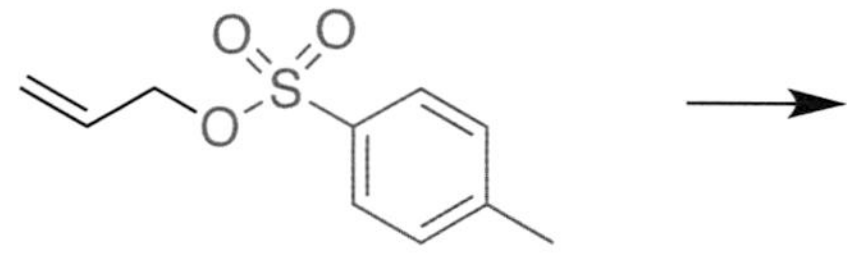

———————————————
allyl carbocation and O⁻Ts

hydrogen
phosphate

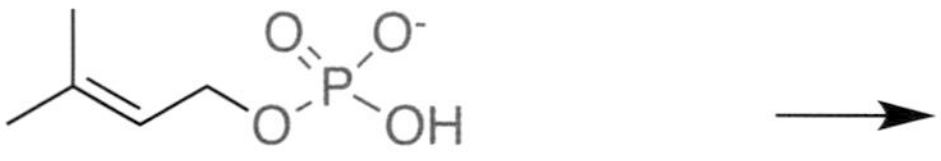

———————————————
allyl carbocation and hydrogen phosphate

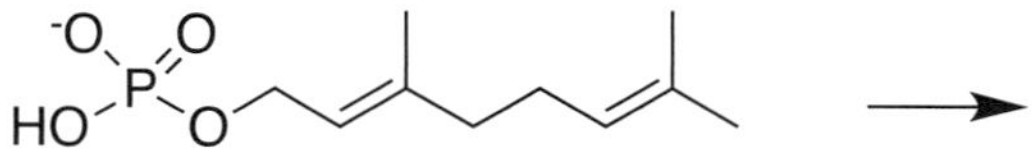

geraniol hydrogen phosphate

———————————————
an allyl carbocation and hydrogen phosphate

Show the products of the following dissociation processes.

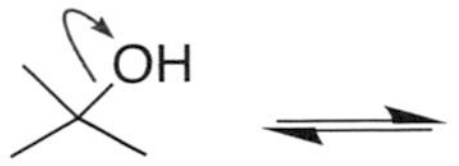

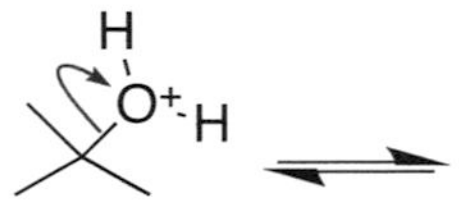

carbocation and hydroxide

carbocation and water

Water is a much *better / worse* leaving group than hydroxide, so the pathway on the *left / right* is more favorable, whereas the one on the *left / right* does not proceed at all.

Some poor *leaving groups* can be converted into better ones by protonating them: *true / false*.

Complete the following diagrams including curly arrows to show electron flow.

H+

-H₂O

fast / slow

protonated intermediate

carbocation intermediate

H+

-HOAc

protonated intermediate

carbocation intermediate

In the last example, only protonation of O^1 / O^2 is stabilized by resonance from the other oxygen.

Carbocations *can / cannot* combine with negatively charged nucleophiles to produce neutral molecules. Each of the following reactions gives a single product; show what that is and curly arrows to explain how it is formed.

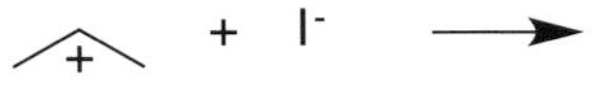

When carbocations combine with *neutral* nucleophiles they form *cations / anions* which may then lose a proton to become neutral, but only if there is a proton that can be lost to neutralize the positive charge.

If the starting materials are enantiomerically pure, the products will be *optically active / racemic*, because the intermediate, *sp / sp² / sp³* hybridized carbocations are *flat / tetrahedral* and the nucleophile can approach from either face.

The following reactions each gives a single product; show that and curly arrows to explain its formation.

intermediate   *product*

CH₂=CHCH₂Cl (allyl chloride) ⇌ $\xrightarrow[-H^+]{EtOH}$

_____   _____

intermediate   *product*

Rigorously, the reaction above has not one but *two* intermediates. Most undergraduate texts ignore the second one for simplicity. Draw the full mechanism below:

CH₂=CHCH₂Cl ⇌ $\xrightarrow{EtOH}$

_____   _____

intermediate   *protonated intermediate*

$\underset{+H^+}{\overset{-H^+}{\rightleftharpoons}}$

_____

product

S$_N$1 reaction of *tert*-butyl chloride with water involves *one / two* intermediates.

S$_N$1 reaction of *tert*-butyl bromide with acetate (MeCO$_2^-$) involves *one / two* intermediates.

S$_N$1 reaction of bromide with allyl chloride involves *one / two* intermediates.

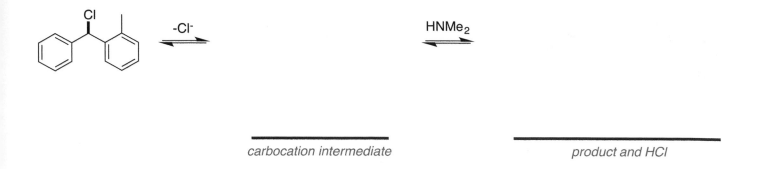

carbocation intermediate

product and HCl

Using exactly the same format as above, draw mechanisms for the following S_N1 reactions showing fast and slow steps and clear curly arrows to depict electron flow.

a

Ph   Cl

Ph   Ph

trityl chloride

heat in
→
water
-HCl

trityl alcohol

b

geranyl phosphate

Cl^-
→
$-PO_4^{3-}$

geranyl chloride

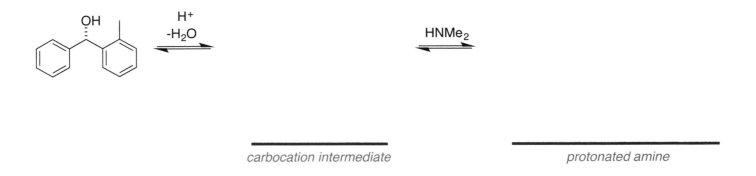

carbocation intermediate

protonated amine

In the reaction above, the reagent added could be an ammonium salt of the form $H_2N^+Me_2$ X^- where X^- is a non-nucleophilic anion (*eg* hydrogen sulfate, hydrogen phosphate).

Kinetics Of S$_N$1

Complete the following mechanism and reaction profile: show curly arrows, indicate if each step is fast or slow by showing corresponding relative energy barriers on the energy profile, and indicate if the process involves an intermediate or not.

OH   H+
      fast / slow

-H₂O
fast / slow

Nu⁻
fast / slow

protonated intermediate

carbocation

energy

reaction progress

At constant acid concentration, the rate of the reaction above *is / is not* proportional to the concentration of the starting alcohol. Complete the following:

rate is proportional to

rate =

_____   _____

where k is the rate constant.

The S_N1 reaction of triphenylmethyl chloride with sodium cyanide proceeds *twice as fast / at the same rate / at half the rate* if the concentration of the cyanide salt is doubled.

Carbocation Stability

Rates of S_N1 reactions tend to *decrease / increase* with stabilities of carbocation intermediates.

Rank the stabilities of the carbocations that may be formed from the following alcohols by drawing the carbocation structures on the line below *without using the letter C to show carbon atoms*: ^tBuOH, EtOH, MeOH, $^nPr(CHOH)Et$.

_____

most stable   *least stable*

Indicate qualitative relative rates of S_N1 reactions of the following alkyl halides: ^tBuBr, EtBr, EtI, Et(CHBr)Et, ^tBuI (ignore the possibility of competing reactions) by drawing their structures on the line below *without using the letter C*.

_____

fastest   *slowest*

Write Me⁺, 1°, 2°, and 3° (to stand for methyl, primary, secondary, and tertiary carbocations) in the following diagrams to correctly depict number of p-to-σ interactions, and carbocation stabilities.

show 3°, 1°, 2°, Me
on top of line

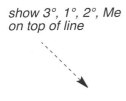

least stable   *most stable*

on bottom of line
show number of p-to-s interactions

Predict the rates of the following reactions of alkyl halides with water assuming they proceed exclusively via S$_N$1 mechanisms (not all will, in fact).

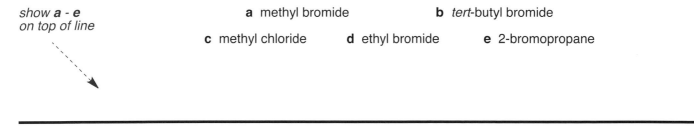

show a - e   **a** methyl bromide   **b** *tert*-butyl bromide
on top of line
                     c methyl chloride   **d** ethyl bromide   **e** 2-bromopropane

fastest   *slowest*

In Et⁺ the sp³ orbitals of the methyl group are tilted a bit *towards / away* from the empty p-orbital of the cation, and this *increases / decreases* the overlap, and therefore the stabilization, relative to a situation in which the orbitals were completely parallel.

In the allyl cation, there is a conformation in which the p-orbital of the carbocation is completely parallel with the p-orbitals that form the π-bond, hence the stabilization of the system overall is *greater / less* than that from hyperconjugation in Et⁺.

Allyl cations are *more / less* stable than many other primary carbocations.

Stereochemistry And S$_N$1

All the reactions shown below begin with optically pure starting materials. Show all the products and circle those that retain any optical activity. Use jagged lines to indicate mixtures of stereomers.

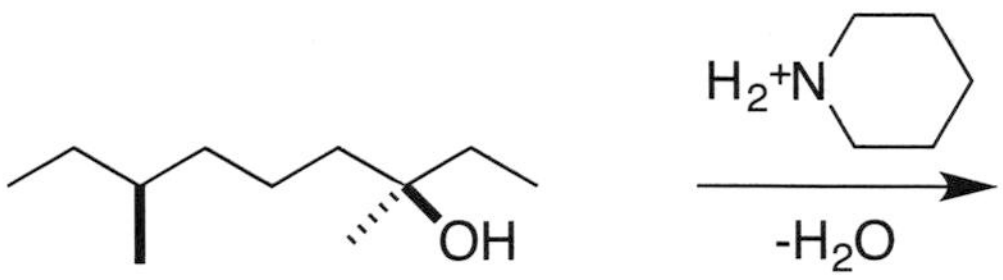

_____

circle if optically active

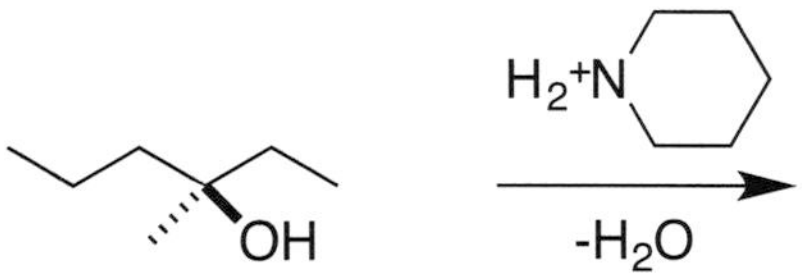

_____

circle if optically active

Identify the product of the following reaction, and indicate if it is optically active.

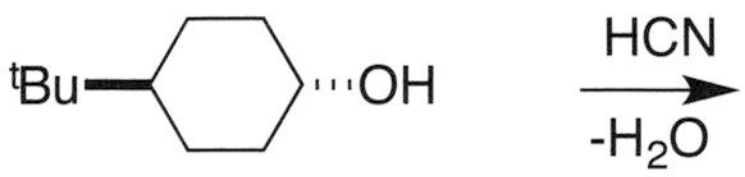

_____

circle if optically active

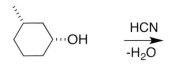

HCN
$\longrightarrow$
$-H_2O$

_____

circle if optically active

HCN
$\longrightarrow$
$-H_2O$

_____

circle if optically active

10 S$_N$2 Displacement At sp^3 Centers

from chapter(s) _____ in the recommended text

A Introduction

Focus
The last section described the S$_N$1 mechanism in which leaving groups leave *before* being replaced by nucleophiles. This section describes a different common pathway, also applicable to many reactions, in which leaving groups leave *as* nucleophiles replace them.

Reasons To Care
Deciding to dissociate and being *forced* to do so are quite different. Increasing the amount of a nucleophile in a S$_N$1 process has no influence on reaction rates, but S$_N$2 processes are accelerated in direct proportion to the amount added. S$_N$1 reactions do not "remember" initial configurations, they just move on, but in S$_N$2 stereochemistries completely flip. Moreover, once a molecule dissociated in the first step in S$_N$1, the highly reactive cationic intermediate is unstable and prone to unproductive side-reactions that may not occur in S$_N$2.

Concepts Involved
hybridization • resonance • electron flow • how mechanism impacts stereochemistry

Objective
This section encourages understanding of differences to enable design of experiments to test if transformations did or did not occur via S$_N$1 or S$_N$2, and recognition of the likely mechanism from rate and stereochemical data. It is an early step towards mechanistic wisdom and enlightenment.

B Differentiating S$_N$1 and S$_N$2

S$_N$2 describes reactions in which one group *replaces another / adds to a molecule* and *in two steps / with first order kinetics / with second order kinetics*.

Inversion of configuration is observed in *S$_N$1 / S$_N$2* processes whereas *S$_N$1 / S$_N$2* mechanisms involve loss of configuration at the site where the reaction occurs.

Nucleophilic substitutions that potentially involve less stable carbocations tend to proceed via *S$_N$1 / S$_N$2* pathways.

Similar reactions that may involve allylic, benzylic, or tertiary carbocations usually feature *S$_N$1 / S$_N$2* mechanisms.

Draw circles around the following substrates that are likely to react with cyanide anion via S$_N$1 reactions, and surround those that probably proceed via S$_N$2 processes with boxes.

Stereochemical Inversion In S$_N$2 Reactions

Draw curly arrows for the following S$_N$2 displacement reactions, and indicate the product including stereochemical details.

Transition states / intermediates in S_N2 displacement processes have geometries that resemble *trigonal bipyramidal / tetrahedral* shapes.

Complete the following representation featured in S_N2 reaction of methyl iodide with phenoxide.

$$PhO^{\delta-} ----\!\!\!\!\!\!\!\!\! \int ------$$

Sophomore organic student Kandy Floss had a habit of retaining one boyfriend (B) until she had lined up her next; we might call that S_B1 / S_B2. Conversely, her classmate Kurt Donothurt had a S_G1 / S_G2 approach, because he tends to let his current girlfriend (G) go before finding another.

Kinetics And S_N2 Pathways

Complete the following mechanism and reaction profile: show curly arrows, indicate if each step is fast or slow by showing corresponding relative energy barriers on the energy profile, and indicate if the process involves an intermediate or not.

product plus by-product

energy

reaction progress

In S_N2 reactions, doubling the concentration of the nucleophile *halves / does not influence / doubles* the reaction rate.

Reaction of methyl iodide with azide is *accelerated / decelerated* by adding more N_3^-.

A substrate that might react via both S_N1 and S_N2 pathways is *more / less* inclined to proceed via the bimolecular route if the nucleophile concentration is very high.

The transition state in a S_N2 reaction is *more / less* charged-localized than carbocation intermediates in S_N1 processes, hence if either pathway could occur S_N1 reactions will be favored if the solvent medium is highly polar.

c Interconversion Of Enantiomers And Diastereomers

Conversion Of Alcohols Into Leaving Groups

Hydroxyl groups *are / are not* good leaving groups in nucleophilic substitution reactions.
Conversion of alcohols into tosylates or mesylates makes them into much *better / worse* leaving groups.
Draw the structures of the following compounds without using the abbreviations *Ts* or *Ms*.

| ^{n}butyl mesylate | ^{i}propyl mesylate | cyclohexyl tosylate |

Draw the products of the following reactions, showing stereochemistry: it is acceptable to use the abbreviations *Ms* and *Ts*.

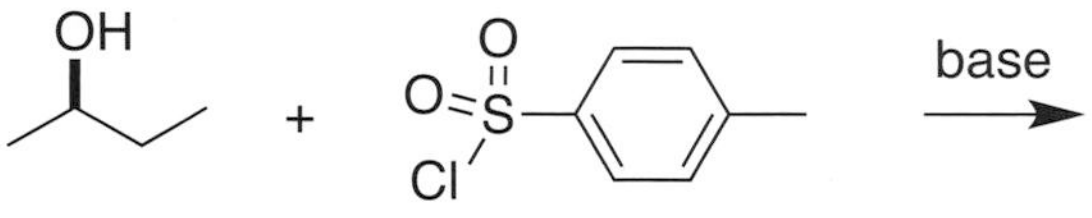

_____

ᵇutyl tosylate

_____

_____   _____

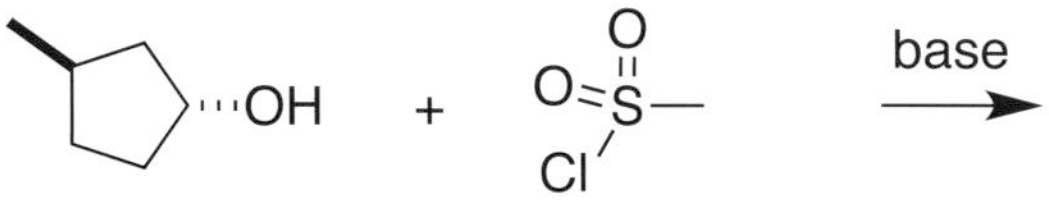

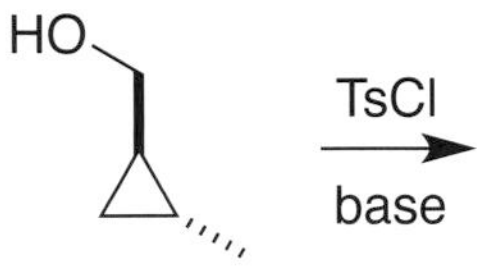

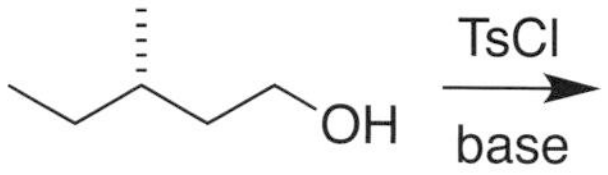

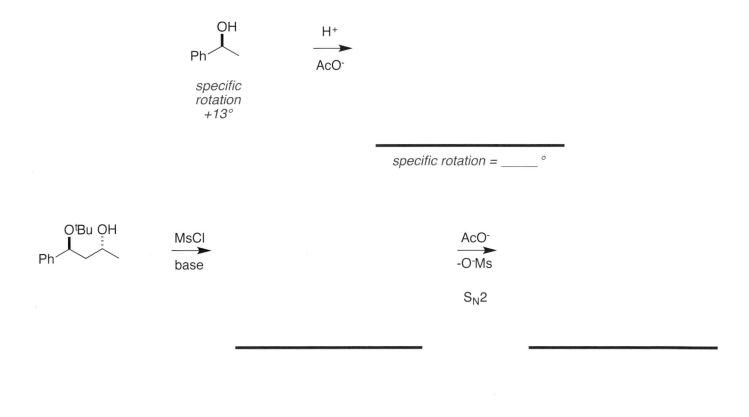

Mesylates and tosylates are *better / worse* leaving groups than hydroxide; they can be formed with *retention / inversion* of configuration at an alcohol center, and displaced in S_N2 processes with complete *retention / inversion / loss* of stereochemistry.

The following questions feature conversion of *O*-acetate groups (OAc) into alcohols via a step called *hydrolysis*. If the oxygen is connected to a chiral center, its configuration does not tend to change.

Show the missing products, indicate key curly arrows at each stage, and pay attention to stereochemistry. If optical rotation data are shown for the starting materials, estimate the specific optical rotation of the corresponding product. The first reaction is most likely S_N1 / S_N2.

specific rotation = _____ °

hydrolysis

MsCl
base

AcO⁻
-O⁻Ms

S_N2

specific
rotation
+42°

——————————   ——————————

hydrolysis

——————————

specific rotation = _____ °

OH

H⁺
AcO⁻

——————————

(i) XS TsCl
(ii) AcO⁻

HO

OH

——————————

product of one S_N1 and one S_N2 reaction

Stereoelectronic Effects

S_N1 / S_N2 reactions occur via approach of a nucleophile along the same trajectory as a leaving group departs.

Substrates that have shapes that preclude approach of a nucleophile in a trigonal bipyramidal *transition state / intermediate* cannot readily undergo bimolecular nucleophilic substitution reactions.

In the following substrates, the symbol X represents a leaving group. Circle the substrates that cannot undergo a S_N2 reaction due to such *stereoelectronic* reasons, and put a box around those that would not be expected to react via either S_N2 or S_N1 pathways.

S_N1 displacements involve interaction of a *HOMO / LUMO* on the substrate with a nucleophile *HOMO / LUMO*.

In S_N1 reactions the LUMO is *the empty p-orbital of the carbocation / filled orbitals on the nucleophile*.

S_N2 displacements involve interaction of a *HOMO / LUMO* on the substrate with a nucleophile *HOMO / LUMO*.

In S_N2 reactions the LUMO is a σ / σ^* orbital.

Show the σ^*-orbitals of the $C - I$ bonds of the following locked iodocyclohexanes, and the direction a nucleophile like cyanide would have to approach from in a S_N2 displacement reaction.

draw C - I σ^*-orbitals and orientation of S_N2 displacement by CN⁻

Circle the iodocyclohexane above that would be least likely to undergo a S_N2 displacement reaction.

D Making Carboxylic Acids And Amines Via S$_N$2 Reactions

Cyanide: A Useful *C*-Nucleophile

Nitriles can be made using cyanide anion in S$_N$2 and S$_N$1 reactions. They can be hydrolyzed with aqueous acid to amides. Predict the products of the following reactions.

This type of transformation (nitrile displacement then hydrolysis) works for *4-MeOC₆H₄I / MeI / BnI / allyl bromide / vinyl iodide* (circle the correct ones).

Phthalimide: Useful *N*-Nucleophile For Syntheses Of Primary Amines

A way to form primary amines is via alkylation of phthalimide, then hydrolysis. Look up the structure of phthalimide and predict the products of the following reactions.

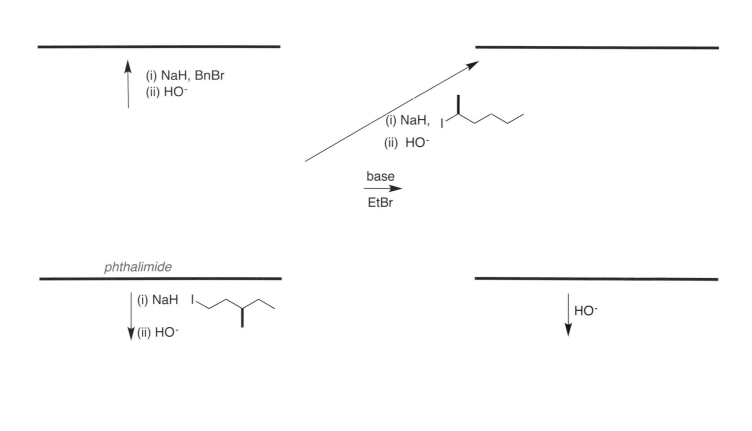

Using this reaction it is possible to make *primary amines / secondary amines / tertiary amines / quaternary amine salts* (strike out impossible).

This so called *Gabriel / Angel* synthesis is a *better / worse* way to make primary amines than by alkylating ammonia.

Throughout, the byproduct is a dianion, *ie* 1,2-($^{-}$OOC)$_2$C$_6$H$_4$ derived from phthalic acid.

11 Elimination Reactions To Form Alkenes

from chapter(s) _____ in the recommended text

A Introduction

Focus

Uni- and bimolecular elimination (E1 and E2) mechanisms are similar to S_N1 and S_N2. S_N1 and E1 both involve carbocation intermediates, the only difference is that in E1 they lose a proton to form alkenes rather than react with nucleophiles to give substitution products. Similarly, S_N2 and E2 are bimolecular processes involving loss of leaving groups, but alkenes rather than substitution products are formed in E2. In E2 reactions, leaving groups are displaced via little cascades of three two-electron shifts (three curly arrows) rather than direct displacement (two ca's). The focus of this section is on elimination reactions.

Reasons To Care

Synthesis of organic molecules often involves formation of $C - C$ bonds with an alcohol group on one of those carbons. That alcohol may not be necessary, and in many cases it is *eliminated* as water to give an alkene, that may then be changed in several ways. This is the situation when bacteria make polyketide natural products, like the anti-cancer compound epothilone B.

epothilone B

E1, E2 and related elimination mechanisms are part of the everyday vocabulary in biological chemistry.

Concepts Involved

hybridization • carbocation stability • electron flow • conformations of acyclic and cyclic compounds • kinetics • stereoelectronic effects

Objective

Questioning at this stage of the *Inquisition* should be easier to endure because of what has been overcome before. There are *always* reactions that have not been encountered before, so the misguided that focus on learning specific transformations will be condemned to perpetual torment. However, the number of concepts involved is small. Grasp these key concepts and fear organic chemistry no more.

B E1 Mechanisms

Complete the following reaction profile (indicate if each step is fast or slow).

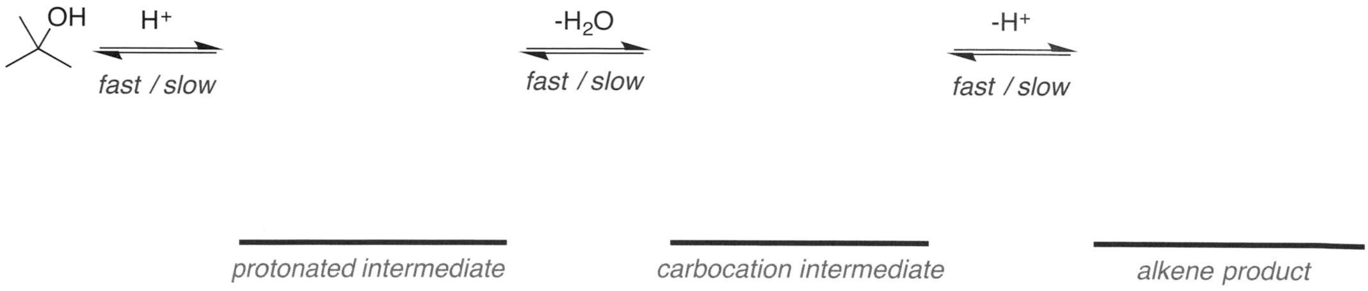

OH   H⁺   -H₂O   -H⁺

fast / slow   fast / slow   fast / slow

protonated intermediate   carbocation intermediate   alkene product

energy

reaction progress

Kinetics

At constant acid concentration, the rate of the reaction above *is / is not* proportional to the concentration of the starting material alcohol. Complete the following:

rate is proportional to   rate =

where *k* is the rate constant.

Carbocation Stability

Rates of E1 reactions tend to *decrease / increase* with stabilities of carbocation intermediates.

Rank the stabilities of the carbocations $^tBu^+$, Et^+, Me^+, $Me(CH^+)Et$ by drawing their structures on the line below *without using the letter C to show carbon atoms*.

most stable   *least stable*

Indicate the rates of E1 eliminations from the following alkyl halides: ^tBuBr, $EtBr$, EtI, $Et(CHBr)Et$, ^tBuI (ignore the possibility of competing reactions) by drawing their structures on the line below *without using the letter C*.

fastest   *slowest*

Bredt's Rule

Circle the alkene-bond geometry that is most stable from the following alternatives.

The hybridization state of the carbon marked with a red dot in *adamantane* below is $sp^3 / sp^2 / sp$ so it has ideal dihedral angles of about *109° / 180° / 120°*. All the carbons in adamantane have *different / the same* hybridization states. Relative to adamantane, the adamantane carbocation shown involves *less / more* ring and bond strain. Circle the conformation of 2-methylbut-2-ene that most closely resembles the configuration around the alkene in *adamantene*; this *is / is not* a stable conformation.

adamantane   *adamantane cation*   *adamantene*

E1 eliminations that result in formation of adamantene *are / are not* favorable.

C E2 Mechanisms

Complete the following reaction profile, carefully indicating all intermediate(s) and transition state(s), and show the charge distribution within the transition state using the symbols δ- and δ+.

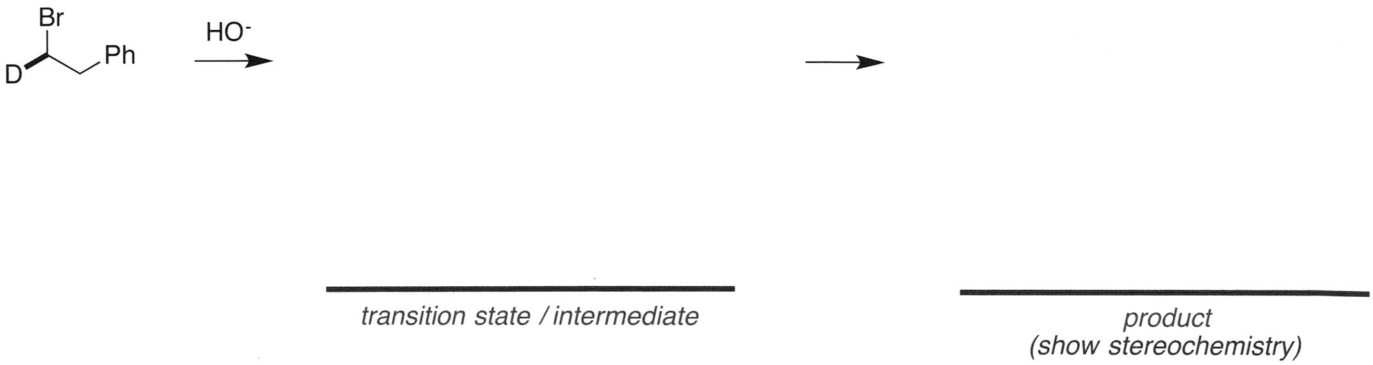

_____
transition state / intermediate

_____
product
(show stereochemistry)

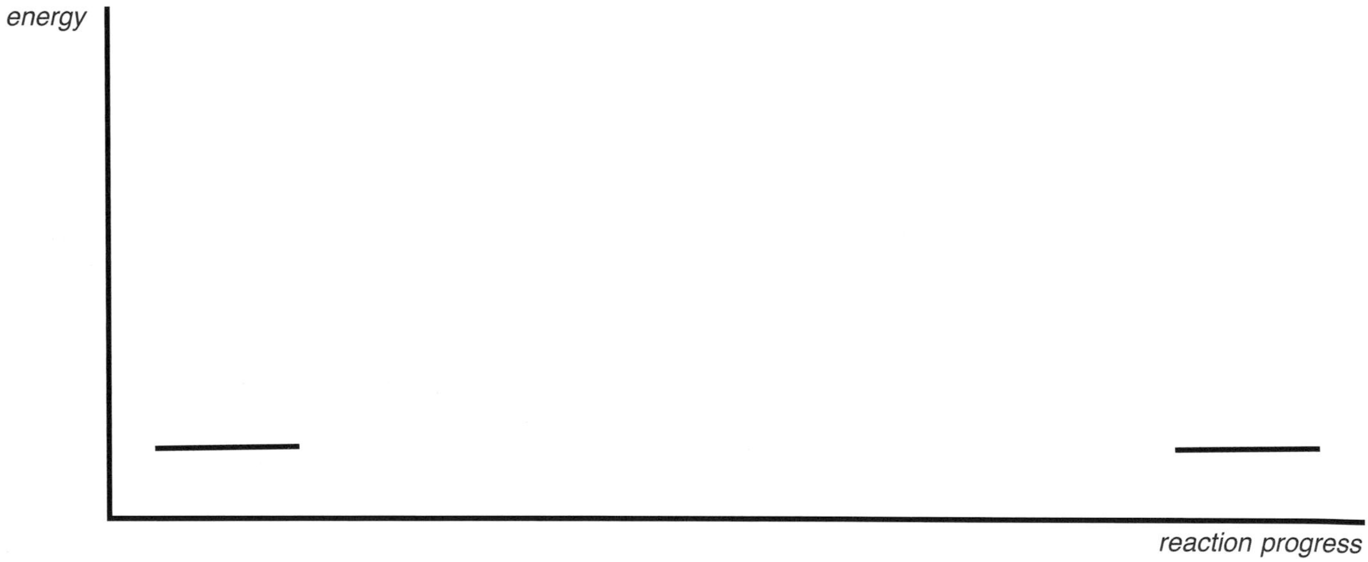

energy

reaction progress

Kinetics

The rate of the reaction above is proportional to the concentration of the substrate and the base. Complete the following:

rate is proportional to   rate =

_____   _____

where k is the rate constant.

Doubling the amount of base *halves / doubles / does not affect* rates of E2 eliminations.

Stereoselectivity

Antiperiplanar refers to a conformation about a bond (here $C - C$) that puts two substituents on *the same / different* sides and *in the same plane / perpendicular*.

Put a circle around the conformation of bromoethane that puts the bromine and the indicated hydrogen antiperiplanar, and similarly draw EtCl in a *syn*periplanar conformer.

---
*synperiplanar
EtCl*

Draw the following molecules in zigzag conformations that have a hydrogen and halogen atom in an *anti*periplanar arrangement, and show the orientations of those atoms clearly.

---	---	---	---
antiperiplanar 1-iodopropane	*antiperiplanar EtBrHCCHMe$_2$*	*antiperiplanar EtMeHCCBrMeEt*	*antiperiplanar ethyl iodide*

Imagine each of the following substrates treated with base to give E2 products via deprotonation of the hydrogen colored red. Draw the Newman projection that puts that hydrogen in an *anti*periplanar orientation with respect to the leaving group, and the alkene that would result from that elimination. Do not change the absolute stereochemistry when drawing the Newman projection.

..... can be represented as

base ⟶

---
complete Newman projection

---
show alkene product

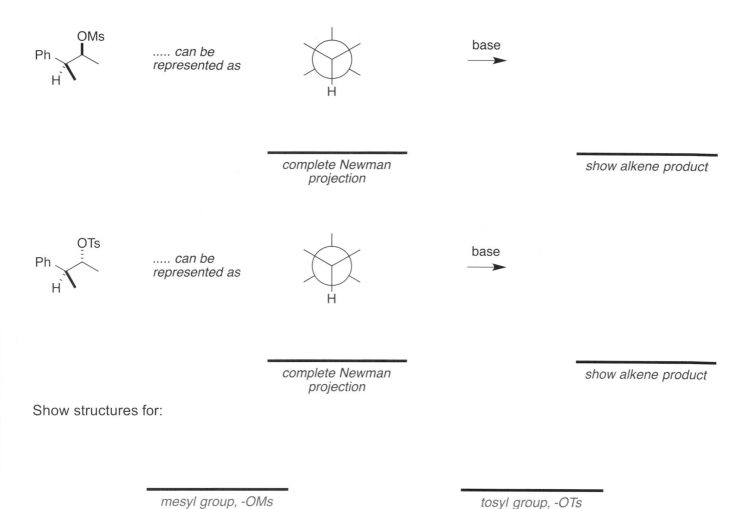

complete Newman projection		show alkene product

complete Newman projection		show alkene product

Show structures for:

mesyl group, -OMs	tosyl group, -OTs

Draw in *all* the hydrogens (if there are any) that are antiperiplanar to a halogen atom in the following molecular conformations.

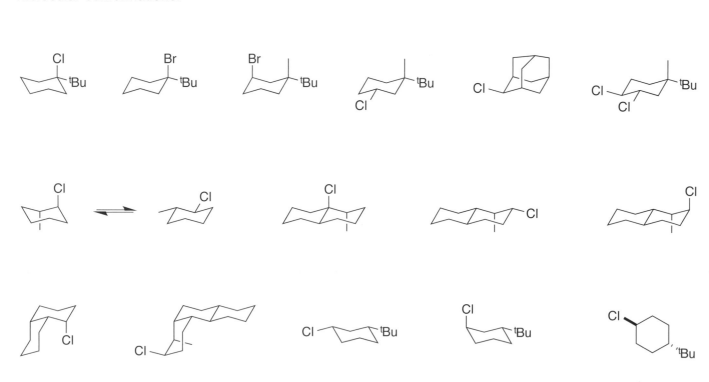

E2-Eliminations are more energetically favorable if the hydrogen that is being deprotonated and the leaving group are *syn / anti*-periplanar.

Give structures of alkyl bromides that could be used to make the following alkenes via *favorable* E2 eliminations (*ie* where no competing E2 mechanisms can give alternative products).

D Factors That Favor E1, E2, S$_N$1, or S$_N$2

Basicity *vs* Nucleophilicity

If an agent Y$^-$ could act as a nucleophile or as a base, then:

(i)   strongly *basic* character of Y$^-$ will increase the rate of *E1 / E2 relative to E1 / E2* reactions and it will tend to favor *E1 / E2* over nucleophilic substitution reactions;

(ii)   weakly *basic* character of Y$^-$ will *retard* the rate of *E1 / E2 relative to E1 / E2* reactions and it will tend to *favor / disfavor E1 / E2* over *nucleophilic substitution* reactions;

(iii)   less *basic* character of Y$^-$ *will / will not* affect the rate of E1 eliminations, but it *will / will not* favor E2 over E1 mechanisms; and,

(iv)   strongly *nucleophilic* character of Y$^-$ will increase the rate of *S$_N$1 / S$_N$2 relative to S$_N$1 / S$_N$2* reactions and it will tend to increase the rates of *S$_N$1 / S$_N$2* over *elimination* reactions.

In cases where E1 and E2 mechanisms compete, the likelihood of preferential E2 *increases / decreases* with the base strength.

Nucleophilicity

Large, hindered nucleophiles/bases, compared to otherwise similar but smaller ones, tend to favor:

(i)   *S$_N$1 / S$_N$2* relative to *S$_N$1 / S$_N$2* reactions; and,

(ii)   *E1 / E2* over *E1 / E2* reactions.

Conversely, small, unhindered nucleophiles/bases tend to favor:

(i)   *S$_N$1 / S$_N$2* relative to *S$_N$1 / S$_N$2* reactions;

(ii)   *E1 / E2* over *E1 / E2* reactions.

Without considering competing elimination reactions, rank the following nucleophiles according to decreasing nucleophilicities: Cl$^-$, I$^-$, N$_3^-$, NC$^-$, H$_2$O, MeO$^-$, NH$_3$

---

most nucleophilic   *least nucleophilic*

Without considering competing nucleophilic substitution reactions, rank the following bases in order of decreasing basicity: Cl$^-$, HO$^-$, H$_2$O, PhO$^-$, NH$_2^-$, NH$_3$

---

most basic   *least basic*

Temperature (and Entropy)

The equation that relates free energy of activation to temperature, entropy and enthalpy is:

$$\Delta G^{\#} = \underline{\qquad\qquad} - \underline{\qquad\qquad}$$

Entropy tends to *decrease* in orienting starting reacting species for the rate determining transition states in *E1 / E2* and *S$_N$1 / S$_N$2* over *E1 / E2* and *S$_N$1 / S$_N$2* reactions.

Low temperatures therefore tend to favor *E1 / E2* and *S$_N$1 / S$_N$2* over *E1 / E2* and *S$_N$1 / S$_N$2* reactions.
High temperatures therefore tend to favor *E1 / E2* and *S$_N$1 / S$_N$2* over *E1 / E2* and *S$_N$1 / S$_N$2* reactions.

E E1cB

Under basic conditions, some substrates generate anions that facilitate elimination of a leaving group on the adjacent carbon. One example of this is removal of 9-fluorenyloxymethyl groups, *ie BOC / FMOC*, used to protect amines as *carbonates / carbamates*. Complete the following mechanism for this deprotection.

draw arrows to depict electron flow

anionic
transition state / intermediate

+ +

product
(methyl phenylalanine)

Fluorenyl anions formed in this protection process have *6 / 8 / 10 / 12 / 14 / 16 / 18* πe, and are therefore *anti-aromatic / aromatic*.

F   Eliminations To Give Allenes, Alkynes, Ketenes And Sulfenes

Draw the products of removing HX from the following molecules, and circle the functional group name of the products.

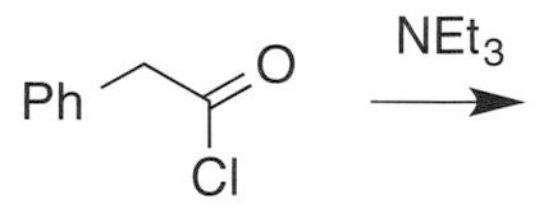

Ph—CH$_2$—C(=O)Cl $\xrightarrow{\text{NEt}_3}$

_____

allene / ketene / sulfene
alkyne

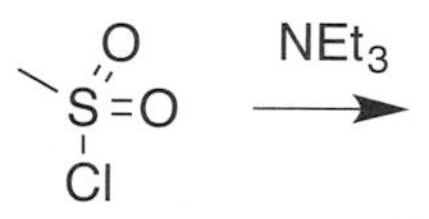

S(=O)(=O)(CH$_3$)Cl $\xrightarrow{\text{NEt}_3}$

_____

allene / ketene / sulfene
alkyne

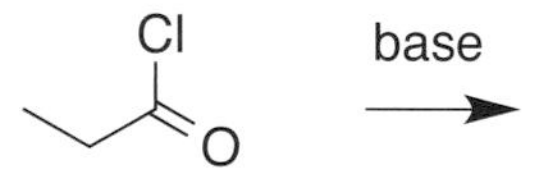

(propanoyl chloride) $\xrightarrow{\text{base}}$

_____

allene / ketene / sulfene
alkyne

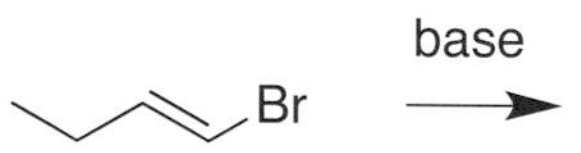

CH$_3$—CH=CH—Br $\xrightarrow{\text{base}}$

_____

allene / ketene / sulfene
alkyne

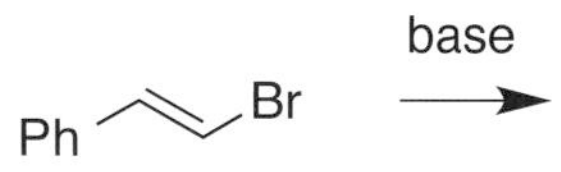

Ph—CH=CH—Br $\xrightarrow{\text{base}}$

_____

allene / ketene / sulfene
alkyne

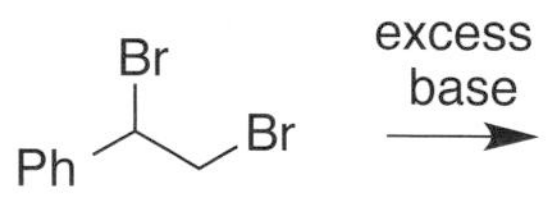

Ph—CHBr—CH$_2$—Br $\xrightarrow{\text{excess base}}$

_____

allene / ketene / sulfene
alkyne

12 Reactions Of Alkenes Via Protonation

from chapter(s) _____ in the recommended text

A Introduction

Focus

Protonation of alkenes gives carbocations. These carbocations are usually not isolated but instead they can react via several different pathways. Factors that cause one pathway to prevail over others include carbocation stabilities, presence of nucleophiles, and opportunities for carbocation rearrangement or proton loss. This section focuses on the possible consequences of protonating an alkene.

Reasons To Care

Classifying reactions that proceed via common mechanisms like S_N1 or S_N2 is a way to simplify organic chemistry. Recognition that a S_N1 pathway is operational, for instance, communicates the mechanism without further consideration. The next level of sophistication is to recognize and evaluate possible mechanistic pathways that become available once a reactive intermediate is generated.

Concepts Involved

hybridization • molecular orbital theory • electron flow • adaptable application of chemical concepts

Objective

Even though protonation of alkenes always gives carbocations, the fate of these carbocations varies with the alkene structure and the molecules around them. Being able to consider the options open to a carbocation is a higher-level skill than learning a mechanism like S_N1 by wrote, and applying it to yet another substrate-nucleophile combination. Only believers can do this; those that believe in their ability to access relative stabilities of carbocations and alkenes, and have faith in their ability to push arrows to describe electron flow.

Survivors can also expect a certain degree of enlightenment from this section. For instance, the *same* carbocations can be formed by loss of a leaving group in S_N1 reactions and by protonating structurally similar alkenes. Alkene protonation followed by reaction of that cation with nucleophiles can give the same products as S_N1 reactions, but they are not S_N1-products because they formed via *addition* to an alkene and not unimolecular substitution of a leaving group. In other words, the same product can be described as a S_N1- or addition-product *depending on how it was formed*. Understand, and the possibilities are endless.

B Protonation Of Alkenes

Generation Of Carbocations Via Protonation

Protons are the *simplest / most complicated* of all electrophiles.

Protons tend to approach alkenes perpendicular to the π-bond, then deviate towards one end of the alkene or the other, giving one neutral *sp^3 / sp^2 / sp* hybridized carbon and a *sp^3 / sp^2 / sp* hybridized carbonium-C.

Alkenes oriented perpendicular to a proton represent a *transition state / intermediate* while the carbonium ion is a *transition state / intermediate*.

Draw protonated alkenes and carbonium ions for the following protonations.

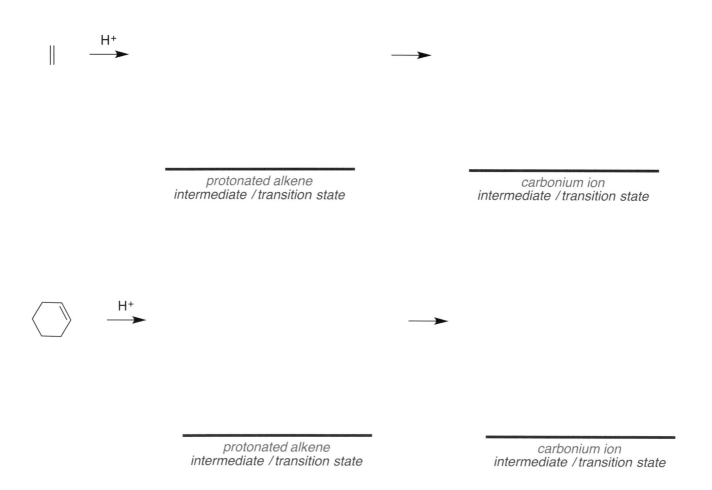

protonated alkene
intermediate / transition state

carbonium ion
intermediate / transition state

protonated alkene
intermediate / transition state

carbonium ion
intermediate / transition state

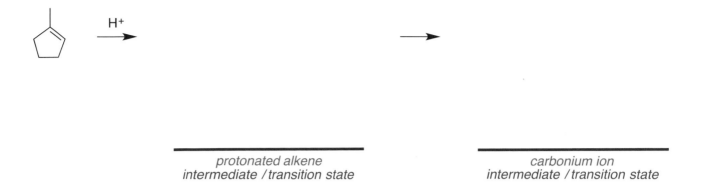

protonated alkene	*carbonium ion*
intermediate / transition state	*intermediate / transition state*

Perpendicular approach of protons on alkenes is favored by frontier orbital interactions, while other trajectories give more stabilization of the developing sp^3 / sp^2 / sp hybridized carbon and sp^3 / sp^2 / sp hybridized carbonium-C.

A Molecular Orbital Picture Of Alkene Protonation

Molecular orbital stabilization occurs when two orbitals mix to generate one that is lower energy than the original orbitals, and when that lower-energy orbital is *more / less* populated with electron density than the original orbitals before mixing.

A proton *does / does not* have a highest occupied molecular orbital (HOMO), so only the *HOMO / LUMO* is relevant when considering frontier orbitals for its interactions. Thus the *HOMO / LUMO* of a proton and the *HOMO / LUMO* of an alkene should be considered when a proton approaches a symmetrical alkene. Complete the following diagram depicting the molecular orbitals for this interaction.

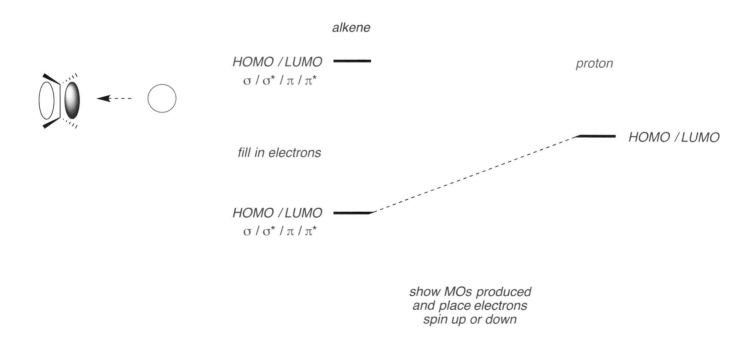

Perpendicular approach of a proton to a symmetrical π-cloud is net *stabilizing / destabilizing*.

C Carbocation Stabilities

Valence bond and molecular orbital approaches are *different types of bonding / alternative theories to explain bonding in general.*

An ethyl cation is stabilized relative to a methyl cation due to mixing of the empty p-orbital (*HOMO / LUMO*) with the filled σ-bonding orbital of a *C-H* bond on the adjacent methyl (*HOMO / LUMO*). Show this interaction by drawing the relevant orbitals in the left hand diagram.

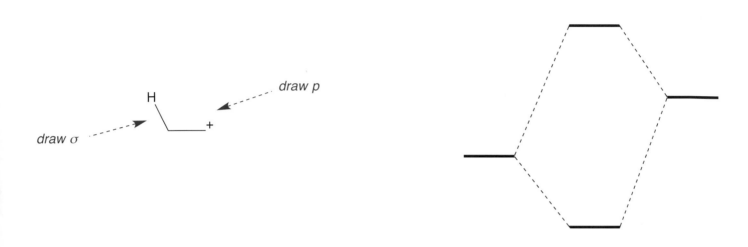

Label the right hand diagram with the following descriptors: *HOMO, LUMO, p-orbital, and σ-orbital.*

The σ-orbital brings *0 / 1 / 2 / 3* electrons into the interaction, whereas the p-orbital bears *0 / 1 / 2 / 3 e⁻*, thus the total number of electrons to place in the new molecular orbitals is _____ ; show these on the diagram above using arrows pointing up or down to represent electronic spin states.

Interaction between the empty p-orbital of a carbocation with the filled σ-bonding orbital of a *C-H* bond on the adjacent methyl can only occur when the orbitals *are in the same plane / reside in perpendicular planes.*

Only one *C-H* bond of the adjacent methyl in an ethyl cation can be involved in this interaction at any instant because the other two *cannot achieve significant orbital overlap / have the wrong sign of the Schrodinger wave equation.*

A secondary propyl cation has *0 / 1 / 2 / 3* adjacent methyl groups, and therefore *0 / 1 / 2 / 3* filled σ- *C-H* bonds that can stabilize by molecular orbital interactions. Secondary propyl cations are *more / less* stable than ethyl or methyl cations because of this.

A *tert*-butyl cation has *0 / 1 / 2 / 3* adjacent methyl groups, and therefore *0 / 1 / 2 / 3* filled σ- *C-H* bonds that can stabilize by molecular orbital interactions. ᵗBu-cations are *more / less* stable than ethyl or methyl cations because of this.

D Alkenes Stabilities

Stabilities of most alkenes *increase with / decrease with / are unaffected by* the number of substituents.

Fill in the π* and allylic σ-orbitals for propene on the diagram below, and complete the molecular orbital diagram to show how they interact.

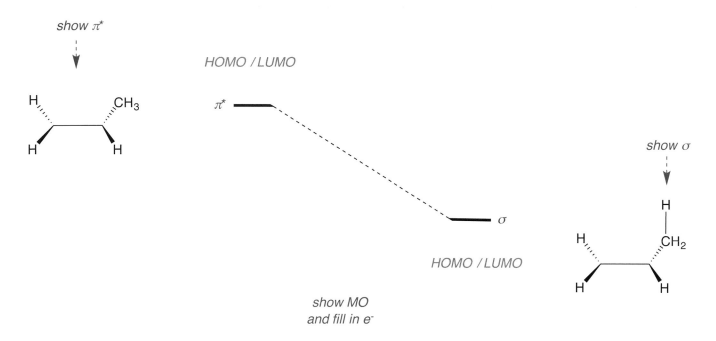

Alkenes can only have the *stabilizing / destabilizing* interactions (above) if they have allylic C – H bonds. Interactions like this explain why more substituted alkenes have *enhanced / diminished* stabilities.

Draw the alkenes below above the line provided to indicate their relative stabilities (remember Bredt's rule).

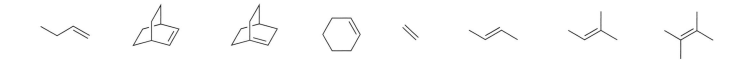

most stable   *least stable*

Heats Of Hydrogenation

Energy is *liberated / taken in* when hydrogen is added across a *C=C* bond.

When hydrogenation reactions give products having the same or very similar energies, more stable alkenes will have *higher / lower* heats of hydrogenation than less stable ones.

The amount of energy liberated on hydrogenation of different compounds to give the same or very similar products *can / cannot* be used to gauge the relative stabilities of the starting materials. Energies involved in such processes are called heats of *hydrogenation / combustion*.

Two profiles for hydrogenation are superimposed on both diagrams below. Identify the two starting materials in each case from two possibilities shown.

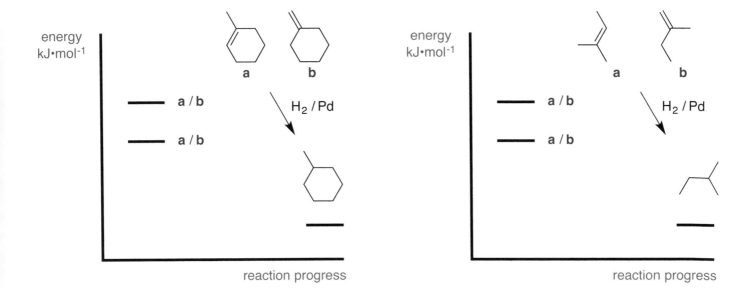

In the example on the left above, *a / b* has the higher heat of hydrogenation, while in the diagram on the right it is *a / b*.

E Acid-mediated Alkene Isomerization

Indicate the most stable alkenes in each of the following pairs, by circling that one.

The least stable alkenes in this series can be protonated to form carbocations, then lose a proton *from a different carbon* to give a different alkene that *is / is not* an isomer of the first. This reaction may be driven to form the most stable alkene, *ie* by *kinetics / thermodynamics*.

Show the carbocation and product alkene for each substrate shown below, and indicate if the equilibrium constant is greater or less than one, based on the relative stabilities of the two alkenes involved.

Ph — $\xrightarrow{H^+}$ — $\xrightarrow{-H^+}$ — $K = \geq 1 / \leq 1$

_____   _____
  carbocation   *alkene*

 $\xrightarrow{H^+}$ — $\xrightarrow{-H^+}$ — $K = \geq 1 / \leq 1$

_____   _____
  carbocation   *alkene*

 $\xrightarrow{H^+}$ — $\xrightarrow{-H^+}$

_____   _____
  carbocation   *alkene*

It is *conceivable / inconceivable* that carbocations can shift groups to isomerize faster than they can lose protons to form an alkene.

F Carbocation Rearrangements

Hydride Shifts

When a hydrogen nucleus (*ie* a proton) migrates with two electrons this is called a *proton / hydrogen / hydride* migration because a proton and two electrons is a *proton / hydrogen atom / hydride anion*.

If alkyl or hydride shifts are possible, the preferred one may be predicted by considering the relative stabilities of the carbocations produced: *true / false*.

Draw curly arrows to describe the following *1,2 / 1,3 / 1,1*-hydride migration reactions, and predict the products.

1,2-Hydride shift reactions involve interactions between filled σ- and empty p-orbitals. Similar orbital interactions *may / cannot* lead to formation of halonium ions (*eg* bromonium).

Considering interactions of single molecules and ions, collisions of protons with *unsymmetrical* alkenes are *most / least* thermodynamically favorable when they lead to the most stabilized carbocation.

Show the most possible carbocation *intermediates / transition states* formed by protonation of the following alkenes, and show curly arrows to depict the reaction flow.

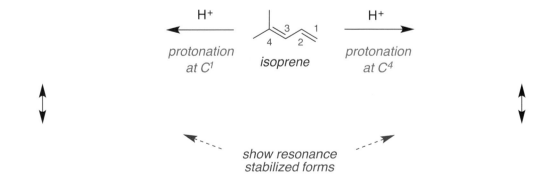

H^+ ← → H^+

least favorable
1° / 2° / 3° carbonium ion

most favorable
1° / 2° / 3° carbonium ion

H^+ ← → H^+

least favorable
1° / 2° / 3° carbonium ion

most favorable
1° / 2° / 3° carbonium ion

H^+ ← → H^+

protonation at C^1   **isoprene**   *protonation at C^4*

show resonance stabilized forms

most favorable
3° carbonium ion

least favorable
1° carbonium ion

Protonation of isoprene at the diene termini (C^1 and C^4 *gives / does not give* a cation stabilized by allylic resonance, while protonation at the internal positions (C^2 and C^3) *does / does not*.

Express the equilibrium constant for the following process in terms of the concentrations of the starting materials and reactants. The free energy change for this reaction involves a *large / small* entropy factor because the number of starting materials *equals / is less / is more* than the number of products.

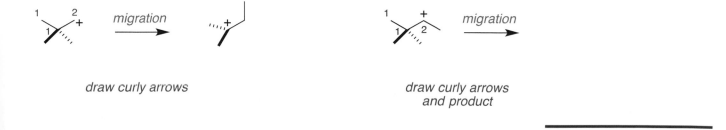

$$K = \frac{\text{conc. of product(s)}}{\text{conc. of substrate(s)}} = \frac{\left[\quad \right]}{\left[\quad \right]}$$

draw the carbocations

The equilibrium constant featured above is *greater than / less than* one.

Alkyl Shifts

Some carbocations can rearrange when electrons in suitably aligned σ-orbitals shift toward the carbocation. When that happens, a group migrates along the chains, and the positive charge appears to shift in the *same / opposite* direction creating a new carbocation.

Carbocation rearrangements are favorable if the cation formed is *more / less* stable than the original one.

In suitable substrates, primary carbocations tend to undergo rearrangements if the products are *primary / secondary / tertiary* carbocations, but secondary ones tend to only migrate to form *primary / secondary / tertiary* carbocations (circle all that apply).

Show curly arrows for the *1,2 / 1,3 / 1,1*-migration reactions shown below, and show the products where necessary.

draw curly arrows

draw curly arrows and product

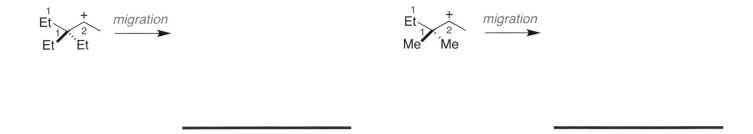

Many groups that can adopt conformations with the p- and σ-orbitals correctly aligned can undergo these migration reactions. If the migrating group is an alkyl then these processes can be called *group tunneling / alkyl shift* reactions.

If relatively free rotation allows different groups to become correctly aligned for 1,2-migration then it is the one *most / least* able to support a positive charge that shifts preferentially. In the example above right, for instance, Et migrates in preference to Me because methyl cations are *more / less* stable than Et^+.

G Electrophilic Addition Mechanisms

Draw curly arrows for addition of an electrophile E^+ to ethene then nucleophilic addition to the carbocation that is formed.

E^+ *fast / slow* Nu^- *fast / slow*

_____   _____
carbocation intermediate   *addition product*

If the activation energy involved in forming a *C-E* bond and breaking a *C=C* bond to form a cation in the first step is greater than that for addition of a nucleophile to the cationic intermediate then the first step will be relatively *fast / slow* compared with the second. Indicate this situation on the diagram above.

Draw the same mechanism for addition of hydrogen bromide and hydrogen cyanide.

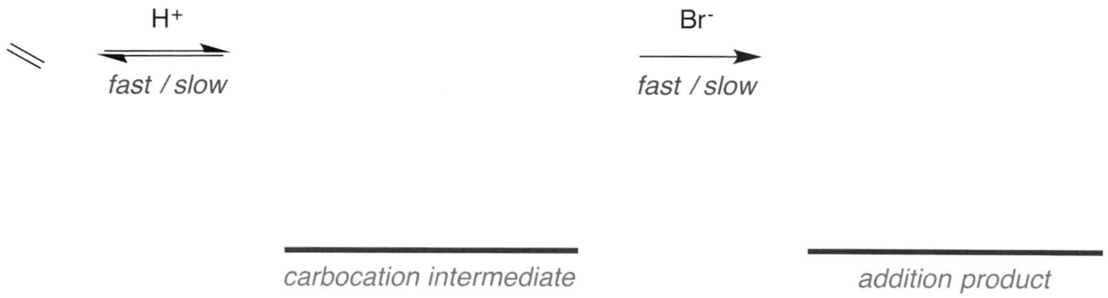

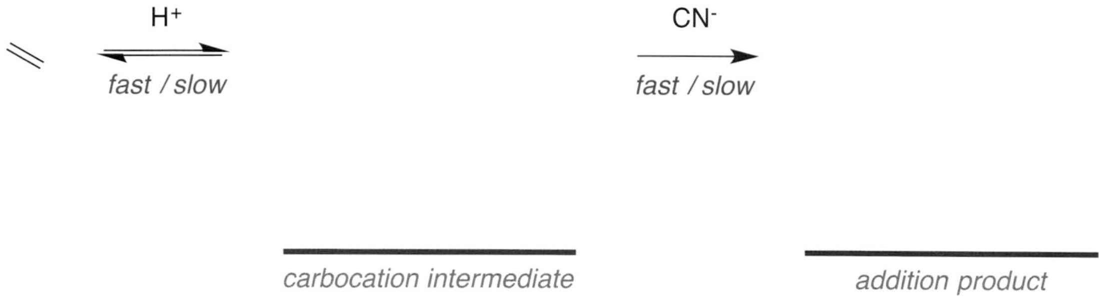

H⁺

fast / slow

Br⁻

fast / slow

_____
carbocation intermediate

_____
addition product

H⁺

fast / slow

CN⁻

fast / slow

_____
carbocation intermediate

_____
addition product

It is possible to draw curly arrows to describe a completely different mechanism for addition of HBr to ethene involving nucleophilic attack of bromide to form a *carbanion*, then reaction of that with a proton.

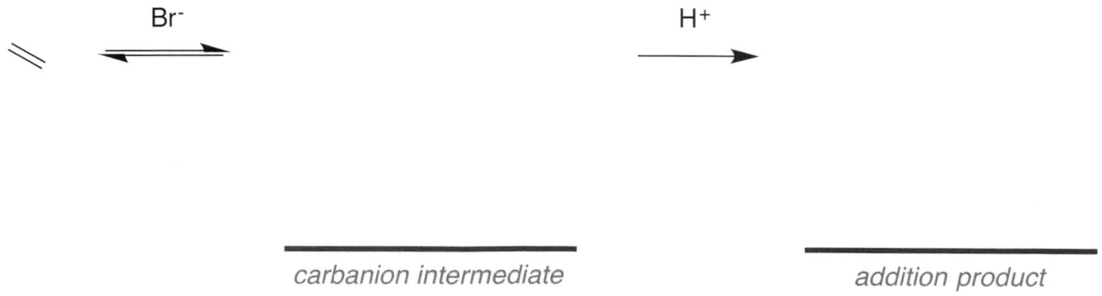

Br⁻

H⁺

_____
carbanion intermediate

_____
addition product

Addition of HBr to ethene *does / does not* proceed in this way.

The following is a list of possible reasons to explain why bromide anion does not add to alkenes. Circle those that seem most significant.

- bromide, being negatively charged, is repelled by electrons in the alkene π-bond
- bromide is too big to add
- carbanions with a bromide on the β-carbon are thermodynamically unstable relative to bromide and alkene
- *C-Br* bonds are so weak compounds containing them are unstable

From here on, consider only the electrophilic attack mechanism. In some reactions the best available nucleophile is *neutral*, so a positively charged entity, usually a *proton / sodium ion*, must be lost to give a neutral addition product. Show this mechanism for hydration of ethene, where the nucleophile is water.

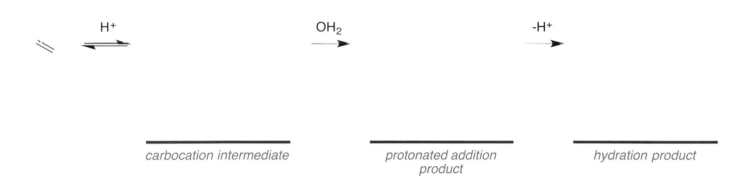

| carbocation intermediate | protonated addition product | hydration product |

H Acid-mediated Hydration Of Alkenes

Electrophilic attack on ethene is less favorable than for most other alkenes because the carbocation formed is *1° / 2° / 3°*.

Hydration of propene could give *one / two / three* possible hydration products in which the *H* and *OH* groups become attached to different carbon atoms, *ie regioisomers / enantiomers*; draw these here.

| 2-propanol | 1-propanol |

Reactions that form one regioisomer selectively are called *chemoselective / enantioselective / regioselective / diastereoselective*.

Unsurprisingly, reactions that involve reaction of one chemical functional group in preference to others are called *chemoselective / enantioselective / regioselective / diastereoselective*.

Suggest terms for processes that form one enantiomer in preference to another, and preferential formation of one diastereomer: _____ and _____, respectively.

Acid-mediated hydration of only some of the following alkenes could involve regioselectivity issues: put a circle around those.

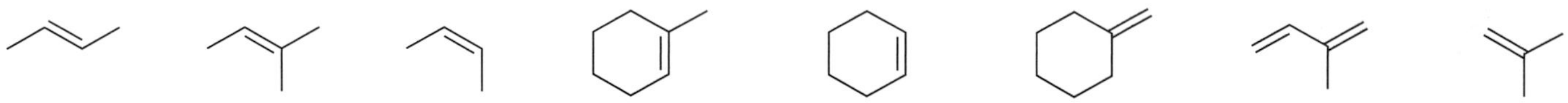

Draw the cations that would be involved in acid-mediated hydration of propene to give 2-propanol and 1-propanol, and indicate their relative stabilities.

_____
gives 2-propanol
more / less stable

_____
gives 1-propanol
more / less stable

Predict the preferred product of the following reactions.

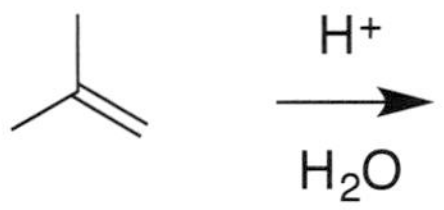

H+
→
H₂O

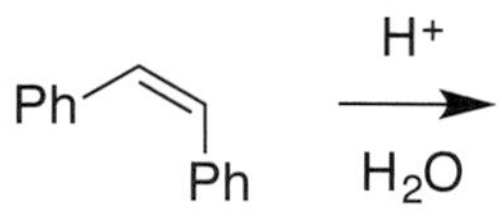

Ph
Ph   H+
→
H₂O

_____   _____

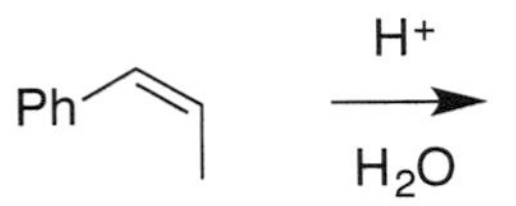

Ph~~ + H+ / H2O →

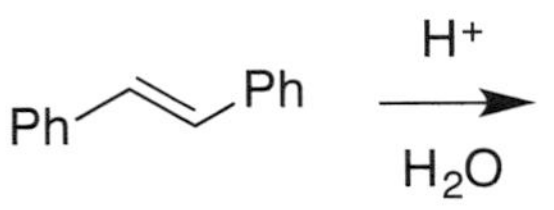

Ph~~Ph + H+ / H2O →

_____

_____

All the reactions above are represented as irreversible. In fact, they are reversible but can be driven to completion in the presence of enough water. In the absence of water the reverse reaction (alcohol to alkene) would occur via a(n) *E1 / SN2 / E2 / SN1* pathway.

Predict the products of the following reactions to form *esters / ethers / epoxides*.

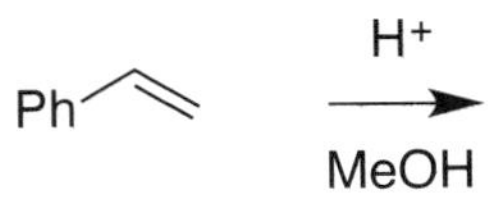

Ph~~ + H+ / MeOH →

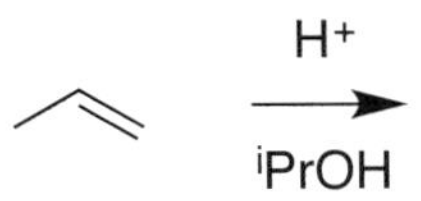

~~ + H+ / iPrOH →

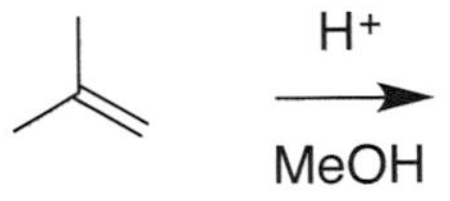

_____

_____

>< + H+ / MeOH →

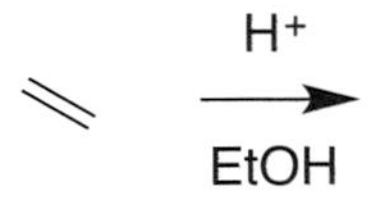

// + H+ / EtOH →

_____

_____

The reactions above *are / are not* hydration reactions, but they are mechanistically similar.

Suggest alkenes that these products could be made from via acid-mediated hydration or similar pathways.

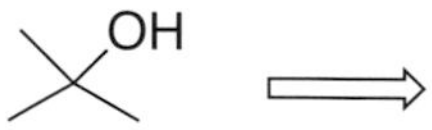

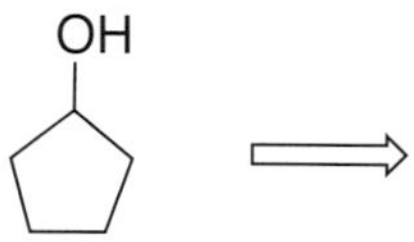

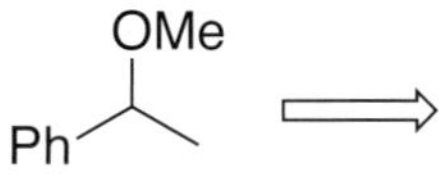

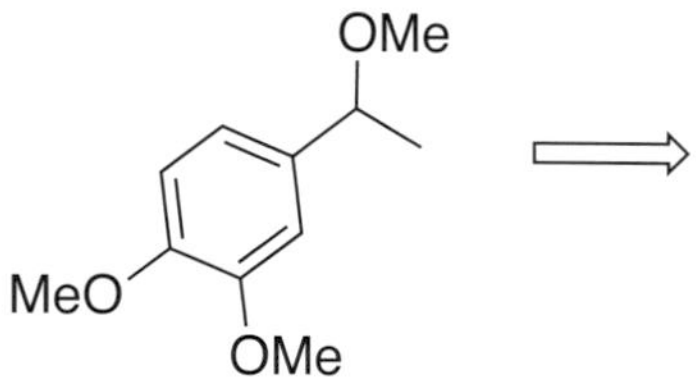

OH (isopropanol structure) ⟹

_____

OH (tert-butanol structure) ⟹

_____

OH (2-butanol structure) ⟹

_____

OH (cyclopentanol structure) ⟹

_____

OMe, Ph (structure) ⟹

_____

OMe, MeO, OMe (aromatic structure) ⟹

_____

Draw circles around those of the following products that could *not* be made by acid-mediated electrophilic addition reactions of alkenes.

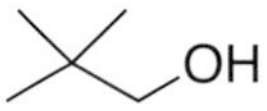

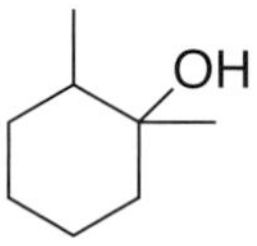

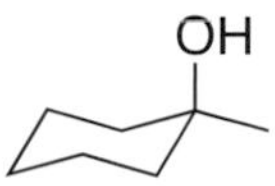

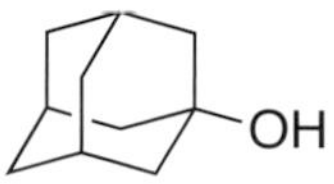

OH   OH   OH   OH   OH   OMe

13 Oxidation States, Hydrogenation, And Hydrogenolysis

from chapter(s) _____ in the recommended text

A Introduction

Focus

Oxidation of an atom occurs when the electron density surrounding it is decreased, while increasing that density is reduction. Organic chemists are aware of the relative levels of electron density around carbon in functional groups, and classify them according to roughly equivalent levels of oxidation. For example, oxidation levels increase in steps from alkane, to alkene, ketone, carboxylic acid, and carbon dioxide. Adding hydrogen *reduces* carbon atoms. Hydrogenation (addition across π-bonds) reduces alkenes to alkanes, and hydrogenolysis (addition across σ-bonds) cleaves C-X links.

Related to hydrogenation and hydrogenolysis is the abstract concept of how many "double bond equivalents" (DBEs) a molecule has. It is abstract because many compounds with several DBEs are *not* alkenes or even multiple-bond-containing.

Reasons To Care

Whenever some substrate is oxidized, a reagent is reduced. Reagents that neither oxidize nor reduce cannot move functional groups between oxidation states. Reducing agents, of which hydrogen is a prime example, move substrates down in oxidation levels, while oxidizing agents move them up. Understanding if a compound is oxidized, reduced, or electronically unperturbed is useful for understanding what is "going on" in a reaction.

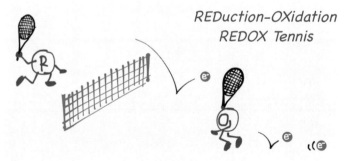

REDuction-OXidation REDOX Tennis

Double bond equivalents can be calculated from the atomic formulae. Knowing the DBEs (from atomic formulae) of compounds of unknown structures can be surprisingly useful when trying to determine what the compound is.

Concepts Involved

addition reactions • electron flow • catalysis

Objective

Oxidation and reductions are common ways in which functional groups are introduced, interconverted, or removed.   The questions here are designed to highlight oxidation levels, and situations in which oxidation or reduction can occur, particularly when hydrogen is the reducing agent.

B Oxidation States In Organic Chemistry

Reduction is *addition / loss* of electrons from the substrate, and *addition / loss* from the reagent.

Oxidation is e^- *addition / loss* from the reagent and *addition / loss* from the substrate.

In organic chemistry, oxidation states can be linked to the number of hydrogen atoms attached to the carbons involved. Low oxidation states of organic compounds have carbons with *more / less* C-H bonds, hence the molecule or functional group in question is more reduced. These molecules have *more / less* C-O, C-N, and C-halogen bonds.

Organic compounds in high oxidation states have *more / less* C-H bonds, and *more / less* C-O, C-N, and C-halogen bonds.

Organize the following compounds in categories as indicated, by placing letters in the boxes provided.

a   b   c   d   e   f CO_2
            g

h   i   j   k CH_2Cl_2 CCl_4 $HCCl_3$ HCOH
                l   m   n   o

lowest oxidation state

_____

one level higher

_____

one more level higher

_____

still another level higher

_____

highest oxidation state

_____

Cyclohexane is at a *higher / lower* oxidation state than hexane.

Classify the following reactions as *oxidation*, *reduction*, or *neutral* (essentially no change in oxidation level) by writing the appropriate term below each.

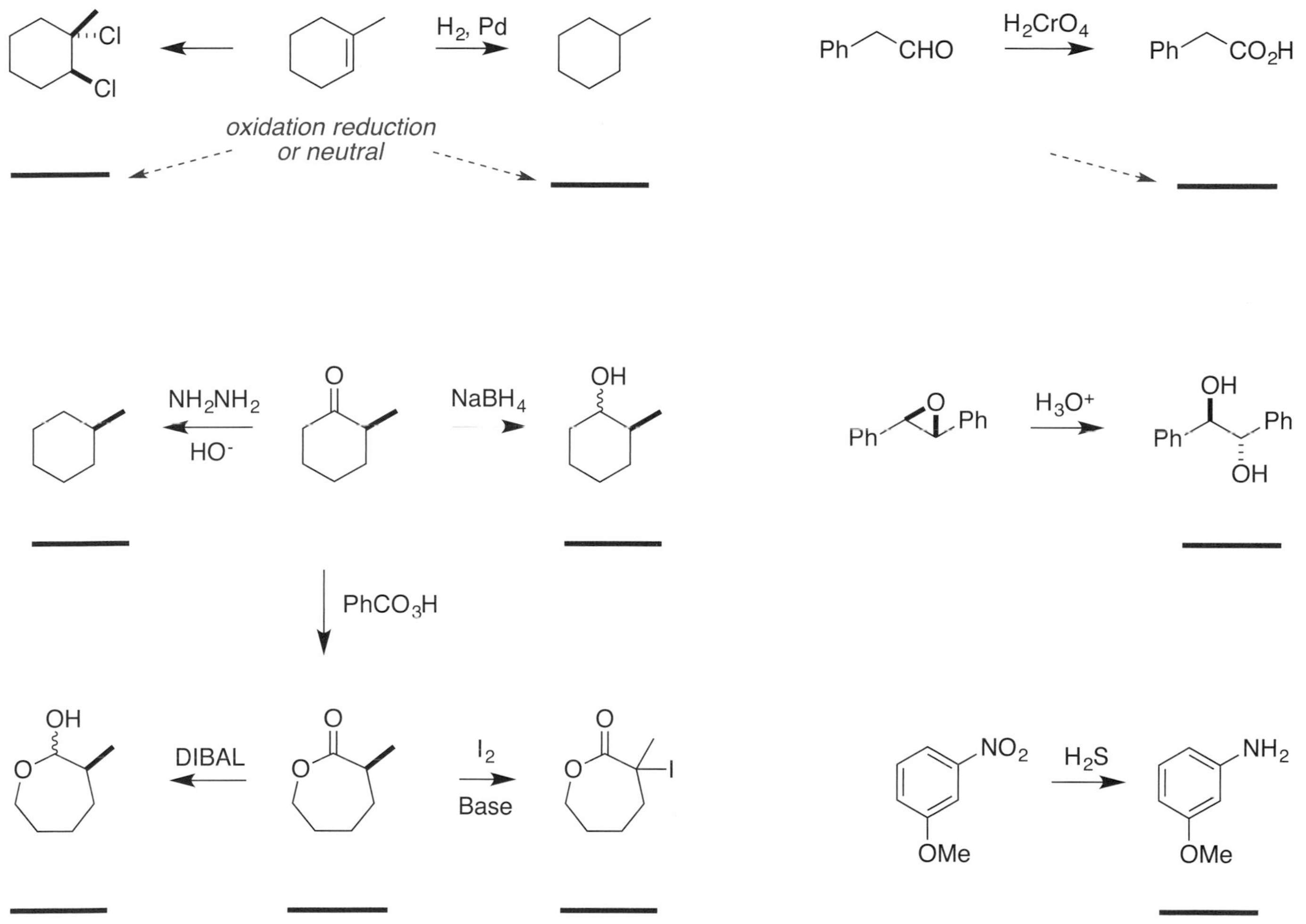

oxidation reduction or neutral

C Addition Of H$_2$

Hydrogenation And Hydrogenolysis

Hydrogenation / hydrogenolysis involves addition of H$_2$ across an unsaturated bond without cleaving the connection between the two atoms.

Hydrogenation / hydrogenolysis involves addition of H$_2$ across a single bond with cleavage.

Addition of hydrogen to an alkene or an aldehyde can be thought of as proceeding via: (i) *homolytic / heterolytic* cleavage of H$_2$ on the surface to the catalyst; and, (ii) near simultaneous addition of the atoms adsorbed onto the surface across a bond, converting that bond to bonds to hydrogen.

Hydrogenolysis is closer to a *radical / ionic* mechanism, than a *radical / ionic* one.

Ignoring the need for a catalyst, draw the hypothetical addition of hydrogen to an alkene and to an aldehyde, using curly arrows for $2e^-$ flow.

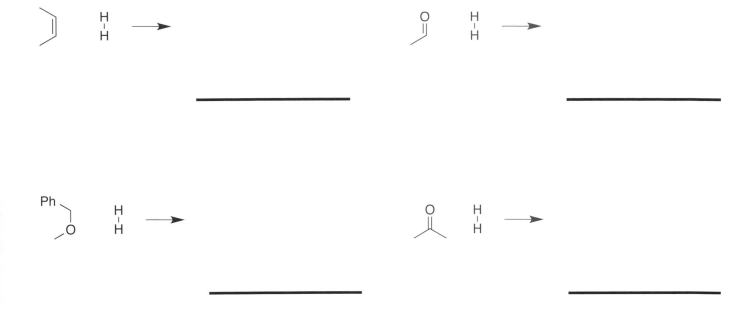

Processes like those above are particularly favorable if the atoms that the hydrogen adds to are inclined to *stabilize / destabilize* a single electron.

Incipient radical character makes hydrogenolysis of benzyl ethers favorable, because the *benzyl / alkoxide* radical is stabilized by resonance.

Aromatic aldehydes, ketones, and esters are *less / more* easily hydrogenated than similar aliphatic compounds, because of radical stabilization.

Development of heterogeneous catalysts, and refinement of the conditions under which they are used, has taken place largely via trial and error testing of alternatives. In the absence of this experience, there are few ways to predict which catalyst and conditions would be suitable for a particular substrate. The following section ignores those details, and focuses on the products which can be formed, and how.

D Hydrogenation

Predict the products of the following hydrogenation reactions (the number of moles of hydrogen absorbed is indicated to help prediction of the product).

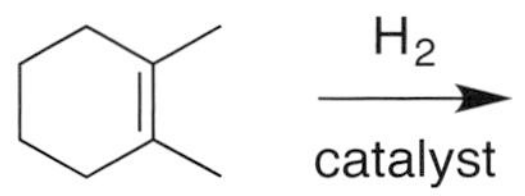
H2
catalyst

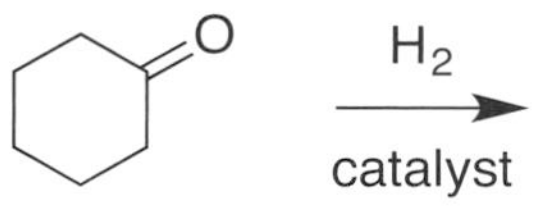
O
H2
catalyst

tip: hydrogenation of benzene rings is hard, but not impossible .....

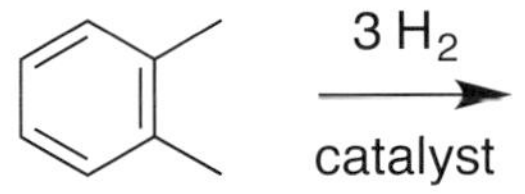
3 H2
catalyst

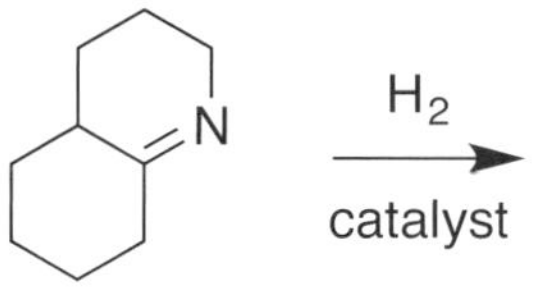
N
H2
catalyst

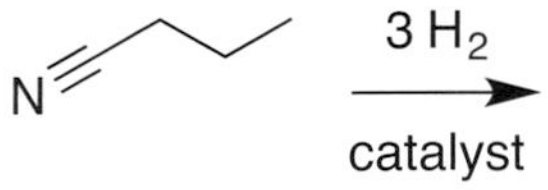
N
3 H2
catalyst

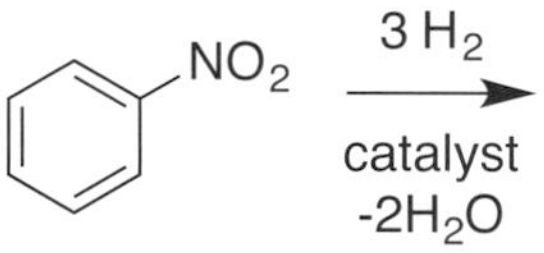
NO2
3 H2
catalyst
-2H2O

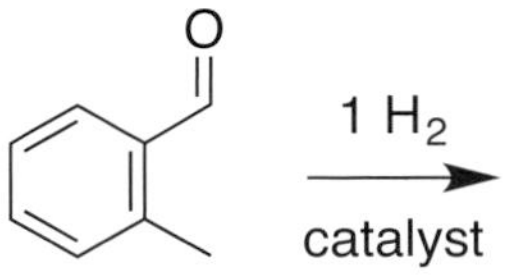
O
1 H2
catalyst

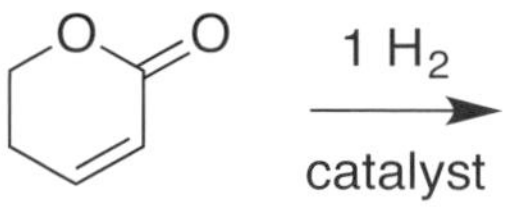
O
O
1 H2
catalyst

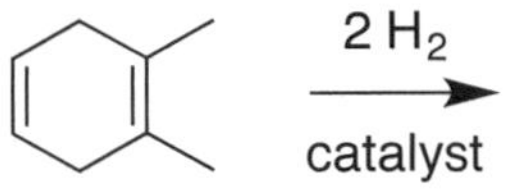

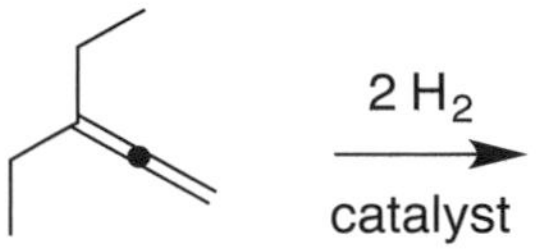

Partial hydrogenations are possible, though the catalyst may need to be deactivated to ensure over-reaction does not occur. Both the following reactions involve only one equivalent of hydrogen.

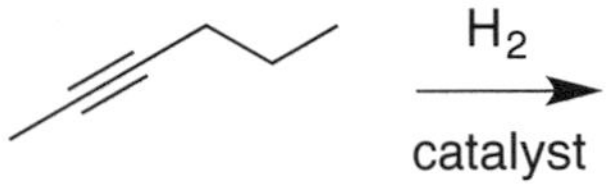

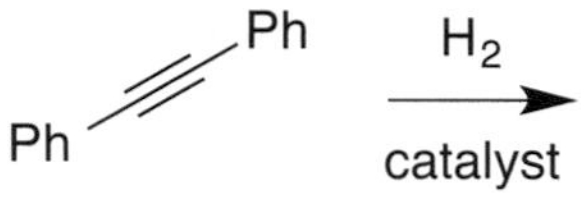

E Hydrogenolysis

Hydrogenolysis refers to addition across *single / double* bonds. Predict the products of the following *hydrogenolysis* reactions (excess H_2 used). The byproduct is only shown below the arrows in the first two reactions.

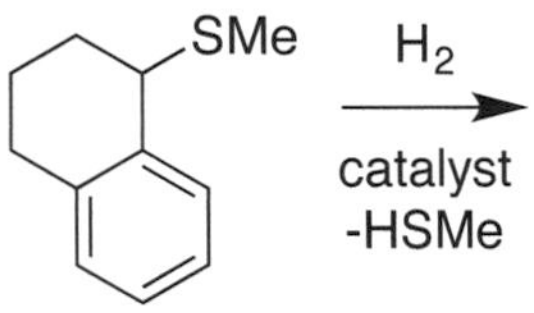

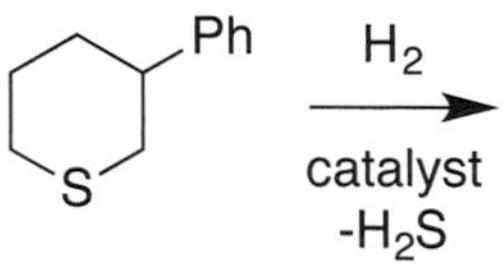

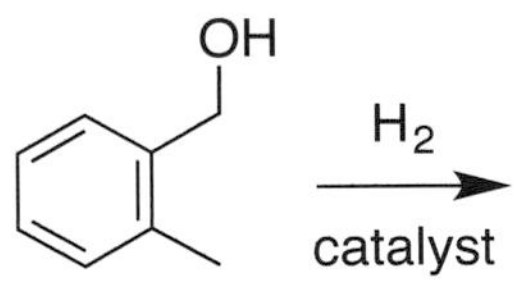

OH

H$_2$

catalyst

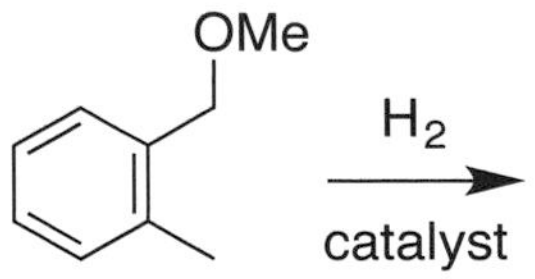

OMe

H$_2$

catalyst

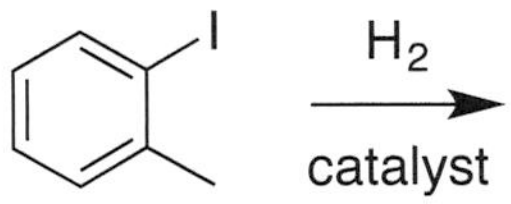

_____

_____

I

H$_2$

catalyst

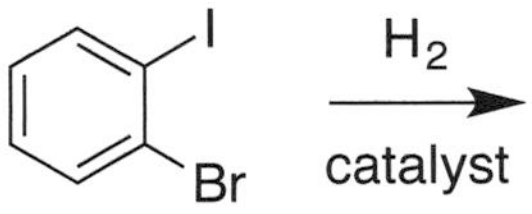

I

H$_2$

Br   catalyst

_____

_____

tip: the following reactions feature *C-S* and *C-Cl* hydrogenolyses …..

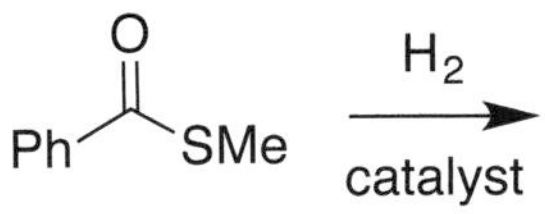

O

Ph   SMe

H$_2$

catalyst

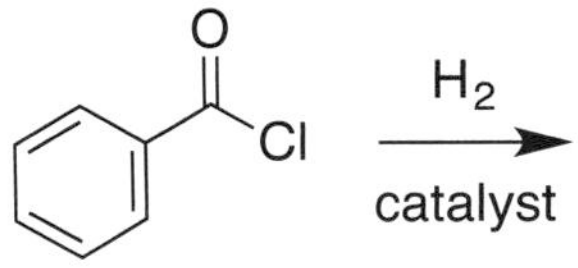

O

Cl

H$_2$

catalyst

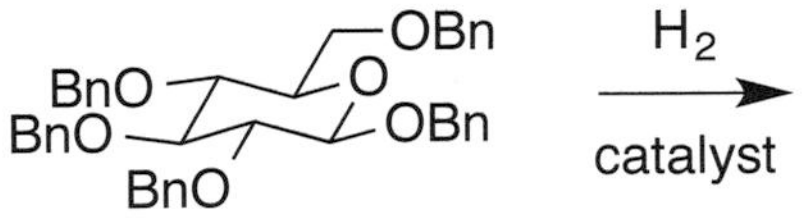

_____

_____

OBn

BnO   O

BnO   OBn

BnO

H$_2$

catalyst

_____

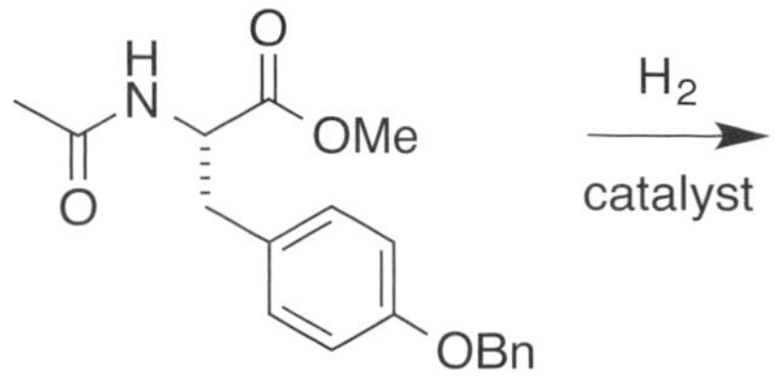
OMe
OBn
H_2
catalyst

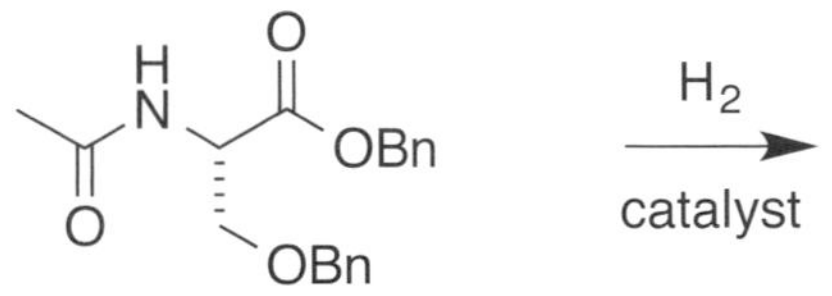
OBn
OBn
H_2
catalyst

tip: how many benzylic carbons are in the following molecule? .....

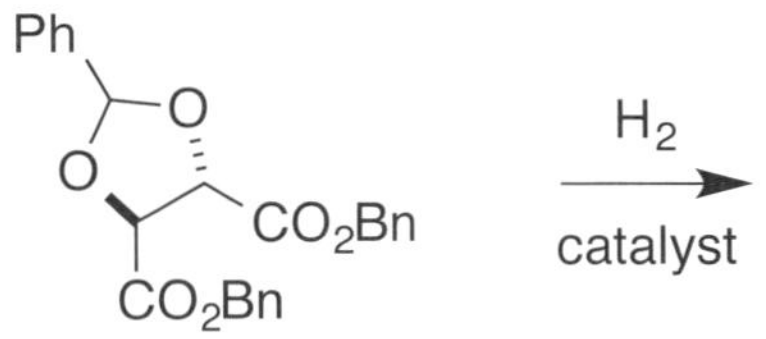
Ph
CO_2Bn
CO_2Bn
H_2
catalyst

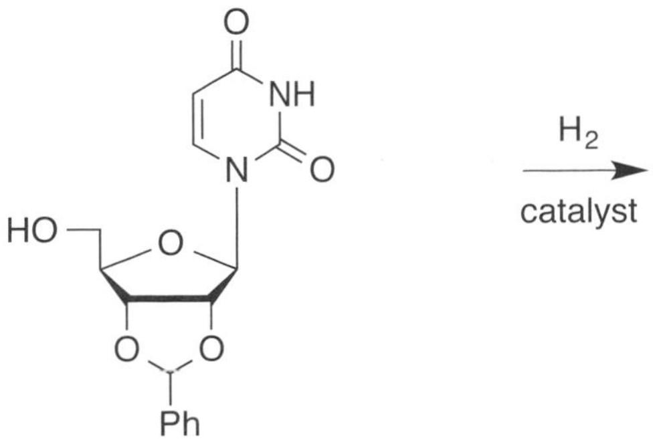
NH
HO
Ph
H_2
catalyst

does not reduce the base

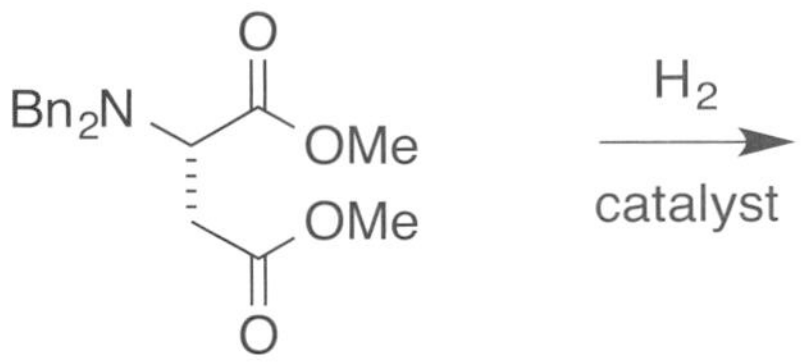

It tends to be *easier / harder* to remove benzyl groups from amines than from alcohols, perhaps because some amine products *poison* the catalyst.

A special case in hydrogenolysis is where a benzyl group is connected to the oxygen of a carbamate, *ie* benzyloxycarbonyl or *Boc / Cbz*. Hydrogenolysis of the benzyl group would leave a hydroxycarbamate, but these are unstable relative to carbon dioxide and amine.

Predict the products of the following reactions.

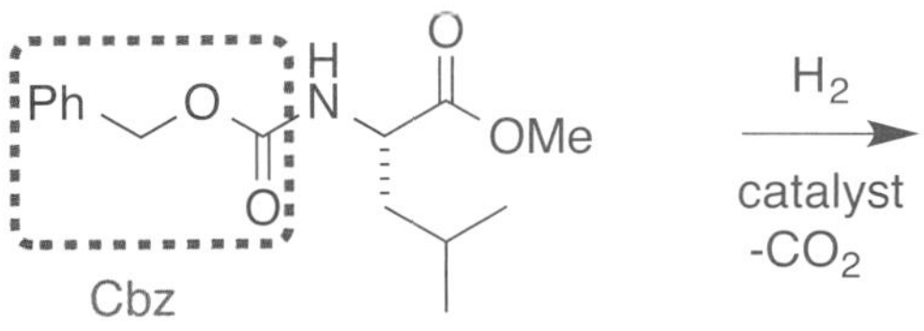

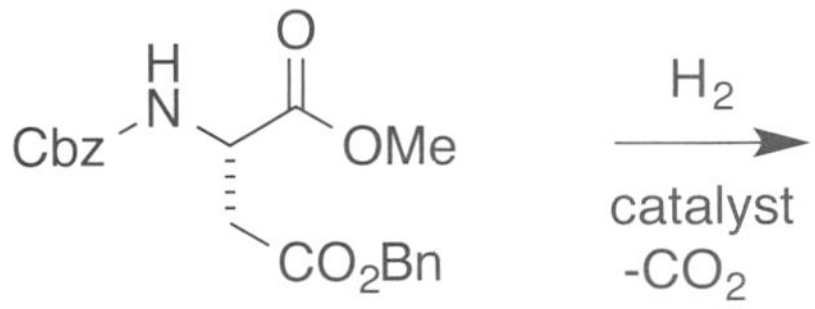

F   Double Bond Equivalents

Double bond equivalents (DBE) or *degree of unsaturation* is a numerical measure of how many molecules of hydrogen must be absorbed by a molecule to convert it into the corresponding acyclic (linear), saturated hydrocarbon. To convert ethene and ethyne into ethane requires *1 / 2 / 3 / 4* and *1 / 2 / 3 / 4* molecules of H_2, respectively.

Conversion of benzene to hexane would require *1 / 2 / 3 / 4* molecules of H_2, one for each of the double bonds and another to cleave the ring.

For hydrocarbons containing n carbon atoms, the DBE *can / cannot* be calculated by subtracting the molecular formula of the compound from C_nH_{2n+2}, then dividing by two (consider propyne and cyclopropene).

DBEs for halogenated hydrocarbons containing n carbon atoms, *can / cannot* be calculated by replacing the halogen atoms with hydrogen then subtracting the molecular formula of the compound from C_nH_{2n+2}, then dividing by two. (Evaluate by considering chloroethene and bromobenzene).

DBEs of acetone and *cis*-1,2-cyclohexandiol are *1 / 2 / 3 / 4* and *1 / 2 / 3 / 4*, respectively.

Evaluate the following assertion: oxygen atoms may be ignored to calculate the DBE, *eg* acetone C_3H_6O may be considered to be C_3H_6. (*True or false*, check by considering *cis*-1,2-cyclohexandiol.)

DBEs of 3-aminopropene and pyridine are *1 / 2 / 3 / 4* and *1 / 2 / 3 / 4*, respectively.

Evaluate the following assertion: formula of molecules that contain nitrogen atoms should be adjusted to remove the nitrogen *and one hydrogen atom* before calculating the DBE, *eg* ethylamine C_2H_7N (DBE = *0 / 1 / 2 / 3*) may be considered to be C_3H_6. (*True or false*, check by also considering 3-aminopropene and pyridine.)

Calculate double bond equivalents for the following substrates.

_____ _____ _____ _____ _____ _____ _____ _____

_____ _____ _____ _____ _____ _____ _____ _____

Double bond equivalents are a "rule of thumb". They *do / do not* apply when calculating unsaturation between two atoms not including carbon (see sulfone and sulfoxide above). They correlate with oxidation states for carbons composed of only *C* and *H*, but addition of O and S obviously changes oxidation state but does not change DBEs.

G Hydridic Reductions

Stepwise reduction of unsaturated bonds via addition of hydride, then a proton, are dealt with later in this *Inquisition*. Use curly arrows to predict which reaction is likely to be easiest based on electronegativities.

easy / hard

_____ _____

14 Halogenation Of Alkenes

from chapter(s) _____ in the recommended text

A Introduction

Focus

Protons are not the only electrophiles that can add to alkenes. Halogens polarize as they approach alkenes and act as electrophiles liberating halide. Molecular orbital (MO) theory indicates halogens have low-lying orbitals that interact with the alkene in ways that are not possible for protons. Indeed, halogens tend to form halonium ions, not carbocations, as the dominant cationic intermediate. Opening of the halonium ions occurs via attack of halide (or perhaps other nucleophiles if present) to give products that are functionalized on both carbons that were alkenes.

Sounds simple? It is not quite that simple because iodine and alkenes are more stable than 1,2-diiodides, and fluorine is not discussed. Consequently, the focus of this section is mostly on chlorination and bromination.

Reasons To Care

Substrate-to-substrate generality is a treasured commodity in organic chemistry. Bromination of alkenes is one of those transformations that so rarely fail that it has been used as a test for alkenes since the early days of organic chemistry. Bromine in organic solvents is brown, but addition of an excess of almost any alkene will consume the brown color. *Trans*-addition of chlorine and bromine to almost any alkene is a reliable friend. The fact that these are *trans*-additions means that the products have defined stereochemistries; this is valuable for both cyclic- and acyclic-alkenes.

Even though iodination of alkenes does not give product, iodine *does* add, reversibly. Addition of iodine catalyzes isomerization of less stable alkene isomers (usually Z-) into their more stable ones.

Finally, bromination of alkenes is used here to introduce the concepts of kinetic and thermodynamic control; several other reactions could be used, but this one is a classic. This explains, for example, why sometimes it is possible to preferentially obtain the *least* stable product in a reaction.

Concepts Applied

electron flow • molecular orbital theory • stereochemistry • interplay of kinetics and thermodynamics

Objective

This section expands on electrophilic attack on alkenes, broadening the scope to processes that have more stereochemical features. Questions require applications of concept *combinations*: electron flow and MO theory, alkene geometry and diastereoselectivity, kinetics and thermodynamics.

186

B Mechanism

Like protons, halogens (X_2) tend to approach alkenes or alkynes *parallel / perpendicular* to the π-bond but, unlike protons, there is an *X - X* bond to become *polarized / delocalized* until *halide* (X^-) and a halonium ion formed.

Hal*onium* ions are *positively / negatively* charged; the *–ium* suffix in that name *is / is not* indicative of this. (Think of other positively charged entities to test if this is true, *ie* NH_4^+, PMe_4).

Chlorination and Bromination

Show mechanisms for halogenation reactions shown below (curly arrows, *etc*) featuring halonium ion *transition states / intermediates*.

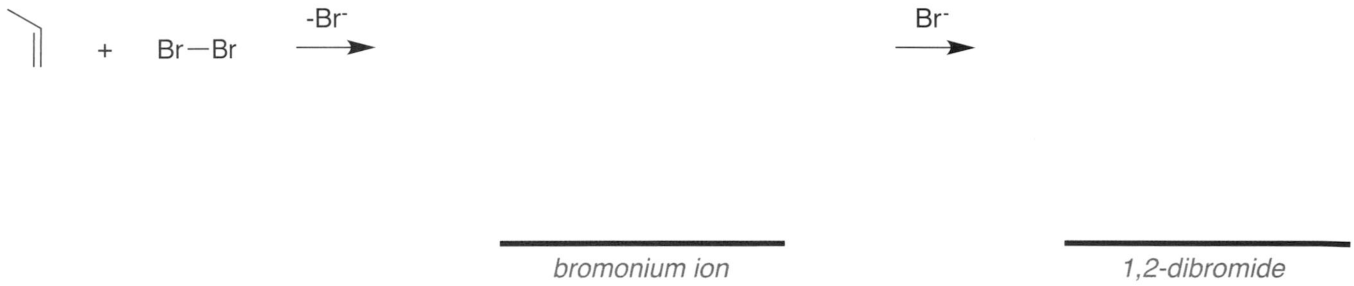

|| + Br—Br $\xrightarrow{-Br^-}$ $\xrightarrow{Br^-}$

———————————
bromonium ion

———————————
1,2-dibromide

+ Br—Br $\xrightarrow{-Br^-}$ $\xrightarrow{Br^-}$

———————————
bromonium ion

———————————
1,2-dibromide

$\xrightarrow[-Cl^-]{Cl—Cl}$ $\xrightarrow{-Cl^-}$

———————————

———————————

Halogens (X_2) are *nucleophiles / electrophiles* while, because of their π-clouds, alkenes are *nucleophiles / electrophiles*. Bromine, for instance, is a *nucleophile / electrophile* because it *has a dipole / becomes polarized* in the presence of high electron density.

Overall, halogenation of alkenes involves rate-limiting *nucleophilic / electrophilic* attack of the halogen on the alkene. Said differently, this is *nucleophilic / electrophilic* attack of the alkene on the bromine. Electron rich alkenes (*eg* those more highly substituted with alkyl substituents) react *faster / slower* than ones that have less or electron withdrawing substituents. Indicate the relative rates of bromination reactions by drawing the following alkenes above the line below without using the letter *C*.

but-1-ene, 1-methylcyclohexene, ethene, *E*-but-2-ene

---

fastest bromination   *slowest bromination*

Halogenation of alkenes are *addition / substitution* reactions involving bonding of one *X*-atom to each alkene-*C*-atom.

A MO View Of Halogenations

Complete the following diagram depicting the molecular orbitals for alkene bromination by filling electrons and the MO levels created.

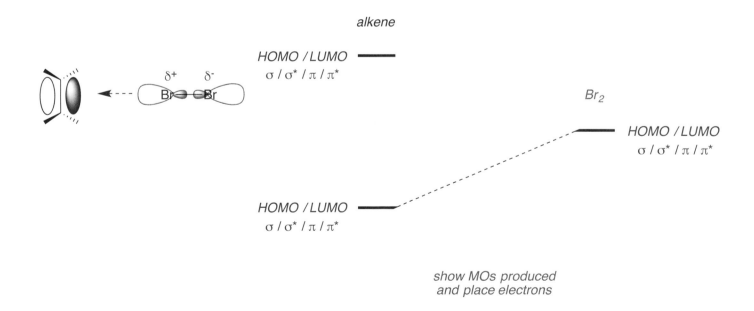

*show MOs produced
and place electrons*

Perpendicular approach of halogens (X_2) to a symmetrical π-cloud is net *stabilizing / destabilizing*, *ie* the energy of the system is reduced.

Interaction of the alkene π-orbitals with empty MOs on X_2 in halogenation is the most important orbital overlap so this is called the *secondary / primary* interaction.

Halogenation of alkenes is further stabilized by a *secondary / primary orbital interaction* between the π^*-orbitals on the alkene and filled orbitals on the bromine. Complete the molecular orbital diagram below to show this (indicate new MO levels and fill in electrons).

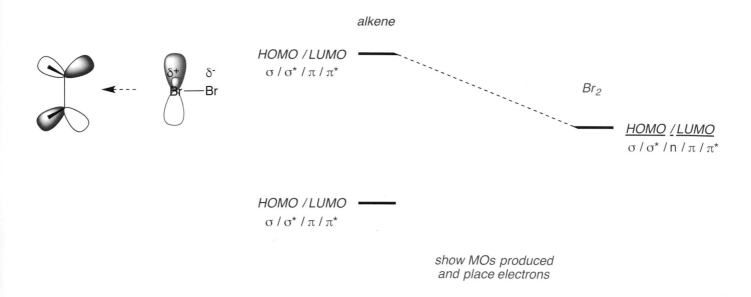

alkene

HOMO / LUMO
$\sigma / \sigma^* / \pi / \pi^*$

Br_2

HOMO / LUMO
$\sigma / \sigma^* / n / \pi / \pi^*$

HOMO / LUMO
$\sigma / \sigma^* / \pi / \pi^*$

*show MOs produced
and place electrons*

Secondary interactions as shown above *do / do not* favor formation of bromonium ions.

Stereospecificity

Bromonium ions in bromination of alkenes, tend to be opened by S_N2 / S_N1 attack of bromide (Br⁻).

Nucleophilic attack on halonium ions occurs *anti / syn* to the halogen atom, consequently alkenes within a ring (*ie endocyclic / exocyclic* ones) give *cis / trans*-dihalide products.

Bromination of cyclohexene *mostly / exclusively* affords the *trans- / cis*-1,2-dibromocyclohexane because approach of bromide to the bromonium ion must occur from the *opposite / same* face as the bromine atom.

In general, halogenation of *cis*-endocyclic alkenes is therefore *stereoselectively / stereospecifically-trans*, meaning it *sometimes / always* gives the *trans*-product.

Show the products of the following reactions, with curly arrows to show electron flow.

Cl—Cl
—————→
-Cl⁻

+Cl⁻
—————→

Show the products of the following reactions.

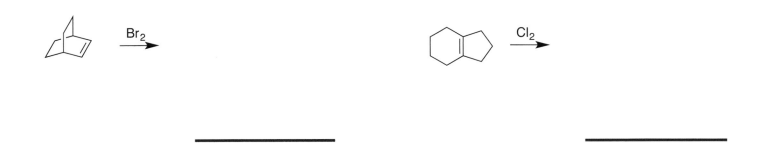

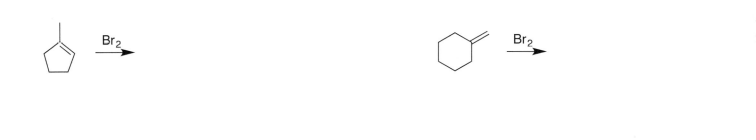

Nucleophilic attack on the following bromonium ion gives *enantiomers / regioisomers*. Draw the enantiomer that corresponds to either trajectory of addition, and assign the stereochemistry.

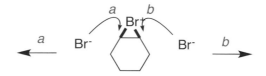

_____   _____
            R,R / R,S / S,S   *R,R / R,S / S,S*

The probability of reaction via pathway *a* and *b* is equal, so the ratio of the two enantiomers formed will be *equal / in favor of route a / favors route b*, ie the product will be *optically active / a racemate* in an organic reaction involving huge numbers of molecules.

It *is / is not* possible to form *meso* stereomers in this reaction.

Often one enantiomer is shown for many reactions in organic chemistry, but it must be the other one is formed in *equal / unequal* amounts; this is true in the reaction below.

Complete the following diagram, paying careful attention to stereochemistry.

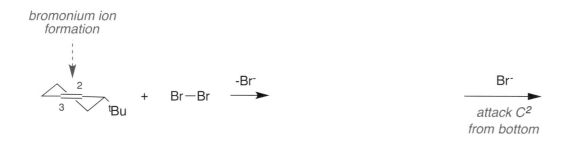

_____   _____
            bromonium ion   *1,2-dibromide*

E-2-butene is shown below with the sp²-hybridized carbon atoms labeled *2* and *3*. Give the products of bromination assuming the bromine attacked the alkene from the top or bottom as indicated and the bromide always attacks at C^2 (it won't!).

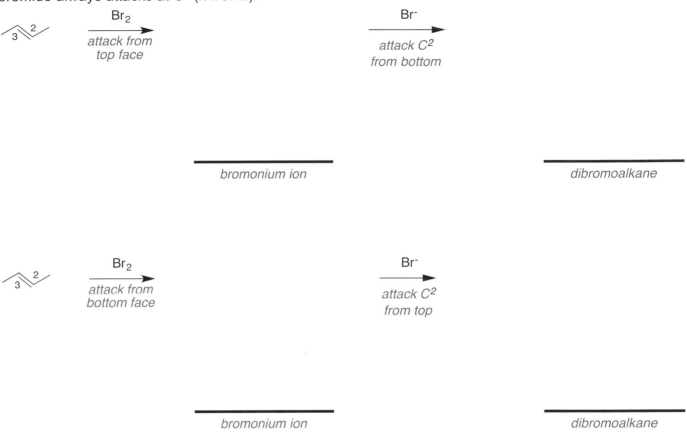

The products from these two reaction pathways are *enantiomers / identical*.

To test the effects of alkene geometry, compare the reactions above, with those below by completing this diagram.

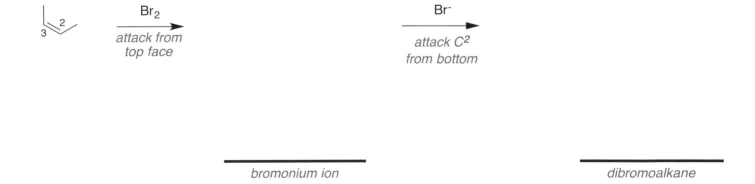

Br$_2$
attack from
bottom face

Br$^-$
attack C^2
from top

bromonium ion

dibromoalkane

When *E*- and *Z*-2-butene react with bromine, the products are racemic *diastereomers / regioisomers*.

Predict the products of the following reactions, carefully showing the relative stereochemistry of any chiral centers.

Br$_2$

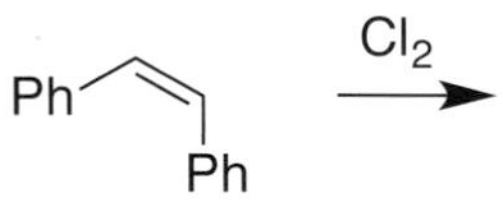

Ph, Ph   Cl$_2$

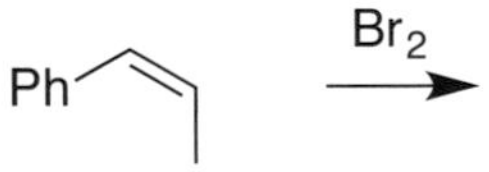

Ph   Br$_2$

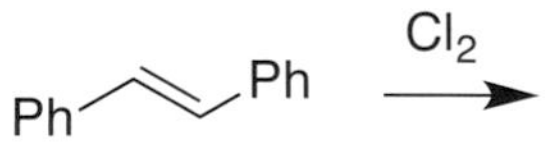

Ph, Ph   Cl$_2$

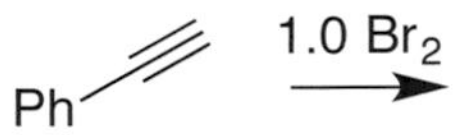

Ph   1.0 Br$_2$

1.0 Cl$_2$

trans-1,2-dibromophenylethene

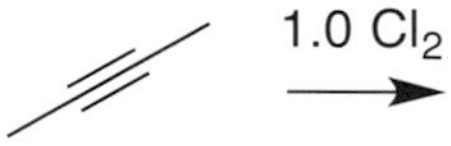

trans-2,3-dichlorobut-2-ene

cis- / trans-   cis- / trans-

Show alkenes that these 1,2-dibromides could be made from.

Iodination

The same mechanisms can be drawn for alkene iodination or bromination and chlorination but iodination does not give product because *the activation energies involved are too high / the product is thermodynamically unstable relative to ethene and iodine.*

Some *Z*-alkenes can be isomerized to their more thermodynamically stable *E*-isomers by treatment with iodine. Complete the following reaction to illustrate how this works for 1,2-diphenylethene (stilbene).

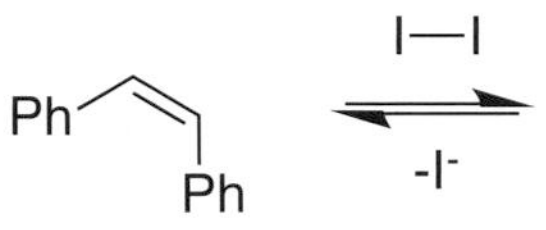

Ph⌒Ph   I—I ⇌ -I⁻   ⇌

───────────

*carbocation
in eclipsed conformation*

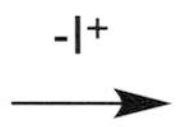

-I⁺ →

───────────

*carbocation
in anti conformation*

E-1,2-diphenylethene

───────────

Predict the predominant products of the following reactions.

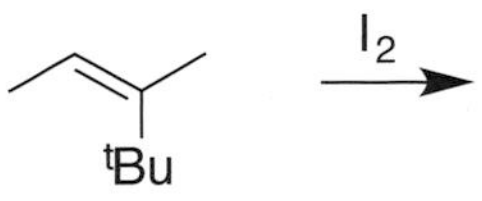

⌐⌐ᵗBu   I₂ →

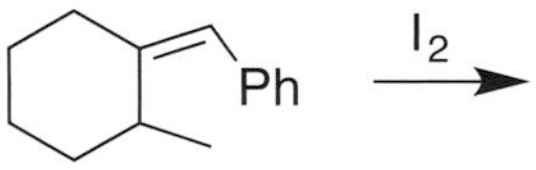

───────────

⬡=Ph   I₂ →

───────────

C Kinetic And Thermodynamic Control

Kinetic Control

Consider an *irreversible* reaction in which a starting material **A** reacts to give products **B** and **C**. There are no intermediates in this process, and, by coincidence, the transition states that lead to **B** and **C** have the same energy.

$$A \longrightarrow B + C$$

Complete the following two diagrams to illustrate cases where **B** is more stable than **C** and *vice versa*.

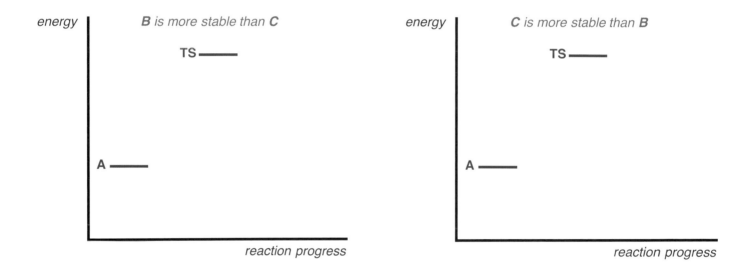

In both diagrams, **B** and **C** must be *higher / lower* energy than **A** since the reaction is irreversible, and the products *can / cannot* surmount the energy barrier necessary to reform **A** but it can be hurdled to give **B** and **C**.

The rate of formation of **B** and **C** in this reaction *is / is not* dependent on the stabilities of these two products; it *is / is not* dictated by the energy barrier for climbing to the transition state from **A**.

When **B** is more stable than **C** the **B:C** product ratio will be *>1 / 1 / <1*, and when **C** is more stable than **B** it will be *>1 / 1 / <1*.

A more common situation is that the transition states leading to **B** and **C** have *different* energies. Complete the following diagrams for an *irreversible* process in which **B** forms faster than **C**; it is best to do this using different color lines to connect **B** and **C** with **A**. Again, assume there are no intermediates.

$$A \longrightarrow B + C \qquad \textit{or better expressed as ....} \qquad B \longleftarrow A \longrightarrow C$$

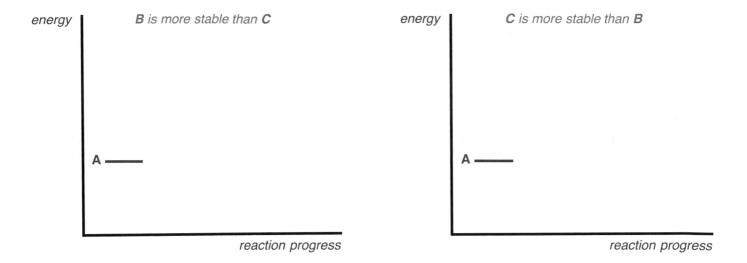

In the situation outlined above, the **B:C** ratio will be determined by their relative *stabilities / rates of formation*, and it will *be invariant / change* as the reaction progresses. In this case the **B:C** ratio is a *kinetic / thermodynamic* one.

Thermodynamic Control

Consider the same reaction, where the relative stabilities are exactly the same as above, except the products revert back to **A** under the reaction conditions, *ie* the process is *reversible / irreversible* and **B** and **C** have *different* energies in a *reversible* process in which **B** forms faster than **C**.

$$ \text{B} \;\rightleftharpoons\; \text{A} \;\rightleftharpoons\; \text{C} $$

At the very beginning, before any **B** and **C** have formed, the rate ratio for formation of products, **B:C** will be *>1 / 1 / <1*, and *will / will not* change as the reaction progresses.

Eventually, when the process has come to equilibrium, the ratio of **B** and **C** will be defined by two equilibrium constants that relate the concentrations of each to the **A**; express these below.

$$ K_B = [\quad] / [\quad] \quad \text{and} \quad K_C = [\quad] / [\quad] $$

At equilibrium, the K_B / K_C ratio *is / is not* another constant, K_{BC}, where:

$$ K_{BC} = [\quad] / [\quad] $$

and the **B:C** ratio is *dependent on / independent of* the concentration of **A**.

In this example, kinetic and thermodynamic controls are *non-coincident / coincident* insofar as they both favor the same product.

At the beginning of the reaction the **B:C** ratio is determined by the relative *stabilities of the products / activation energy barriers* but at the end it is governed by the relative *stabilities of the products / activation energy barriers*.

These ratios are *the same / different* but they both favor the same product.

Non-coincident Kinetic And Thermodynamic Control

Occasionally there are reactions where a product **B** forms faster than **C**, but **C** is more stable and both products equilibrate with the starting material **A**. From here on, assume **B** and **C** are both more stable than **A**, and only the activation energies involved change. Show this on the diagram provided.

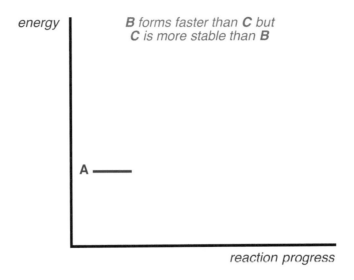

B forms faster than **C** so it is the *kinetic / thermodynamic* product; it forms *reversibly / irreversibly*.

C is the *kinetic / thermodynamic* product; it forms *reversibly / irreversibly*.

At equilibrium, the least stable product **B** would *be favored / be disfavored / form exclusively / will not be observed* because it will revert as the reaction proceeds and *reversibly / irreversibly* forms **C**.

Finally, consider a very special case where **B** forms faster than **C**, but **C** is more stable and *only the least stable product B could equilibrate with the starting material A*. Show this on the diagram below.

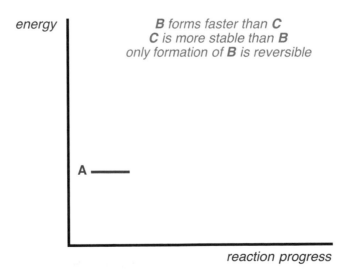

B forms faster than **C** so it is the *kinetic / thermodynamic* product; only **B** forms *reversibly / irreversibly*.

C is the *kinetic / thermodynamic* product; it forms *reversibly / irreversibly*.

At equilibrium, the least stable product **B** would *be favored / be disfavored / form exclusively / will not be observed* because it will revert as the reaction proceeds and *reversibly / irreversibly* forms **C**.

In both types of non-coincident kinetic and thermodynamic control a *kinetic / thermodynamic* product would form preferentially in the early stage of a reaction, then be mostly, or completely, transformed into a different *kinetically / thermodynamically* controlled product later.

Bromination Of 1,3-Butadiene: Non-coincident Kinetic And Thermodynamic Control

Addition of one equivalent of bromine to 1,3-butadiene can be described in the following way:

1,4-dibromide
more stable

1,2-dibromide
less stable

In this reaction, the 1,2-dibromide forms quickly in the early stages of the reaction, *ie* it is the *kinetic / thermodynamic* product.

The amount of 1,2-dibromide *increases / decreases* as the reaction time is extended, and the concentration of 1,4-dibromide *increases / decreases*.

Suggest a reason that the 1,2-dibromide might be *less* stable than the 1,4-isomer related to the degree of substitution of the alkene products: _____

_____

_____.

The 1,2-dibromide might form faster than its 1,4-isomer because direct attack of bromide on the bromonium ion occurs in preference to nucleophilic attack on the alkene next to it.

Nucleophilic attack on alkenes tends to be much *less / more* favorable than electrophilic attack; in fact, it *does / does not* proceed unless there are electron-withdrawing groups attached to the alkene (*eg* halonium ions).

D Halogenations In Nucleophilic Solvents

Consider relative electronegativities of carbon and bromine, then circle the representation of a bromonium ion that is most accurate.

Nucleophiles add to the carbon of an unsymmetrical halonium ion that is *best / least* able to support the incipient positive charge.

Regio- / chemo-selectivity is important when bromination of unsymmetrical alkenes is performed in the presence of a better, or more abundant, nucleophile than bromide because the reaction can produce different *epimers / regioisomers*.

Circle the preferred products of the following reactions.

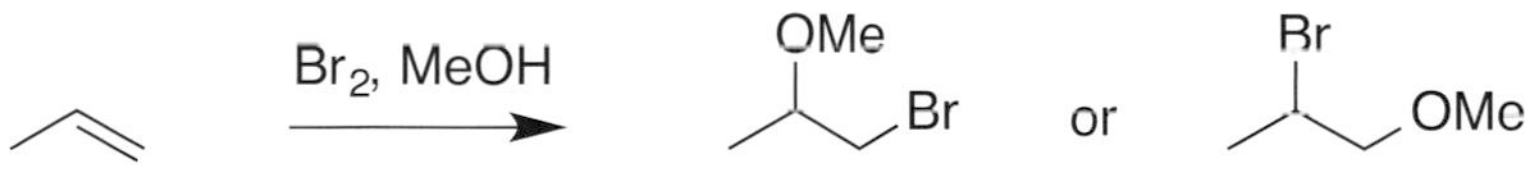

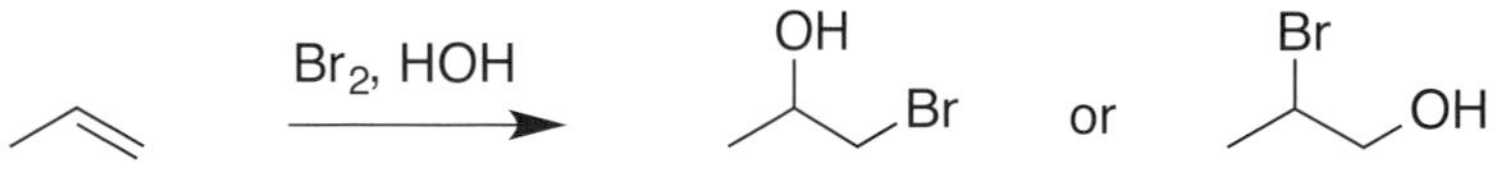

Br$_2$, MeOH

or

Br$_2$, HOH

or

Opening of bromonium or chloronium ions by water is called a *halohydrin / chlorohydrin* reaction.

If the alkene substrate is unsymmetrical, halohydrin reactions will generate products with the halogen on the carbon least able to support a negative charge because *this is the precursor to the most stable cation / the nucleophile attack at the most substituted carbon is sterically favored.*

Give the preferred regioisomeric product of reaction of hydroxide or water with the following bromonium ions.

Ph—⟨Br+ $\xrightarrow[\text{-H}^+]{\text{H}_2\text{O}}$ _____

⟨Br+ $\xrightarrow[\text{-H}^+]{\text{H}_2\text{O}}$ _____

⟨Br+ $\xrightarrow{\text{HO}^-}$ _____

Ph—⟨Br+ $\xrightarrow{\text{HO}^-}$ _____

Considerations regarding potential carbocation stabilities *are / are not* likely to apply to ring opening of epoxides.

15 Epoxidation Of Alkenes, And Epoxides

from chapter(s) _____ in the recommended text

A Introduction

Focus

This *Inquisition* is not about memorizing reagents, but a few epoxidation agents are introduced here to illustrate how to represent electron flow in epoxidation reactions. This section is about how to form epoxides and their reactivities.

Reasons To Care

Like chlorination and bromination, epoxidation of alkenes is a reliable transformation, and the product epoxides are spring-loaded electrophiles for nucleophilic displacement reactions. Unsymmetrical epoxides can open at either carbon, and orientations for popping them open are governed by media pH and nucleophile reactivity; reaction at one site in preference to a similar one is called regioselectivity, and epoxide opening is an excellent example of how regioselectivity can vary with conditions.

Highly reactive organic molecules do not survive in living organisms. Alkyl bromides, and many alkyl chlorides, will non-selectively alkylate the first nucleophiles they encounter when introduced into a cell or into an animal, and this inevitably leads to toxicity. Epoxides are alkylating agents but their reactivity is relatively attenuated. For instance, bacteria manage to produce the anti-microbial fumagillin and the anti-cancer compound neocarzinostatin without poisoning themselves. However, the presence of an epoxide in a biologically active molecule suggests it will covalently bind to some, and probably many, biomolecules.

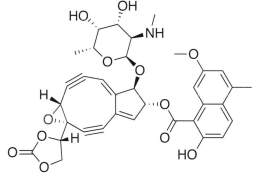

fumagillin   *neocarzinostatin*

Concepts Involved

additions to alkenes • electron flow • alkene oxidation • ring strain • S_N2 • acids and bases • stereochemistry

Objective

Epoxidation reactions are easy to understand, but there is regiochemical ambiguity about where nucleophiles tend to add. After this questioning, there should be no such doubts.

B Reagents And Mechanism

Bromination of alkenes can be drawn as loss of a bromide leaving group *pulling / pushing* electrons away from the other bromine in Br_2 as that electrophilic bromine approaches the alkene.

Each of the following diagrams has one curly arrow missing; fill it in accurately in all three cases.

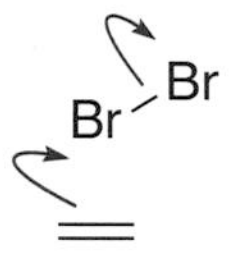

bromination

epoxidation
general
X is leaving group

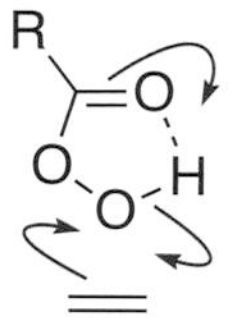

epoxidation
with peracid

Epoxides are *2 / 3 / 4* membered rings containing oxygen.   Like Br_2 in bromination, agents for epoxidation possess a leaving group that *pulls / pushes* electrons away from an oxygen which becomes more polarized and *electrophilic / nucleophilic* as it adds to an alkene.

Two common agents for epoxidizing alkenes are *meta*-chloroperbenzoic acid (mCPBA) and dimethyldioxirane (DMDO). Check these structures online, and fill them in here, and predict the structure of the material that is left after these agents donate oxygen.

mCPBA

product after donation
of oxygen

dimethyldioxirane

product after donation
of oxygen

Epoxidation involves *nucleophilic / electrophilic* attack of an oxidant on an alkene that therefore acts as a(n) *nucleophile / electrophile*.

Epoxidation of alkenes is a(n) *addition / substitution* reaction.

Show the mechanisms and products of the following reactions.

epoxidation of propene with peracetic acid

peracetic
acid

$\longrightarrow$

_____   _____
propene   propene oxide

epoxidation of cyclohexene with m-chloroperbenzoic acid (mCPBA; look up structure)

mCPBA

$\longrightarrow$

_____   _____
cyclohexene   cyclohexene oxide

Give the products of epoxidations of the following alkenes.

   mCPBA ⟶

⟶ mCPBA

mCPBA ⟶

⟶ mCPBA

DMDO ⟶

DMDO ⟶

Complete the following diagram depicting the molecular orbitals for this interaction by showing the new MO levels and filling in electrons.

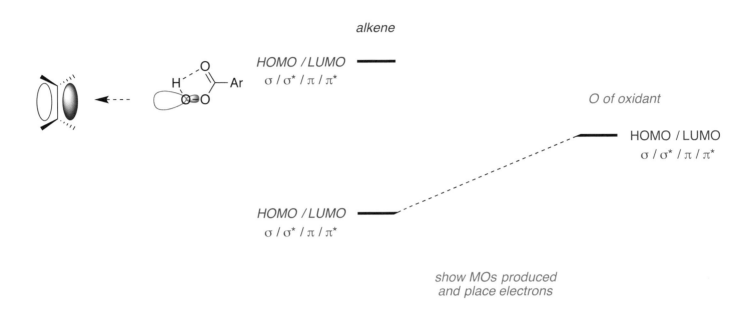

alkene

HOMO / LUMO
$\sigma / \sigma^* / \pi / \pi^*$

O of oxidant

HOMO / LUMO
$\sigma / \sigma^* / \pi / \pi^*$

HOMO / LUMO
$\sigma / \sigma^* / \pi / \pi^*$

show MOs produced
and place electrons

c Rates Of Epoxidation

Indicate the relative rates of epoxidation by drawing the following alkenes above the line below without using the letter *C*: but-1-ene, 1-methylcyclohexene, ethene, *E*-but-2-ene

fastest epoxidation   *slowest epoxidation*

D Stereospecificity

Formation of some epoxides is almost impossible due to strain issues; circle those for which this applies:

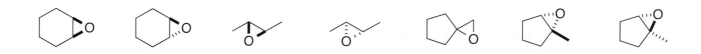

Reagents like DMDO and mCPBA are *stereospecific* insofar as the geometry of the double bond is 100 % *conserved / inverted* in epoxidation reactions mediated by these reagents.

Predict the products of the following epoxidations reactions

mCPBA

mCPBA

————————————
cis / trans

————————————
cis / trans

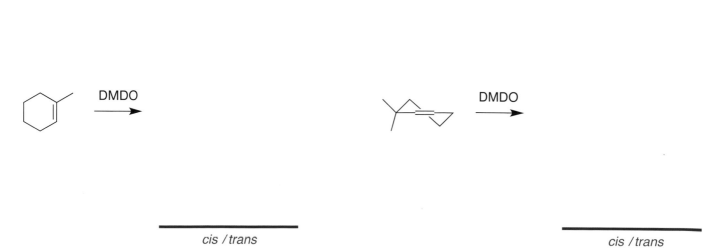

DMDO

DMDO

————————————
cis / trans

————————————
cis / trans

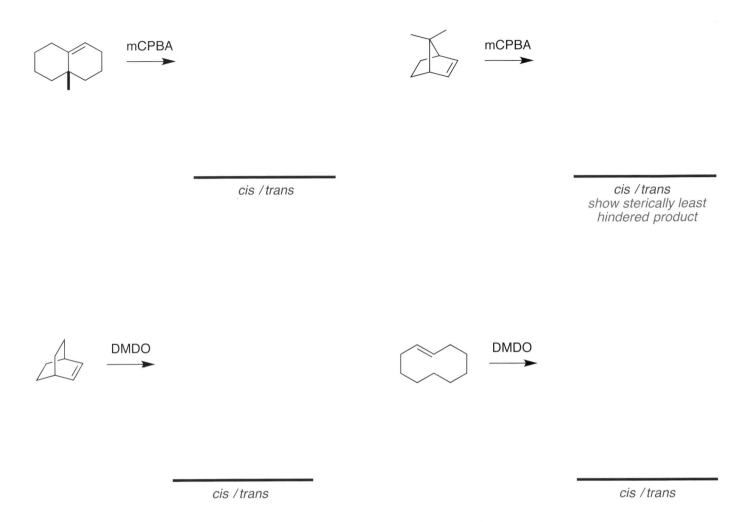

_____
cis / trans

_____
cis / trans
show sterically least
hindered product

_____
cis / trans

_____
cis / trans

In general, epoxidations of endocyclic *cis*-alkenes *always / never* give the *cis / trans* epoxide, but, of course, not all cyclic alkenes have *cis*-geometries.

For acyclic alkenes, the stereospecificity of epoxidation reactions also has to reflect the geometry of the alkene.

Predict the products of the following epoxidations reactions.

_____
cis / trans

_____
cis / trans

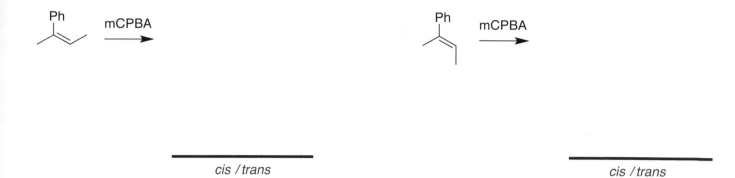

cis / trans   _cis / trans_

Show the alkenes the following epoxides were made from via reaction with DMDO.

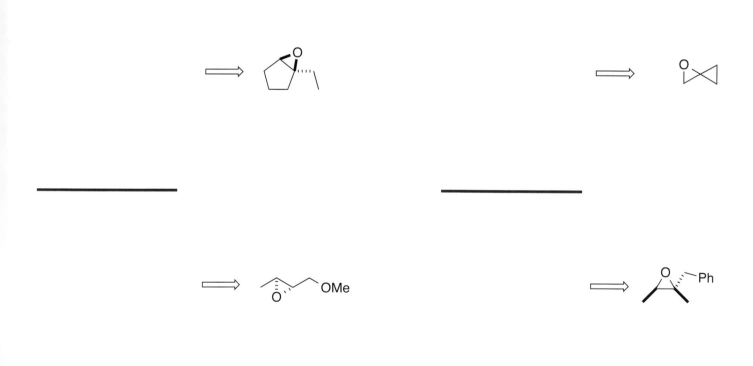

E Regioselectivity Of Epoxide Ring Opening Reactions

Under Neutral Or Basic Conditions

There are at least two possible outcomes when an unsymmetrical epoxide is attacked by a nucleophile; at least two *regioisomeric / epimeric* products could be formed.

In the absence of acid, nucleophilic attack on epoxides occurs on the least hindered epoxide terminus, *ie* it is largely dictated by *steric / electronic* factors.

Show curly arrows to illustrate formation of those two possible products, show the products, and predict the one that should be favored for the following reactions that are performed under basic conditions.

+ O⁻Me ⟶   +

———————————————   ———————————————
major / minor   *major / minor*

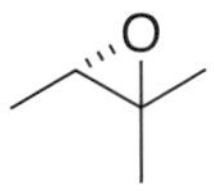

+ ⁻CN ⟶   +

———————————————   ———————————————
major / minor   *major / minor*

Ph + N₃⁻ ⟶   +

———————————————   ———————————————
major / minor   *major / minor*

A small amount of minor product may be formed in these transformations so they are *regiospecific / regioselective* and not *regiospecific / regioselective*.

Under Acidic Conditions

Protonation of unsymmetrical epoxides activates both *C – O* bonds in unsymmetrical epoxides, but the bond leading to the most stabilized {incipient} carbocation is stretched the most. Circle the product drawing that illustrates this best for the following protonation reactions.

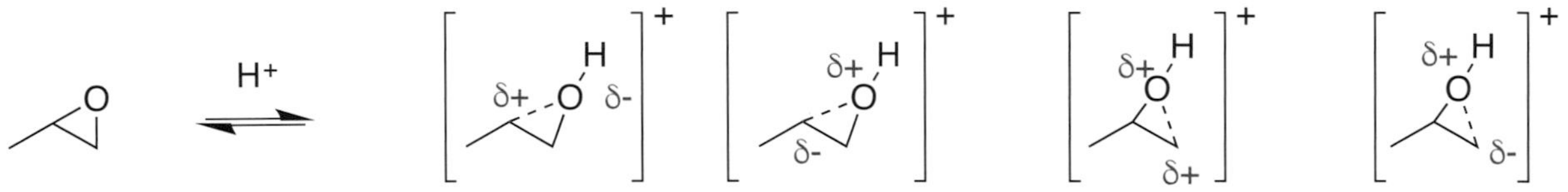

circle the most favorable form

Predict the products of the following reactions (after deprotonation).

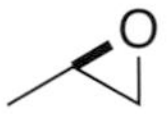 + $PhNH_2$ $\xrightarrow{H^+}$ ______ + ______

major / minor *major / minor*

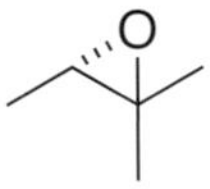 + HOEt $\xrightarrow{H^+}$ ______ + ______

major / minor *major / minor*

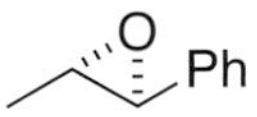 + OH_2 $\xrightarrow{H^+}$ ______ + ______

major / minor *major / minor*

Show curly arrows to depict the mechanism of the following reactions.

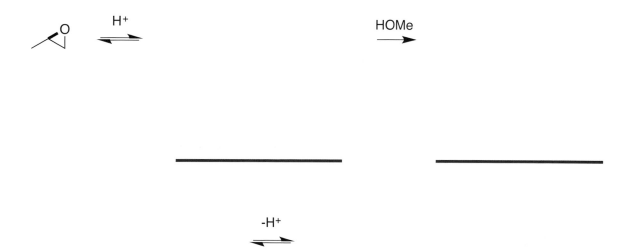

Take care regarding the stereochemistry in this final example.

16 Cycloadditions To Alkenes And Alkynes

from chapter(s) _____ in the recommended text

A Introduction

Focus

Electrophilic additions to alkenes follow a pattern: alkenes (nucleophiles) react with electrophiles forming cationic intermediates, then nucleophiles add to these. Cycloadditions, particularly ones involving molecules with nucleophilic and electrophilic centers resonating over the termini of a three-atom arrangement (1,3-dipolar compounds), do *not* behave in this way. Instead, it is as if the alkene behaves like a wire, shorting an electrostatic potential by connecting the positive and negative sites.

This section is about these types of reactions, particularly 1,3-dipolar compounds (three atoms) adding to alkynes or alkenes (two), *ie* [2 + 3] cycloadditions.

Reasons To Care

Anyone working in a laboratory likes general, reliable, reactions, and the people who love them the most are those who find synthesis hard. Some cycloadditions are called "click reactions" because they are so easy to perform and nearly always work that almost *anyone* could do them. Many biochemists and biologists have heard of the click reactions, and some even perform them. Moreover, azide-alkyne cycloadditions are robust; neither organic azides nor alkynes react with the types of organic compounds found in cells, for instance, and when they are mixed in or around cells they somehow find each other. When two functional groups are destined to combine only with each other that is called "chemoselectivity" (think: *Love, true love.*).

Alkene cleavages with oxidizing agents like ozone or permanganate and periodate are not so chemoselective, but they are reliable, and useful, for instance in chopping a complex molecule into more easily identified fragments to deduce what parent compound is.

Concepts Involved

electron flow • regioselectivity • chemoselectivity • oxidation • ring strain • heat of hydrogenation

Objective

Introduction of some reactions used in synthetic and biological chemistry, and another way that electron flow occurs.

B Nomenclature Of Cycloadditions

Cycloadditions can be classified according to how many atoms are in the newly formed ring. Formation of three-membered rings via cycloadditions can only be [2 + 1] processes, but *[4 + 2] / [1 + 2] / [3 + 2]* could lead to five-membered rings (circle all that apply).

Write a descriptor, *eg* [5 + 1], below each of the following cycloaddition reactions.

cyclopropanation	Diels-Alder	click reaction	ozonolysis	dihydroxylation

This section focuses on a few cycloadditions relevant to biological chemistry.

C Carbene Additions [2 + 1] (Cyclopropanations)

Reagents that contribute one atom to a ring in cycloadditions must be able to expand their valency by two: *true / false*.

Carbenes have only *5 / 6 / 7* electrons in the valence shell of carbon. Consequently, a singlet carbene can donate a pair of electrons to an alkene, and receive a pair in return, thus expanding the valency of carbon to *3 / 4 / 5*. A leaving group *is / is not* required in cyclopropanations featuring carbenes.

Carbenes can be sp^2 hybridized with *an empty p-orbital / a diradical structure, ie singlet / triplet* forms, or sp^3 hybridized with *an empty p-orbital / a diradical structure, ie singlet / triplet* forms. Both are typically represented as (circle the correct one in each set):

carbene	dimethylcarbene	dibromocarbene

214

Complete the following cyclopropanation mechanisms (show all curly arrows, and/or draw product).

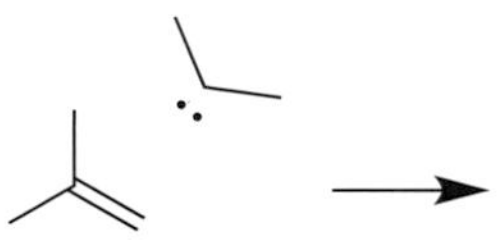

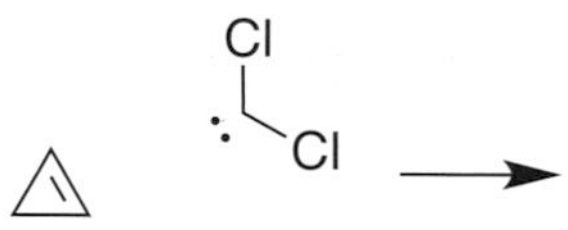

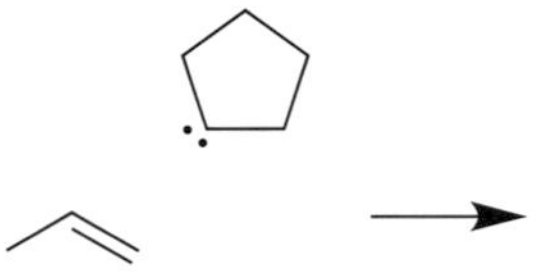

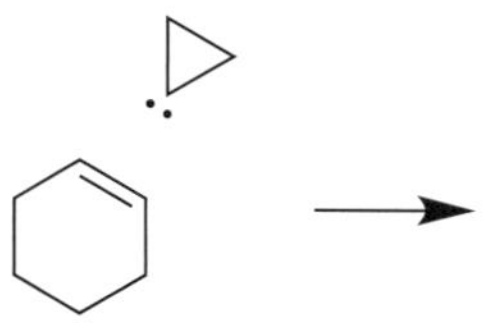

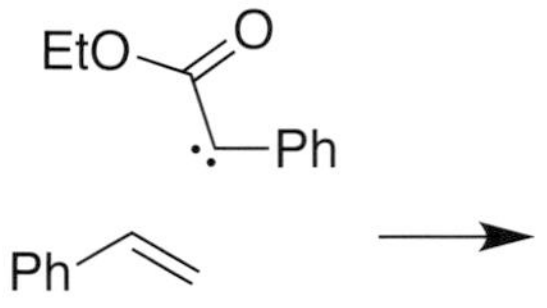

_____

_____

_____

_____

show only trans-product

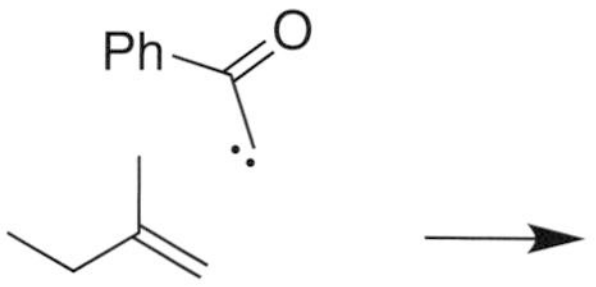

show only trans-product

Substances that have two rings sharing a single carbon are called *spiro- / spiral- / spooky*-compounds.

D Ozonolysis [2 + 3]

Ozone is generated by electrical discharge in an oxygen atmosphere. It smells like *a sea breeze / rotten eggs / don't smell it you clown, it's highly toxic* (circle all that apply).

Treatment with ozone, *ie hydrogenation / ozonolysis*, then quenching with a mild reducing agent, cleaves alkenes to give *aldehydes / epoxides / ketones / alkynes* at either terminus (select all that apply).

Predict the products of the following ozonolyses.

Ph⟍⟍ (i) O$_3$ / (ii) Me$_2$S →   +   _____

⬡ (i) O$_3$ / (ii) Me$_2$S →   +   _____

Ph⟍⟍ (i) O$_3$ / (ii) Me$_2$S →   +   _____

⬡= (i) O$_3$ / (ii) Me$_2$S →   +   _____

⬡⬡ (i) O$_3$ / (ii) Me$_2$S →   _____

⬡ (i) O$_3$ / (ii) Me$_2$S →   _____

A retro-[2 + 3] is a *cycloaddition so old it has gone out of fashion then came back again / a ring cleavage to 2 and 3 atoms components.*

Show the alkenes that gave these aldehydes after ozonolysis.

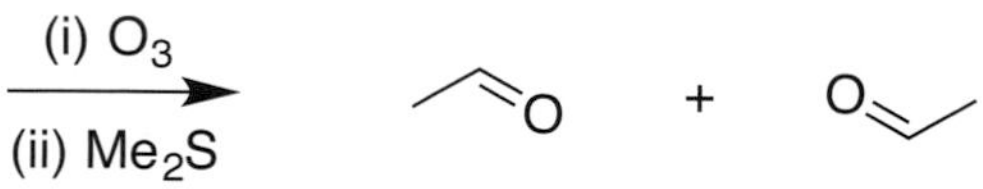

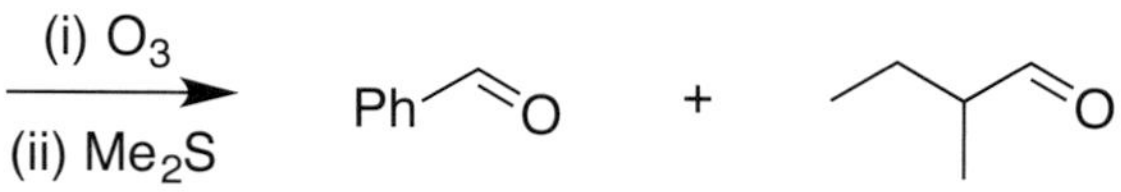

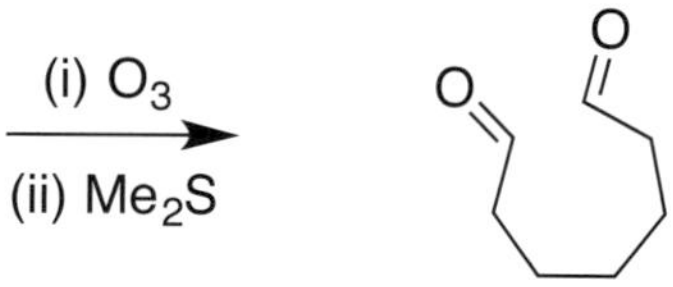

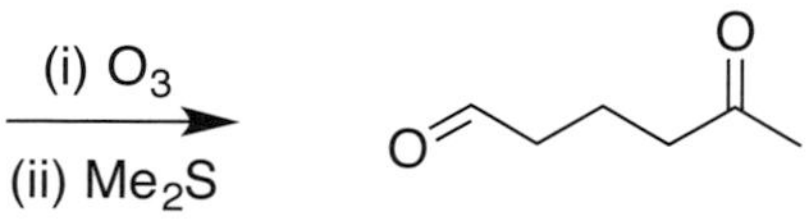

$$\xrightarrow[\text{(ii) Me}_2\text{S}]{\text{(i) O}_3}$$

+

_____

$$\xrightarrow[\text{(ii) Me}_2\text{S}]{\text{(i) O}_3}$$

Ph   +

_____

$$\xrightarrow[\text{(ii) Me}_2\text{S}]{\text{(i) O}_3}$$

_____

$$\xrightarrow[\text{(ii) Me}_2\text{S}]{\text{(i) O}_3}$$

_____

Complete the following reaction mechanism filling in curly arrows or missing products where necessary.

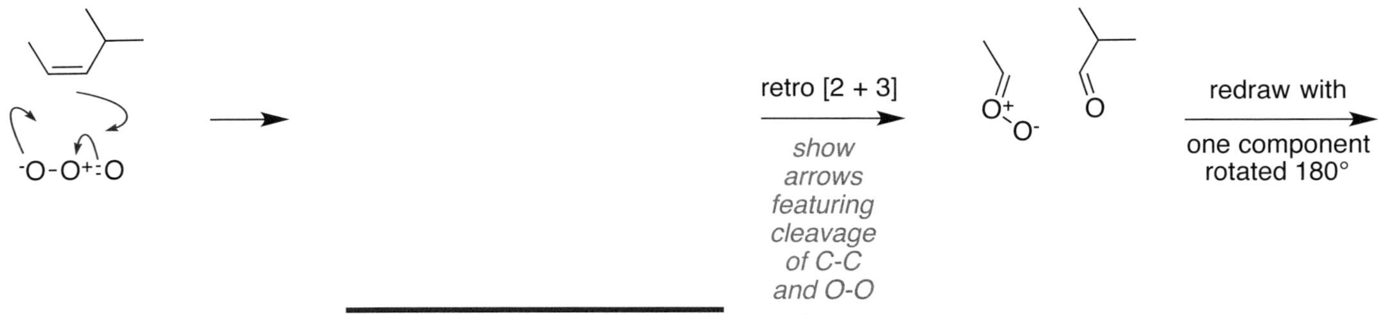

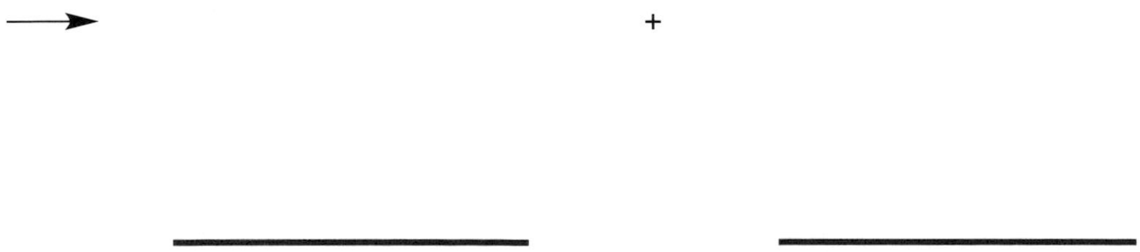

retro [2 + 3]

show arrows featuring cleavage of C-C and O-O

redraw with one component rotated 180°

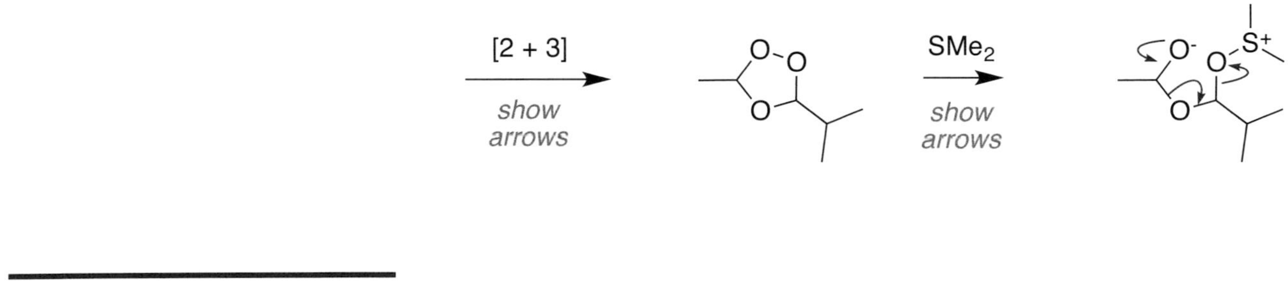

[2 + 3]

show arrows

SMe₂

show arrows

+

Aldehyde or ketone products, and carbonyl oxide intermediates, in ozonolysis reactions may be *reduced / oxidized* to alcohols if the mixture is treated with sodium borohydride, or *reduced / oxidized* to acids if treated with hydrogen peroxide.
Show the products of the following reactions.

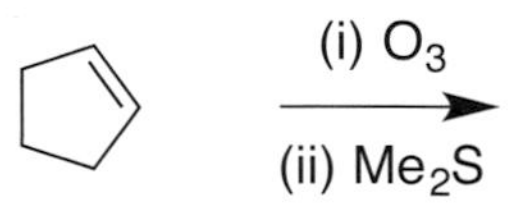

(i) O_3

(ii) Me_2S

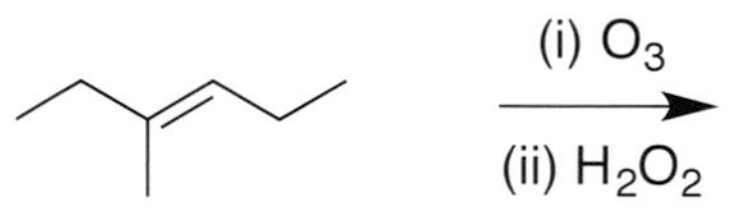

_____

(i) O_3

(ii) H_2O_2

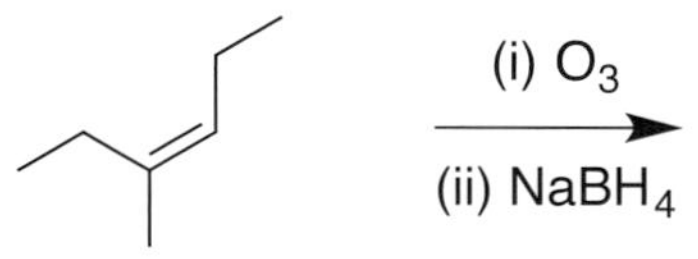

_____

(i) O_3

(ii) $NaBH_4$

_____

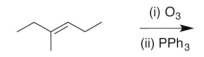

(i) O$_3$

(ii) PPh$_3$

(i) O$_3$

(ii) NaBH$_4$

(i) O$_3$

(ii) H$_2$O$_2$

E Dihydroxylation [2 + 3]

A dihydroxylation adds _____ hydroxyl groups to an alkene.

Fill in the intermediate and product of these reactions.

O=Os(O)(O)=O

⟶

hydrolysis
⟶
then remove
metal salts

_____   _____

O=Mn(O)(O⁻)=O

⟶

hydrolysis
⟶
then remove
metal salts

_____   _____

Cycloadditions of these metal oxides to alkenes occur with *syn / anti* face specificity.

Draw osmium tetroxide additions to alkenes to give osmate esters, then hydrolyzed to diols for the following alkenes. Show curly arrows only for the first step.

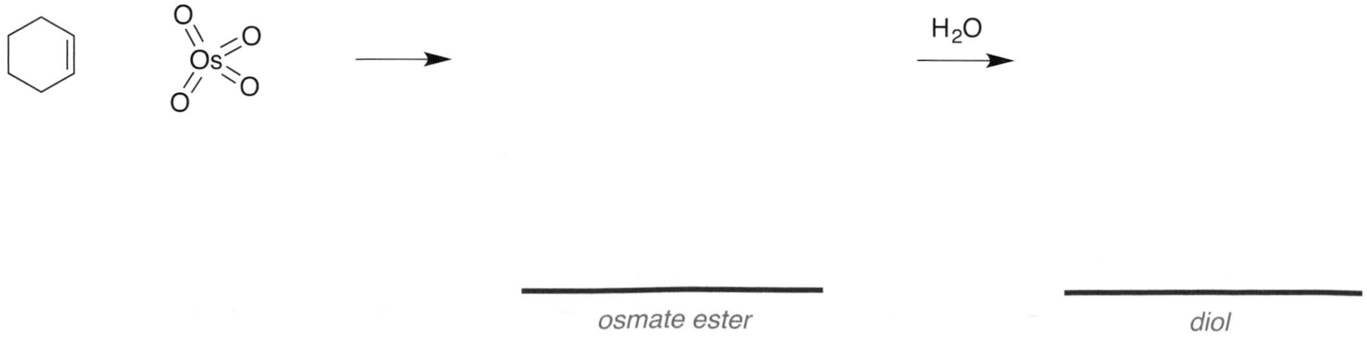

⟶   H₂O ⟶

_____   _____

osmate ester   *diol*

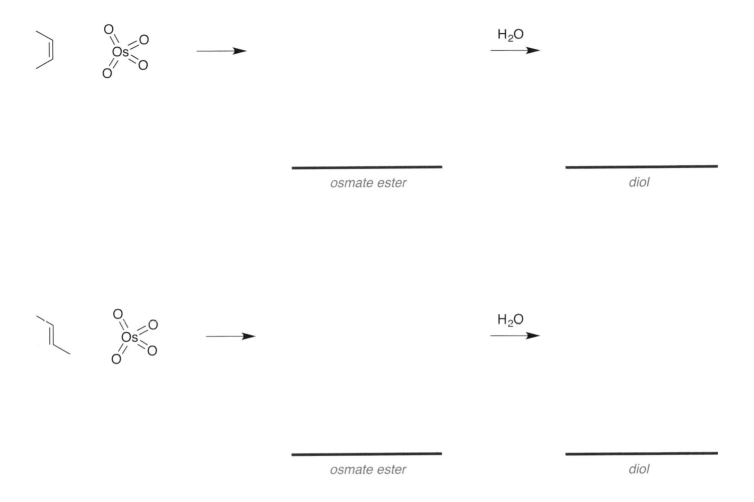

osmate ester   diol

osmate ester   diol

Dihydroxylation with osmium tetroxide is stereospecifically *trans / cis*.

This is *like / unlike* generation of diols via epoxidations and acid-mediated ring opening of the epoxide with water, which gives net *trans / cis* addition of hydrogen peroxide across an alkene.

Unfortunately, OsO$_4$ is highly toxic and expensive, but the reaction can be made to work catalytically by adding more than one equivalent of an amine oxide, relative to the alkene. Two typical amine oxides used are trimethylamine *N*-oxide and *N*-methylmorpholine-*N*-oxide (NMO).

Show the structures of these amine oxides here.

trimethylamine-N-oxide   *NMO*

Give the products of the following reactions.

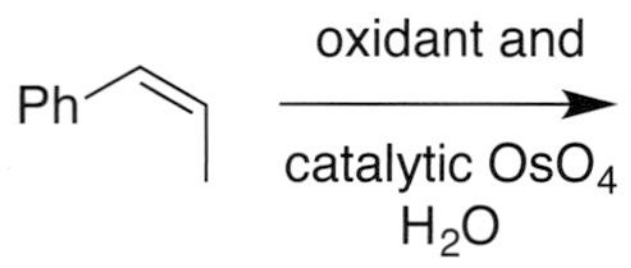

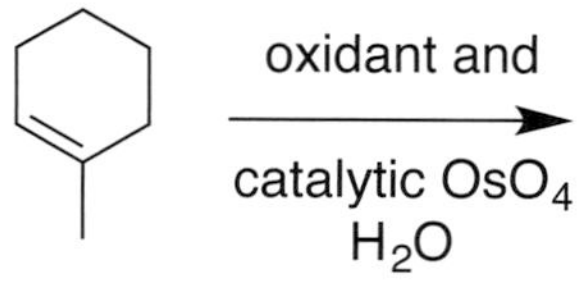

(cyclopentene structure) $\xrightarrow{\text{mCPBA}}$

$\xrightarrow[\text{H}_2\text{O}]{\text{H}^+}$

_____

_____

Ph (cis-alkene structure) $\xrightarrow[\substack{\text{catalytic OsO}_4 \\ \text{H}_2\text{O}}]{\text{oxidant and}}$

(1-methylcyclohexene structure) $\xrightarrow[\substack{\text{catalytic OsO}_4 \\ \text{H}_2\text{O}}]{\text{oxidant and}}$

_____

_____

show stereochemistry

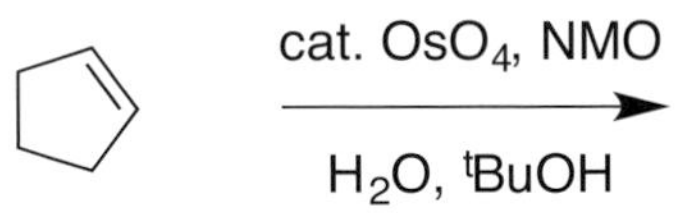

cat. OsO$_4$, NMO

$\xrightarrow{}$

H$_2$O, ^{t}BuOH

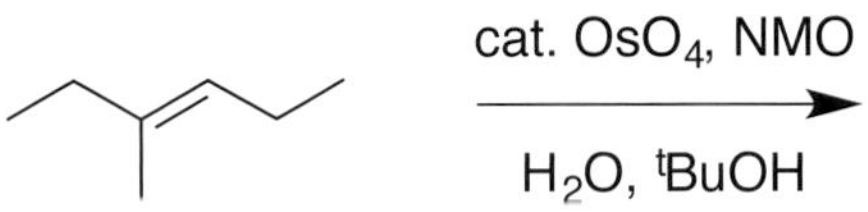

———————————————

cat. OsO$_4$, NMO

$\xrightarrow{}$

H$_2$O, ^{t}BuOH

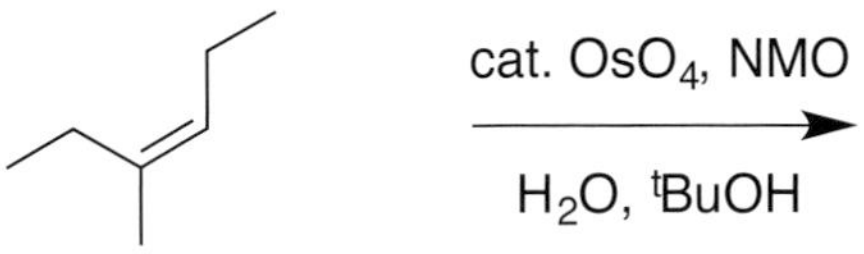

———————————————

cat. OsO$_4$, NMO

$\xrightarrow{}$

H$_2$O, ^{t}BuOH

———————————————

F Periodate Cleavage

Diols are cleaved to aldehydes or ketones via treatment with periodic acid (or HIO_4). The iodine of periodic acid (HIO_4) is in the *+8 / +7 / +6 / +5* oxidation state; it is *oxidized / reduced* in this reaction to HIO_3 which is in the *+8 / +7 / +6 / +5* oxidation state. Show clear curly arrows for the *second step* following transformation.

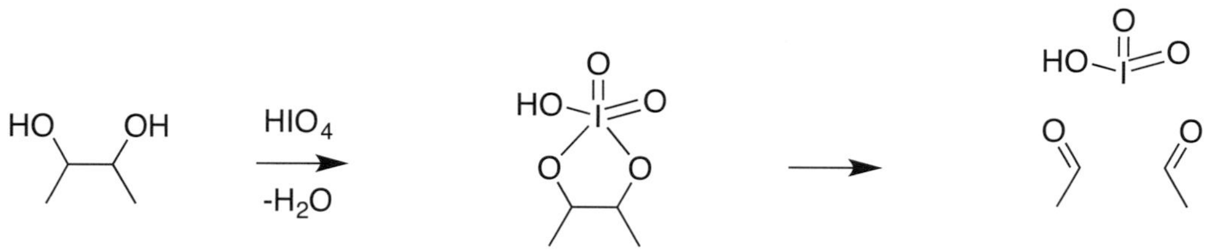

Show the intermediates and products in the following reactions

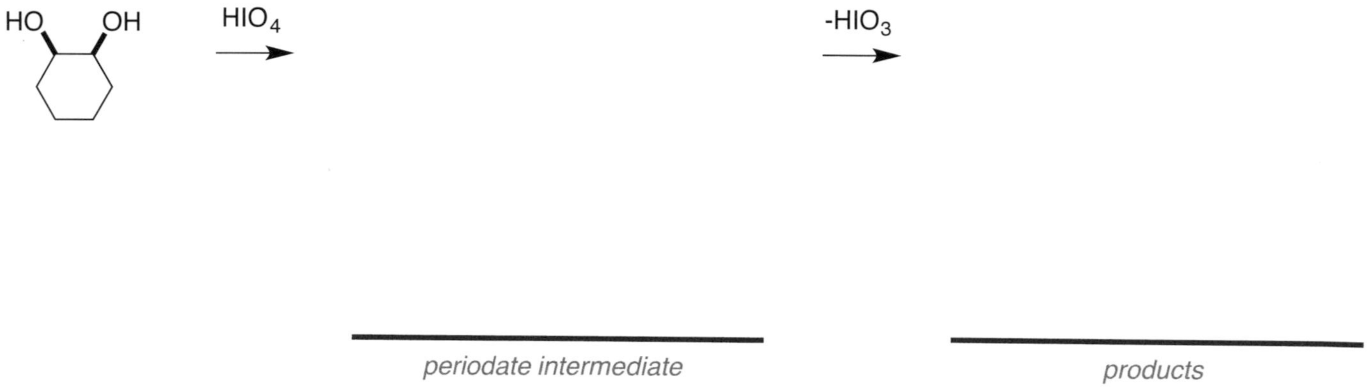

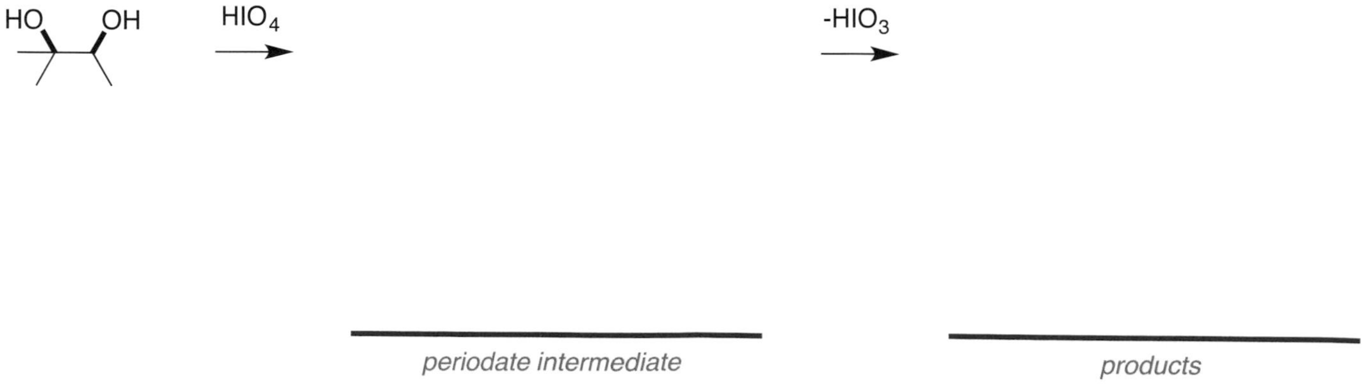

_____   _____
     periodate intermediate   *products*

_____   _____
     periodate intermediate   *products*

G Azide-Alkyne "Click Reactions" [2 + 3]

A terminal alkyne is a *C – C* triple bond *at the end of a chain / an incurable disease*.

Heating an organic azide and a terminal alkyne together causes them to undergo a *[3 + 2] / [4 + 1] / [4 + 1]* cycloaddition. Two *enantiomers / regioisomers / diastereomers* are always formed in this reaction, *ie* it is *diastereoselective / regioselective / enantioselective / chemoselective*.

Complete the following by adding curly arrows and the product.

Ph─≡   heat   ⟶   +   heat   ≡─Ph

⁻N=N⁺=N   ⁻N=N⁺=N
   \   \

_____   _____
  1,4-addition product   *1,5-addition product*

Copper(1+) salts can substitute the *H-C*sp alkyne hydrogen, and this leads to exclusive formation of the 1,4-cycloaddition product, *ie* the reaction becomes 100% *regioselective / chemoselective*.

Draw the products of the following reactions.

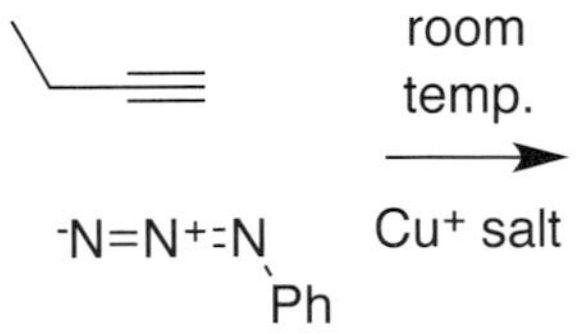

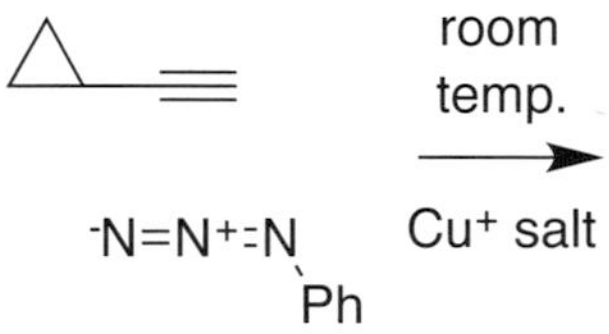

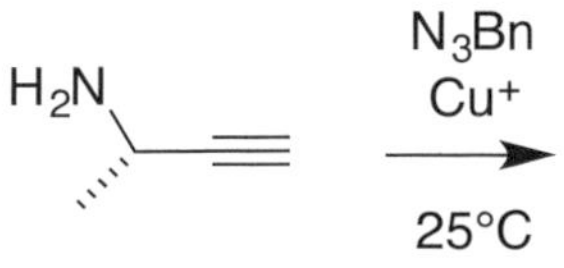

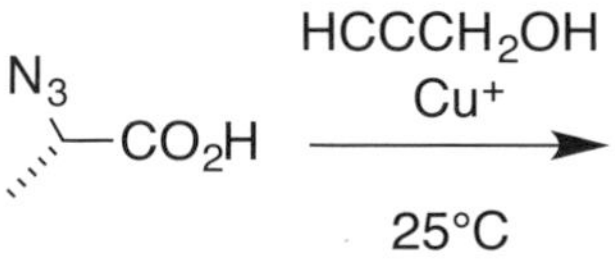

\─≡   room temp.   ⟶   △─≡   room temp.   ⟶
⁻N=N⁺=N   Cu⁺ salt   ⁻N=N⁺=N   Cu⁺ salt
    Ph   Ph

_____   _____

H₂N\─≡   N₃Bn / Cu⁺ / 25°C ⟶   N₃\─CO₂H   HCCCH₂OH / Cu⁺ / 25°C ⟶

_____   _____

Biological molecules (*eg* proteins, DNA, RNA, carbohydrates) have many different organic functionalities, but *none / most* of them react quickly with azides or with alkynes.

If an azide and alkyne combination is introduced into a mixture containing biomolecules it may proceed with formation of few by-products, *ie* this type of click reaction is *diastereoselective / enantioselective / chemoselective*.

In experiments with cells, however, moderate concentrations of copper ions are cytotoxic, and cells are *more / less* stable when heated above 37 °C. Consequently, chemists have devised another way …..

Complete the following diagram of the thermal cycloaddition of 2-butyne with azidoethanol, with curly arrows of course, and mark the hybridization state of the carbons marked with red dots.

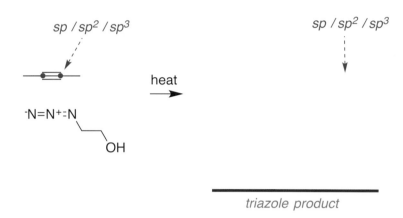

$sp / sp^2 / sp^3$

$sp / sp^2 / sp^3$

heat

⁻N=N⁺=N

OH

triazole product

In 2-butyne the ideal geometry around the "red dot carbons" is *109 / 120 / 180°*, whereas in the triazole product it is *109 / 120 / 180°*.

Indicate the relative stabilities of the following alkynes, based on ring strain factors, by writing *1* under the most stable, *2* under the next, *etc*.

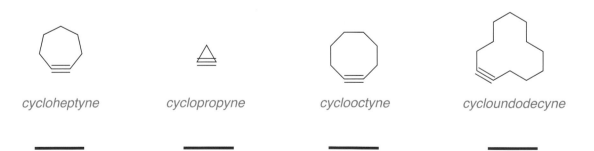

cycloheptyne   *cyclopropyne*   *cyclooctyne*   *cycloundodecyne*

_____   _____   _____   _____

One of these cyclic alkynes has never been made; put a circle around that one. Another of these is extremely difficult to isolate; draw a square around that one. Heat is liberated when alkynes are hydrogenated to alkanes, and this is called the heat of *ozonolysis / hydrogenation / combustion* for that substrate. Of those shown above, the alkyne that liberates most heat in this reaction is the *least / most* strained, *ie* _____ .

Hydrogenation changes alkyne sp-hybridized carbons to *sp / sp² / sp³*, thereby making those carbon atoms *more / less* able to fit in medium-size rings.

Click reactions of cycloalkynes change alkyne sp-hybridized carbons to *sp / sp² / sp³*, thereby making those carbon atoms *more / less* able to fit in medium-size rings.

Two of the alkynes shown below undergo room temperature cycloadditions with organic azides at a convenient rate in the absence of catalyst; these particular compounds can be conveniently connected to a biomolecule via organic reactions, circle those two.

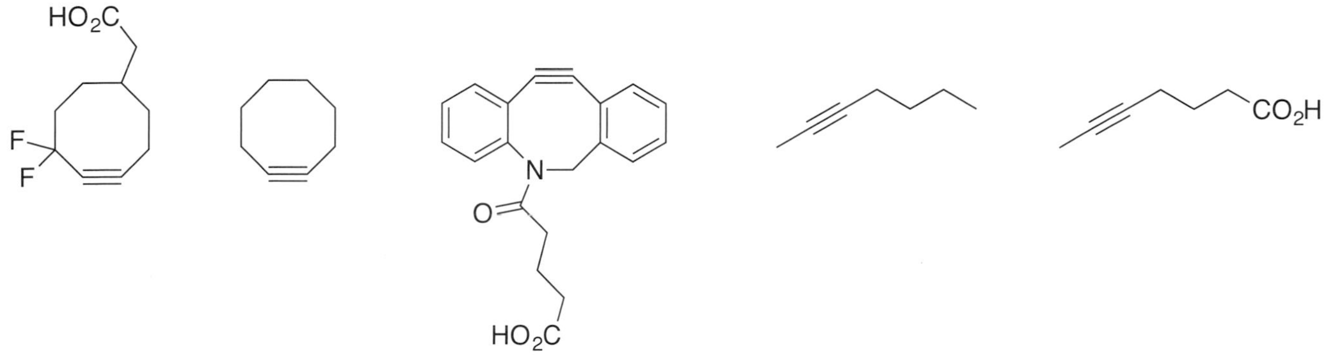

Alkynes like the ones circled above *can / cannot* be coupled to a biomolecule or biomarker then used for click reactions in cells that are specially modified to contain azides. Reactions like these *do / do not* need copper salts to proceed at room temperature.

17 Benzene And Aromaticity

from chapter(s) _____ in the recommended text

A Introduction

Focus

Orbital symmetry dictates the energetic levels of molecular orbitals in aromatic compounds. Combination of p-orbitals from sp^2-hybridized carbons gives a low-lying bonding molecular orbital, then degenerate sets of two at higher levels. Thus, placing 2, 4, 6, 10 e^- is favorable, and the $4n + 2$ rule is valid. The focus of this section is understanding and recognizing aromaticity.

Reasons To Care

crixivan

Aromaticity is everywhere. All the nucleobases in DNA and RNA have aromatic heterocycles, several of the amino acids have side-chains with aromatic functionalities, and a significant fraction of small molecule pharmaceuticals are aromatic compounds.

Molecular orbital theory explains why aromatic compounds are stable, less reactive than they would otherwise be, and why they are UV chromophores. Aromaticity explains why alkenes and arenes are chemically different.

Concepts Involved

MO theory • resonance • heats of hydrogenation • hybridization

Objective

Recognition of the features of aromatic molecules, and ones that destabilize related compounds that are not.

B Common Aromatic Compounds

As the name implies, aromatic compounds tend *to / not to* smell. They also tend to react *in the same way as / differently to* aliphatic compounds. Industrially they can be formed by distillation from *oil / plants*, or by heating petroleum to a high temperature over *a catalyst / a reductant*.

Draw benzene and some examples of aromatic compounds here (do not use examples from next question):

_____

benzene

_____

_____

Show structures for the following common aromatic compounds (can be found on Wiki).

_____

toluene

_____

benzyl alcohol

_____

phenol

_____

para-xylene

_____

aniline

_____

benzaldehyde

_____

styrene

_____

tosic acid

_____

benzoic acid

_____

1,2-dimethylbenzene

_____

meta-dichlorobenzene

_____

para-bromobenzoic acid

---

ortho-bromophenol

1,3-dichlorobenzene

4-iodoaniline

2-bromostyrene

1,3-diphenylbenzene

---

para-phenyliodobenzene

---

ortho-Me$_2$C$_6$H$_4$

1,3-Bn$_2$C$_6$H$_4$

---

para-(Me$_2$N)BrC$_6$H$_4$

Rigorous names for *monosubstituted* benzenes are based upon "benzene" provided the substituent does not have more *C*-atoms than the benzene ring, *ie* ____. Draw the following:

---

chlorobenzene

---

tert-butylbenzene

---

nitrobenzene

Benzenoid compounds are those that *do / do not* contain heteroatoms.

Benzene rings tend to make compounds containing them *lipophilic / hydrophilic* sometimes leading to aggregation and insolubility in water.

If the substituent has more carbon atoms than a benzene ring, then the ring is named as a "phenyl" substituent. Draw the following compounds:

_____

3-phenylheptane

_____

2-methyl-4-phenyloctane

_____

phenylcyclopropane

_____

1-bromo-2-cyclobutylbenzene

_____

2-phenylheptane

_____

1-phenylnaphthlene

One of those names is wrong! Give it the correct name: _____.

Draw jagged lines that separate a hydrogen atom from:

_____

phenyl group in benzene

_____

benzyl group in toluene

_____

1-naphthyl group in naphthalene

C Heats Of Hydrogenation And Aromaticity

Energy is *liberated / taken in* when hydrogen is added across a C=C bond.

The amount of energy liberated on hydrogenation of different compounds to give *the same* product *can / cannot* be used to gauge the relative stabilities of the starting materials. Energies involved in such processes are called *heats of hydrogenation*.

Benzene is *more / less* stable than expected from the heats of hydrogenation of cyclohexene (-118 kJ/mol) and 1,3-cyclohexadiene (-230 kJ/mol); specifically, the heat of hydrogenation of benzene (-206 kJ/mol) is *less / more* than expected.

Complete hydrogenation of all these molecules gives *hexane / cyclohexane*; illustrate this in a simple diagram in which that same product is at a baseline.

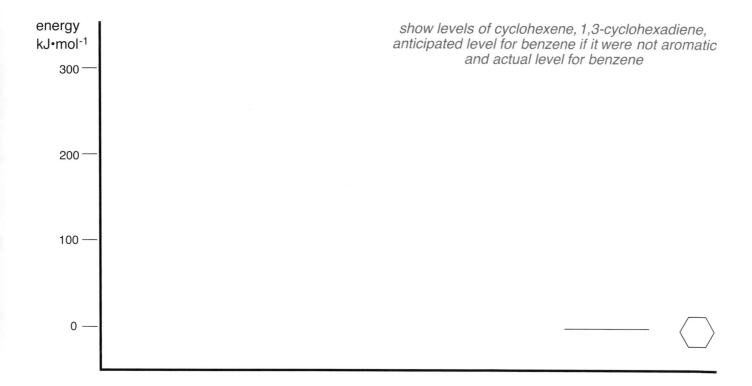

show levels of cyclohexene, 1,3-cyclohexadiene, anticipated level for benzene if it were not aromatic and actual level for benzene

All the C-C bonds in benzene are the same length (139 pm), between typical *C-C* (154 pm) and C=C (134 pm) bonds; the structure is a perfectly symmetrical hexagon, and all the C-C-C bond angles are *109° / 120° / 180°*; each carbon is sp^3 / sp^2 / sp hybridized, and has an empty *s / p* orbital.

Electron densities on the carbons are *different / equal*.

Draw resonance structures of benzene and illustrate these characteristics (*C-C* bond lengths, *C-C-C* bond angles, hybridization state) on your diagram:

In molecular orbital theory, combination of 6 *p*-orbitals gives *3 / 6 / 12* molecular orbitals. Complete the following for the 6 *p*-orbitals on the 6 carbon atoms in benzene combining into molecular orbitals.

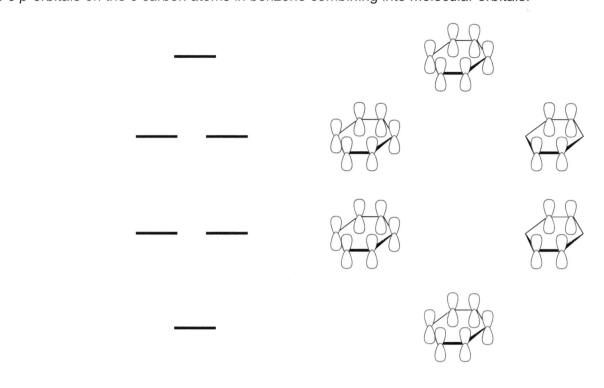

Aromatic molecules must be *acyclic / cyclic, conjugated / unconjugated, planar / non-planar*, and they must have $4n + 2$ π-electrons (n = integer). This is called *The Hückel Rule / Dewar's Principle*. Based on the diagram above, verbalize why $4n + 2$ might be a highly significant number for aromatic compounds:

_____

Indicate *aromatic* or *non-aromatic* for each of the following molecules; if they are *non-aromatic* give the reason.

aromatic or
not aromatic because _____
_____ .

aromatic or
not aromatic because _____
_____ .

aromatic or
not aromatic because _____
_____ .

aromatic or
not aromatic because _____
_____ .

aromatic or
not aromatic because _____
_____ .

aromatic or
not aromatic because _____
_____ .

aromatic or
not aromatic because _____
_____ .

aromatic or
not aromatic because _____
_____ .

aromatic or
not aromatic because _____
_____ .

aromatic or
not aromatic because _____
_____ .

D Predicting Aromaticity

Carbocycles

Draw the *p*-orbitals involved for the cycloheptatrienyl cation (shown bottom right on previous page), and indicate the number of electrons that each orbital brings to the delocalized system above the ring. Throughout, there is no need to draw in the double bonds, just show the p-orbitals.

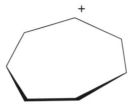

Draw the *p*-orbitals involved for the cyclopentadienyl *anion*, and indicate the number of electrons that each orbital brings to the delocalized system above the ring. This ion is *aromatic / non-aromatic*.

There are *2 / 3 / 4 / 5* resonance structures for the 1-ethyl-2-methylcyclopentadienyl anion.

Draw the *p*-orbitals involved for the cyclopentadienyl *cation*, and indicate the number of electrons that each orbital brings to the delocalized system above the ring. This ion is *aromatic / non-aromatic*.

Draw the *p*-orbitals involved for the cyclopropenyl *cation*, and indicate the number of electrons that each orbital brings to the delocalized system above the ring (*note:* there is a double bond in this cation). This ion is *aromatic / non-aromatic*.

There is/are *1 / 2 / 3* resonance structures for the 2-ethyl-1-methylcyclopropenyl cation, and it is *flat / puckered*.

Draw the *p*-orbitals involved for the cyclopropenyl *anion*, and indicate the number of electrons that each orbital brings to the delocalized system above the ring. This ion is *aromatic / non-aromatic*.

Draw the *p*-orbitals involved for the cyclopropenyl *radical*, and indicate the number of electrons that each orbital brings to the delocalized system above the ring. Radicals have one unpaired electron. This radical is *aromatic / non-aromatic*.

Circle the compound(s) from the selection below that are predicted to be aromatic based on the $4n + 2$ rule.

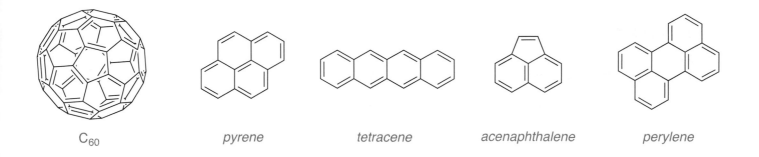

C$_{60}$ pyrene   tetracene   acenaphthalene   perylene

The $4n + 2$ rule *is / is not* inviolable.

18 Electrophilic Attack On Benzene

from chapter(s) _____ in the recommended text

A Introduction

Focus

Alkenes and halogens combine in addition reactions and there are no by-products. However, aromatic compounds tend to react with halogens to give *substitution* products with loss of HX (X = halide). That difference, attributed to a favorable deprotonation that leads to regeneration of aromaticity, is the focus of this section.

Reasons To Care

One mechanism (electrophilic attack then loss of a proton) explains how a wide variety of electrophiles can be substituted onto benzene rings. In synthetic organic chemistry this allows elaboration of aromatic rings with halides, nitro, sulfonic acid, acyl groups, and more.

Outside of synthetic chemistry, in biological systems, electrophilic aromatic substitution of benzenoid is *uncommon* because the conditions necessary to force electrophiles to add can only be achieved if the benzenoid compound is particularly reactive (*eg* a phenol).

Concepts Involved

aromaticity • resonance • hybridization • electron flow • electrophilic additions to alkenes• carbocation rearrangements

Objective

Electrophiles *substitute* onto aromatic rings, but they tend to *add to* alkenes. The reason for this difference is that it is energetically more favorable for arenes to lose a proton and regain aromaticity. This section is to make sure the people agree on the similarity and understand the reasons for the difference. Factors that stabilize the cationic intermediates by resonance should also be known.

B Electrophilic Bromination Of Alkenes And Benzene Compared

First Step: Approach Of Electrophile

There *is / is not* a difference in the way electrons distribute when bromine approaches ethene and cyclohexene.

Electrons *do / do not* distribute in a similar way when bromine approaches benzene.

In the cationic intermediate **I**, there are *1 / 2 / 3* hydrogen atoms on C^1 and *1 / 2 / 3* on C^2.

Attack of bromine on ethene is *faster / slower* than on benzene because for benzene *aromatic / hyperconjugative* stabilization is lost.

Second Step: Loss Of Positive Charge

In the reaction of bromine with benzene the second step is loss of a *proton / bromide*.

Bromination of ethene and of benzene, proceed differently because only benzene can regain *aromatic / hyperconjugative* stabilization in that second step.

addition / substitution   *addition / substitution*

Draw addition and substitution products for the following alkenes (assume both reactions occur).

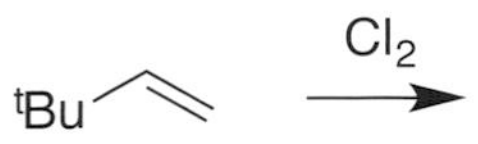

ᵗBu ⟍⟍ —Cl₂→

———————————
addition product

———————————
possible substitution product

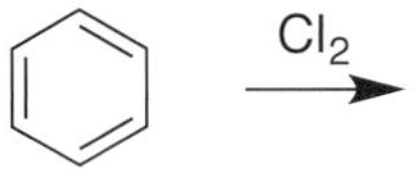

⬡ —Cl₂→

———————————
addition product

———————————
substitution product

The simplest electrophile to substitute H with is a deuteron D⁺ (a *heavier / lighter* isotope of a proton).

Electrophilic attack of a deuteron on benzene is *the same as / different to* nucleophilic attack of benzene on a deuteron.

When a deuteron approaches (because it is electrostatically *attracted to / repelled by*) the π-electrons of benzene, it polarizes them, and eventually forms a bond.

The process described above breaks one of the double bonds and leaves a positive charge on a carbon adjacent to where the deuteron added, as shown below.

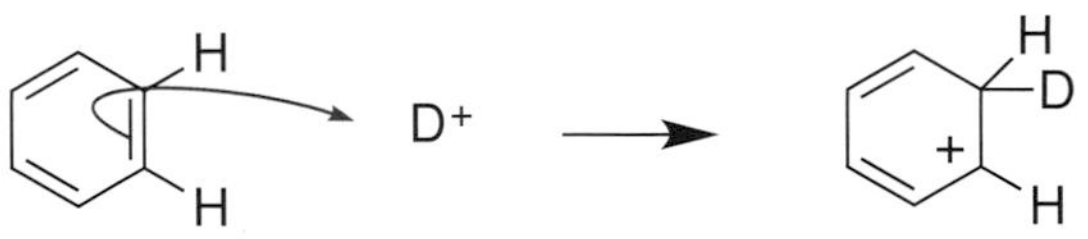

⬡ H / H D⁺ → ⬡ H,D / + H

The cationic *intermediate / transition state* formed in the step above is *aromatic / non-aromatic.*

Benzene *loses / retains* its aromatic stabilization energy when the deuteron adds, so this process is likely to be *fast / slow.*

Draw the same type of diagram for addition of the following electrophiles to benzene.

Cl+

Br+

---

a nitronium ion, NO$_2$+

---

a sulfonium ion, HSO$_3$+

---

a methyl carbocation, Me+

---

an acylium ion, MeCO+

After a deuteron adds to benzene there are two entities that could dissociate: a deuteron or a proton. Loss of a deuteron reforms benzene, hence addition of a deuteron to benzene is *reversible / irreversible*.

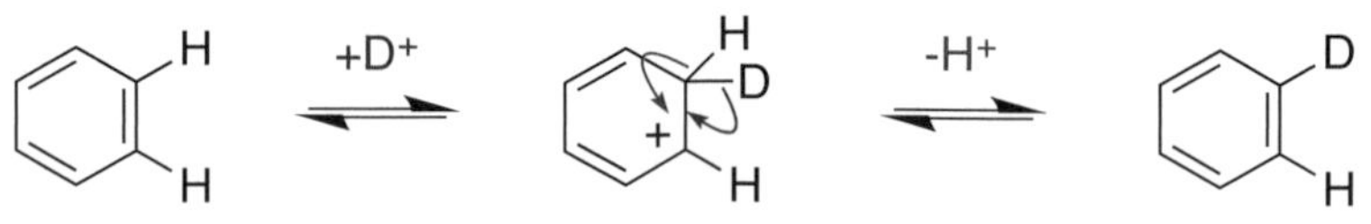

C Halogenation Of Benzene

Chlorine, bromine, and iodine alone are *sufficiently / insufficiently* electrophilic to react with benzene, but the X-X molecules can be polarized to a state in which one atom has enhanced electrophilicity.

This is illustrated below for chlorine interacting with iron(3+) chloride (ferric chloride), and for bromine with aluminum tribromide.

$$Cl-Cl \quad + \quad FeCl_3 \quad \longrightarrow \quad Cl^{\delta+}\text{-}\text{-}Cl\text{-}\text{-}\text{-}Fe^{\delta-}Cl_3 \qquad\qquad Br-Br \quad + \quad AlBr_3 \quad \longrightarrow \quad Br^{\delta+}\text{-}\text{-}Br\text{-}\text{-}\text{-}Al^{\delta-}Br_3$$

Halogens are activated by the Lewis *acid / base* in these reactions.

Complete the following diagrams for halogenation of benzene and formation of a substitution product (draw curly arrows throughout).

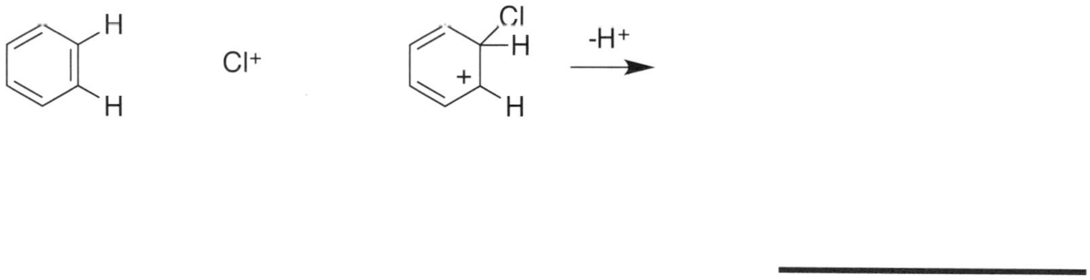

Cl⁺ → product with Cl and H, cation intermediate, -H⁺

Br⁺ →(slow)   →(fast, -H⁺) _____ *bromination*

I⁺ →(slow)   →(fast, -H⁺) _____ *iodination*

D Sulfonation And Nitration Of Benzene

Sulfonium ions are formed by protonating sulfur trioxide; it takes a *weak / strong* acid, sulfuric, to do this.

Solutions of SO_3 in sulfuric acid are called fuming sulfuring acid or *oleum / opium*.

Nitronium ions are made by *deprotonating / protonating* nitric acid with sulfuric acid, then water is lost to give the nitronium ion. Draw curly arrows on the following reactions to illustrate how sulfonium and nitronium electrophiles are formed.

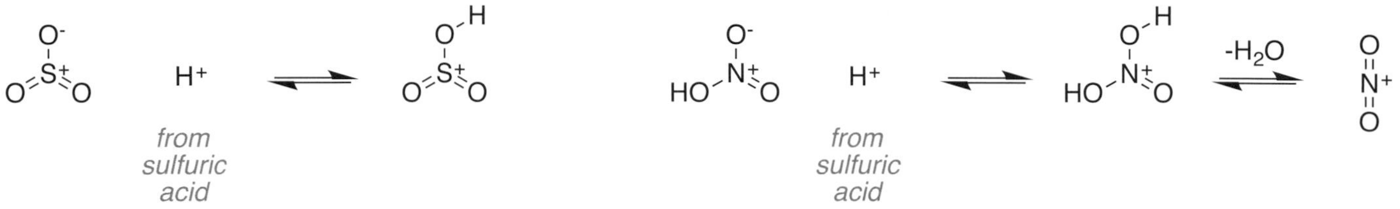

Complete the following mechanisms for sulfonation and nitration of benzene.

sulfonation

nitration

E Acylation Of Benzene (Friedel-Crafts)

Electrophilic acylation reactions rely on generating *carbocations / acylium ions*. Lewis acids give acylium ions when they are combined with acid halides or acid anhydrides. Complete the following diagrams to illustrate that process.

_____
acylium

_____
acylium

Cyclic anhydrides are interesting because they give acylium ion equivalents functionalized with carboxylic acid groups. Illustrate this below showing acyclic acylium species formed in the reactions below.

_____
acylium

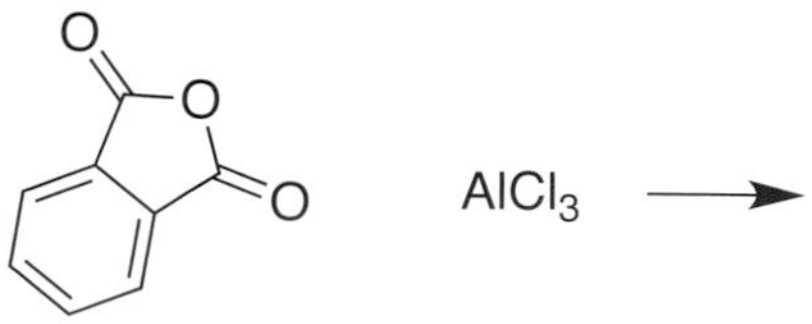

_____
acylium

Complete the following mechanism for Friedel-Crafts acylation of benzene.

slow ⟶   fast ⟶
                                              -H⁺

_____   _____

Products of electrophilic acylation reactions are *esters / ketones*.

These products have *more / less* electron rich aromatic rings than the starting materials, and therefore *do / do not* tend to react with another acylium ion to give diketones.

Predict the products of the following *acylation* reactions.

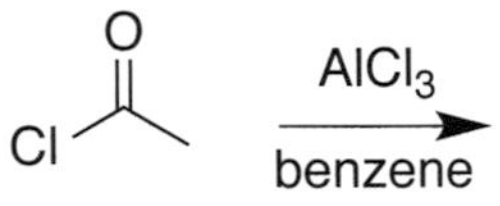

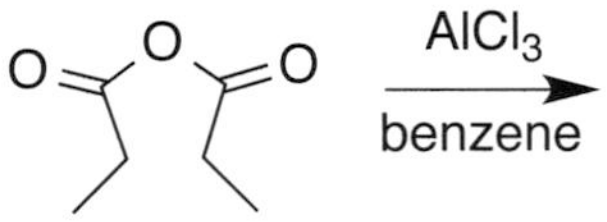

AlCl₃
benzene

_____

AlCl₃
benzene

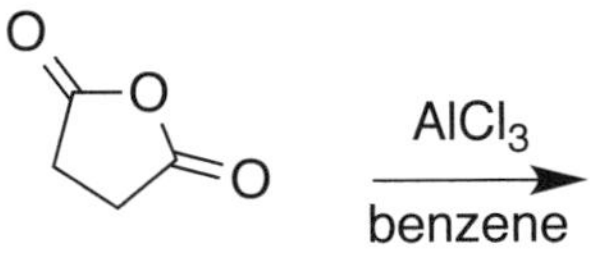

_____

AlCl₃
benzene

_____

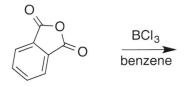

BCl_3 / benzene →

OMe — Ac_2O, BF_3, CH_2Cl_2 →

OMe

In the last example, the carbon atoms that could react are all *equivalent / different*.

F Alkylation (Friedel-Crafts)

Electrophilic alkylation reactions proceed via *carbocations / acylium ions*.

Lewis *acids / bases* give these reactive intermediates when they are combined with alkyl halides.

Complete the following diagrams to illustrate aromatic alkylation process.

$\wedge$Br $AlCl_3$ →

$\times$I $SnCl_4$ →

This mode of generation is most useful when the reactive intermediates *do / do not* rearrange before they react with the aromatic compound.

Methyl, ethyl, *tert*-butyl, benzyl, and simple symmetrical allyl, carbocations tend *to be / not to be* vulnerable to rearrangement reactions, so this issue *is / is not* a concern for those electrophiles.

Complete the following mechanism of Friedel-Crafts alkylation of benzene, showing clear curly arrows to depict the electron flow.

methylation

Show the intended monoalkylation products of the following reactions.

Products of electrophilic alkylation reactions are *alkylbenzenes / arylbenzenes*, these are *more / less* electron rich than the starting materials, and therefore *do / do not* tend to add a second reactive intermediate; Friedel-Crafts alkylation reactions *are / are not* therefore prone to deliver more than one alkyl group, *ie* over alkylation.

Carbocation Rearrangements Revisited

Hydrogens on β-carbons relative to the positive charge in a carbocation can migrate to the atom having the positive charge if this occurs faster than competing reactions of the carbocation.

The hydrogen migrates with both electrons associated with it, so this type of reaction can be referred to as a *proton / hydrogen atom / hydride* shift.

Draw accurate curly arrows to represent this in the following rearrangements.

This type of reaction is likely to occur if the carbocation formed is *more / less* stable than the original one. Circle the carbocations below that can rearrange via *H*-shifts.

CH$_3^+$

Alkyl groups stabilize adjacent positive charges, hence the order of carbocation stabilities *increases / decreases* from tertiary, through secondary, to primary.

Sometimes carbocations can undergo rearrangements that involve shift of carbanions; this tends to be favorable if the carbocation formed is more stable than the original one.

Show arrows and products to complete the following shift mechanisms.

^{13}C label

19 Ultraviolet And Fluorescence Spectroscopy

from chapter(s) _____ in the recommended text

A Introduction

Focus

Short wavelength, high energy, quanta promote electrons from ground state energy levels to excited states. When superimposed on these transitions, variations for vibrational energy levels are small but significant enough that UV absorbance span a broad range of wavelengths.

Most molecules that absorb UV quanta relax to the ground state mostly via vibrational pathways (*ie* thermal relaxation processes). Some more rigid conjugated molecules relax via shift of the electron that was in the excited state back to the ground state, emitting a photon as "fluorescence". This electron is always longer wavelength than the UV absorption for that molecule.

UV absorption and fluorescence emission are the focus of this section.

Reasons To Care

Many assays in the biological sciences feature colorimetric detection (relying on a change of color). These include ELISA assays involving binding of monoclonal antibodies, and MTT assays to measure the number of cells that remain alive after a test treatment. UV assays can be used for qualitative measurement of concentrations, or qualitative detection.

Fluorescence detection is usually around ten times more sensitive than UV. Fluorescent small molecule probes can be used to label cell organelles or attached other molecules to track where they move in cells (Figure 1). Modern super-resolution techniques allow this to be done with resolution even below the diffraction limit. Fluorescent probes can be used to quantitate accumulation of experimental drugs in organs of laboratory animals, and they can be used to stain tumor cells selectively so that surgeons may spot them more easily than is otherwise possible.

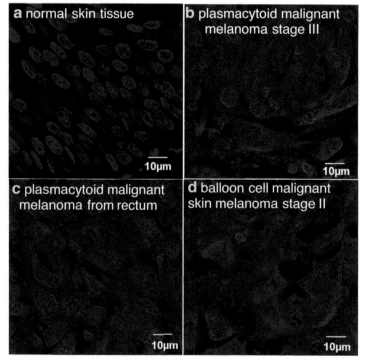

a normal skin tissue

b plasmacytoid malignant melanoma stage III

10μm

10μm

c plasmacytoid malignant melanoma from rectum

d balloon cell malignant skin melanoma stage II

10μm

10μm

Figure 1. Tissues treated with a red fluorescent small molecule that detects a receptor on the surface of metastatic melanoma cells, and a blue one that stains all nuclei. **a** Normal skin tissue (only nuclei stain). **c** – **d** Human melanoma cells stain red indicating receptor is present.

Concepts Involved

electromagnetic spectrum • MO theory • aromaticity • resonance

Objective

Questions to probe the fundamentals of UV and fluorescence, and an introduction into the types of organic dyes and fluors used in biological sciences, and elsewhere.

B Fundamental Physics

Quanta of UV radiation are *less / more* energetic than those corresponding to vibrational states in IR, and less energetic than quanta corresponding to the *radiowave / X-ray* range of the electromagnetic spectrum.

Absorption of quanta in the UV region corresponds to promotion of an electron from a *ground / excited* state energy level to a(n) *ground / excited* one.

The wavelength of the maximum absorption of a UV peak ($\lambda_{\text{max abs}}$ in nm) is *inversely / directly* proportional to the *energies / number* of the quanta involved, and the degree of absorbance is *inversely / directly* related to their *energies / number*.

UV absorbances tend to be *broad / sharp* peaks because promotion of an electron can place it within different *X-ray / IR-vibrational* states in the excited energy level.

Groups that absorb quanta in the UV are called *chromophores / UV-phores*, and these include aromatic systems, conjugated alkenes, nitro compounds, and conjugated alkynes.

In general, the more extended a conjugated system is, the larger its UV *cross-section / footprint* and the *less / more* photons it absorbs.

C Molecular Orbital Diagrams Of Alkenes, Dienes, and Polyenes

Conjugated polyenes are ones in which *C=C* double bonds are linked by *just one / more than one single* *C-C* bond.

Indicate if the following alkenes are conjugated or non-conjugated (the black dot in the allene indicates a carbon that is shared by two double bonds).

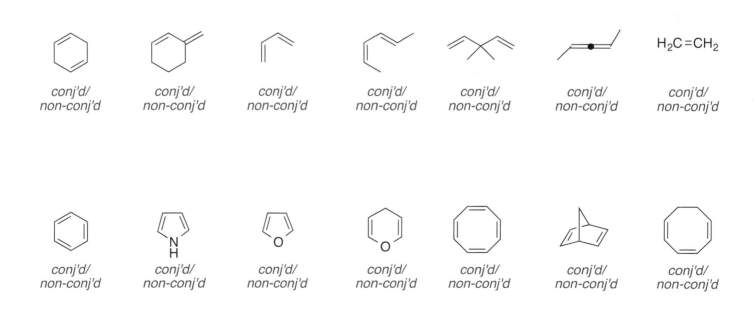

conj'd/ non-conj'd	conj'd/ non-conj'd	conj'd/ non-conj'd	conj'd/ non-conj'd	conj'd/ non-conj'd	conj'd/ non-conj'd	conj'd/ non-conj'd

conj'd/ non-conj'd	conj'd/ non-conj'd	conj'd/ non-conj'd	conj'd/ non-conj'd	conj'd/ non-conj'd	conj'd/ non-conj'd	conj'd/ non-conj'd

β-carotene *conj'd / non-conj'd*

isoprene
conj'd / non-conj'd

limonene
conj'd / non-conj'd

squalene *conj'd / non-conj'd*

arachidinoic acid *conj'd / non-conj'd*

porphyrin *conj'd / non-conj'd*

Conjugation *is / is not* possible between unsaturated double and triple bonds, and those that contain heteroatoms.

Indicate which of the following molecules have an alkene conjugated to alkynes.

phosphoiodyns A
conj'd / non-conj'd

debilisone
conj'd / non-conj'd

Molecular orbital theory is *an alternative to / a less convenient form of* valence bonding to describe chemical bonding.

When *n* atomic orbitals mix they *always* form *n / n + 1 / n − 1* molecular orbitals.

For monoenes, two π-molecular orbitals (MOs) are formed from the *1 / 2 / 3* parallel, unhybridized p-orbitals on each carbon.

One MO has less energy than the starting p-orbitals, the other has more, and these are called *bonding / antibonding* π- and *bonding / antibonding* π*-orbitals, respectively.

Maximal / minimal overall stabilization occurs when 2e occupy the π-orbital.

Fill in the electrons into the following MO diagram, label features of it with the terms *bonding*, *antibonding*, π-, π*-, and fill in the signs of the wave equation that give the MOs indicated.

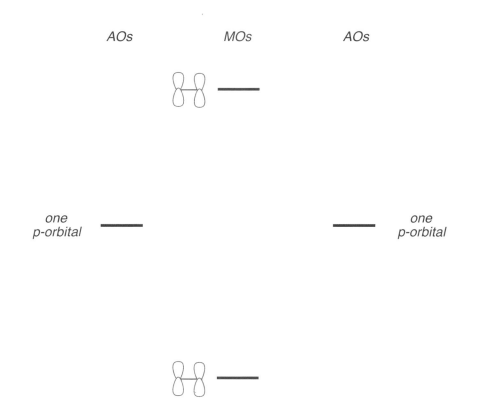

When an electron in a MO is promoted from a π- to a π*-orbital that corresponds to quanta in the *X-ray / ultraviolet / near IR* region resulting in an *excited / bored* state of the molecule that normally relaxes to the ground state via loss of *γ-rays / radiowaves / IR / NMR* energy.

Systems with more double bonds in conjugation have *larger / smaller* cross-sections, therefore they absorb *less / more* photons from a white light source (quanta of many wavelengths).

This corresponds to the *absorbance / adsorption* of the *chromophore / fluorophore*, and that is expressed in terms of *extinction coefficients*.

A more conjugated polyene has a *larger / smaller* extinction coefficient than a less conjugated one.

252

The following is to predict if conjugation increases or decreases energies of quanta absorbed by alkenes in the electronic region via MO diagrams for progressively more π-conjugated.
Complete the following MO diagrams for 1,3-butadiene and for 1,3,5-hexatriene placing electrons, using the terms *bonding*, *antibonding*, π-, π*-, and fill in the signs of the wave equation that give the MOs indicated.

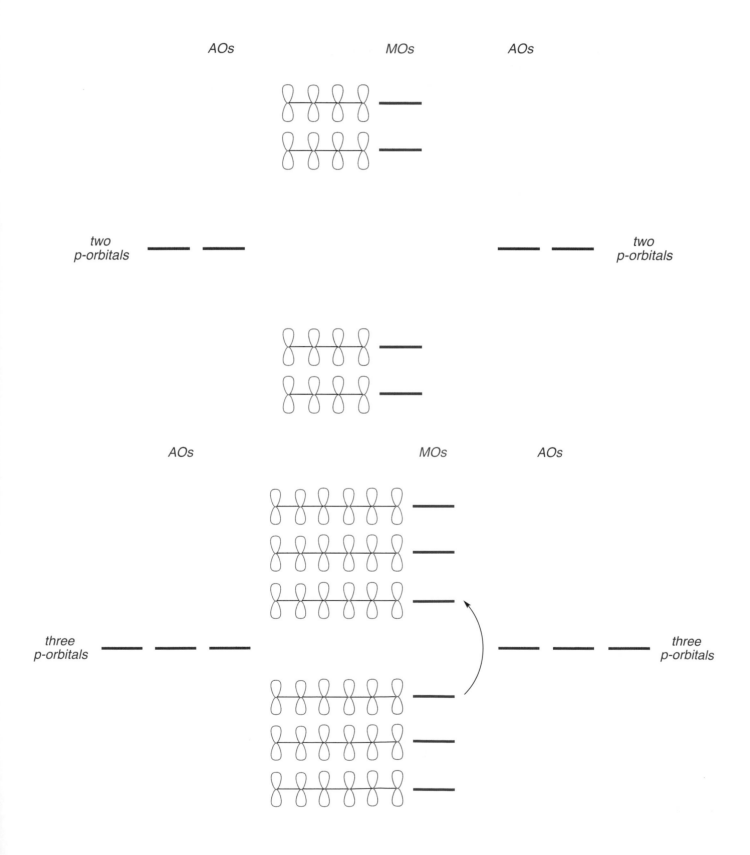

D UV Spectroscopy

More conjugation *increases / decreases* the gap between the highest occupied molecular orbital (HOMO) and the lowest unoccupied molecular orbital (LUMO).

Increased conjugation therefore corresponds to absorbance of *lower / higher* energy quanta of *increased / decreased* wavelengths.

Infra-red (IR) absorptions correspond to transitions between *vibrational / electronic* energy states, while *vibrational / electronic* transitions correspond to quanta in the ultra-violet (UV) region.

Thus *IR / UV* transitions correspond to stretching bonds, and electrons are promoted from one molecular orbital to one higher in energy by *IR / UV* quanta.

Energies involved for *IR / UV* transitions are greater than ones for *IR / UV*.

Transitions **A**, **B** and **C** correspond to *IR / UV* transitions, while **D**, **E**, and **F** are between *IR / UV* states.

Based in Boltzman's distribution concepts, in a collection of molecules the number of quanta absorbed by transitions **D**, **E**, and **F** are likely to be *greater / less* than for transitions like **G**.

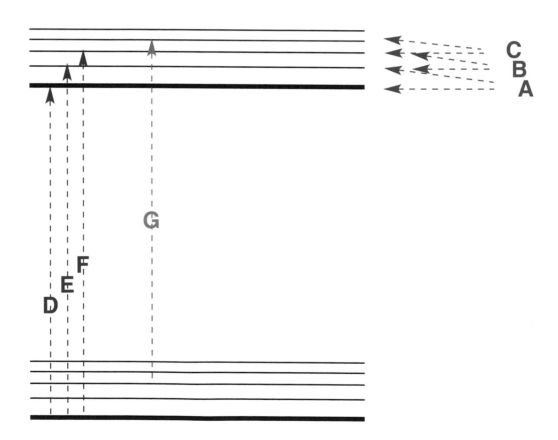

UV absorptions are relatively broad because they involve transitions between *multiple / only one* vibrational level(s) for each electronic transition.

For a reaction with components having UV chromophores, elevating the temperature of a reaction by 10 °C enables a molecule to overcome a *higher / smaller* energy barriers than leaving it in the Texas sunshine.

E Fluorescence Spectroscopy

Transitions **A**, **B** and **C** in the following diagram correspond to *IR / UV / fluorescence* and transitions between *vibrational / electronic* energy levels.

When a molecule is excited in this way it may relax via transitions like **d** – **g** that correspond to *vibrational / UV / fluorescence* emissions.

After half-lives typically in the *nano / milli*-second range the molecule will relax via emission of *IR / UV / fluorescent* radiation.

This will only occur for relatively *rigid / flexible* molecules for which competing rotational and (mostly) vibrational relaxation processes are relatively slow.

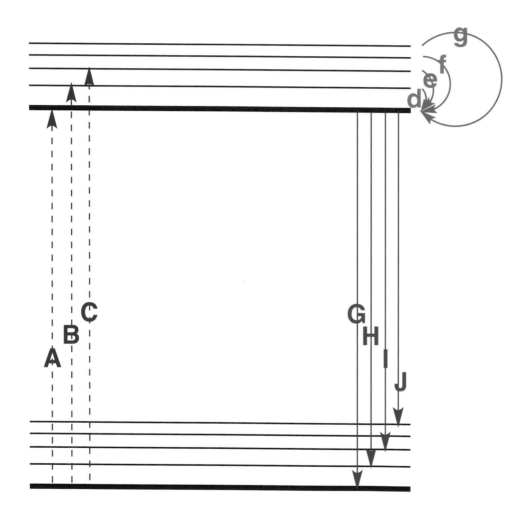

Fluorescent emissions are relatively brilliant hence fluorescence spectroscopy is a *sensitive / insensitive* way of detecting "fluors".

Fluorescence can be used to detect fluor-labeled organelles in cells with *higher / lower* sensitivity than UV spectroscopy, and much *higher / lower* sensitivity than IR.

Many DNA sequencing techniques rely on *fluorescence / IR / UV* spectroscopy because small concentrations of labeled-DNA must be detected.

Fluorescence activated cell sorting (FACS) detects concentrations of cells labeled with different *fluors / IR chromophores*.

Assays using UV to detect reactions mediated by enzymes that liberate a UV-chromophore tend to be about ten times *more / less* sensitive than ones using fluorescent probes.

Fluorescent compounds tend to be relatively *rigid / flexible* structures that shift charges around via resonance (*ie* they have large oscillating dipoles).

The following fluorescent probes have resonance structures that move charges between the red and blue atoms. Show clear curly arrows for this electron flow (on the right to go to the left as well as on the left to go to the right), *and* complete the bonding structures showing careful attention to charges.

a BODIPY

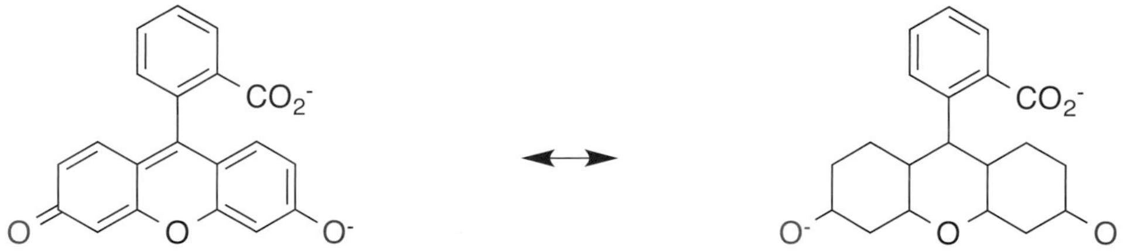

a fluorescein

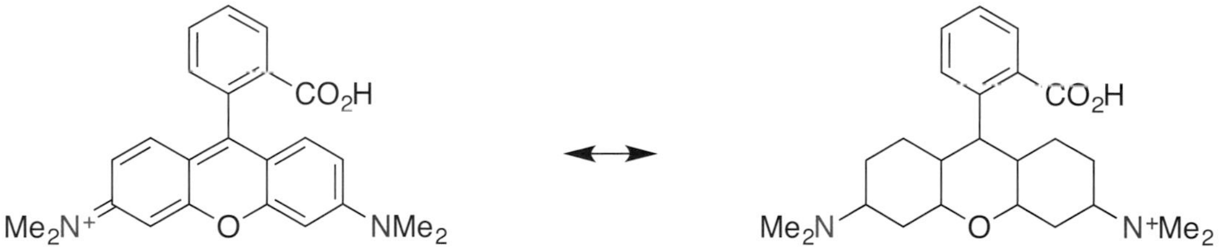

a rhodamine

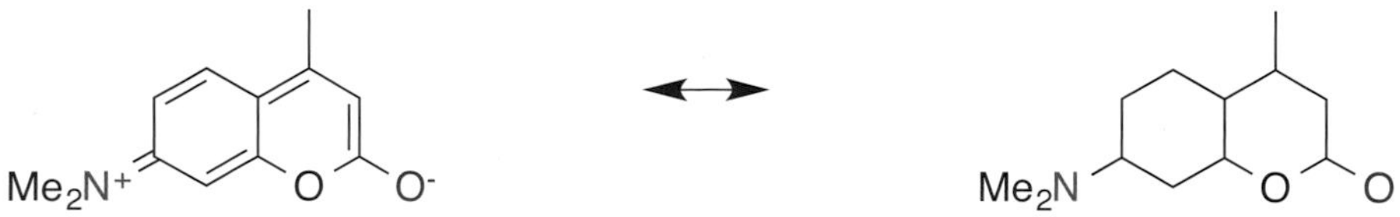

a coumarin

Of the probes shown above, the two which have fluorescence that is most sensitive to pH changes around 7 are the *BODIPY / fluorescein / rhodamine / coumarin*, whereas the *BODIPY / fluorescein / rhodamine / coumarin* is least sensitive to pH.

This is because *BODIPY / fluorescein / rhodamine / coumarins* contain phenolate-O^- groups that can be protonated as the pH is reduced from 7.0.

Fluorescence of the *BODIPY / fluorescein / rhodamine / coumarin* is likely to be most sensitive to the dipole moment of the solvent it is in because the oscillation of charge in this molecule is unsymmetrical.

Which of the fluor solutions below emit the highest energy light *B / G / Y / O / R / V*, and which of them emit at the longest wavelength *B / G / Y / O / R / V*.

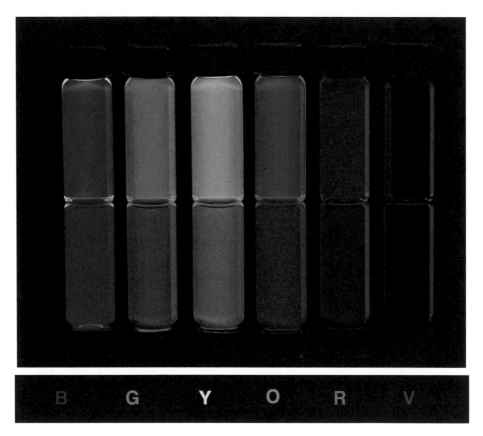

Circle the correct definition of fluorescence quantum yield from the following choices:

$$\frac{\text{\# photons absorbed}}{\text{\# photons emitted}}$$ $$\frac{\text{\# photons emitted}}{\text{\# photons absorbed}}$$ $$\frac{\text{\# photons lost as heat}}{\text{\# photons absorbed}}$$

Circle the correct descriptor of fluor brightness:

quantum yield **x** absorbance at excitation wavelengths   quantum yield **x** absorbance at λ_{max}

absorbance at excitation wavelengths only   quantum yield only   absorbance at λ_{max} only

20 Infrared (IR) Spectroscopy

from chapter(s) _____ in the recommended text

A Introduction

Focus

When IR light of a wide range of wavelengths is shone on organic compounds, bonds will pick the quanta and vibrate like balls (the atoms) on springs (the bonds). They will gyrate backwards and forwards too, in motions that correspond to absorbance of other quanta. Absorbances of quanta by the compound are measured relative to a control beam (that does not pass through the sample) in the IR spectrometer. All these gyrations and oscillations resonate with each other and that results in formation of a fingerprint set of absorbances in the longer wavelength region of the spectra. Distinct absorbances characteristic of functional groups are observed in the higher energy spectral regions. The focus of this section is to understand IR absorbances, and to begin to use them to identify organic compounds.

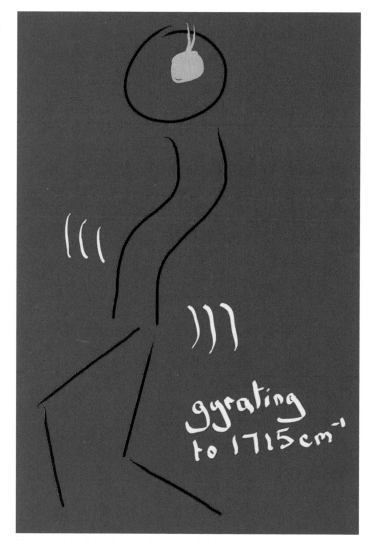

Reasons To Care

FT-IR machines are less expensive, easier to use, and easier to maintain than nuclear magnetic resonance (NMR) and mass spectrometry (MS) equipment. It is possible to run good IR spectra in less than ten minutes, and the information obtained can be highly informative. IR spectroscopy can help researchers confirm they have the compound they think they have, determine if two samples are the same or different, or, in conjunction with other techniques, deduce the structure of an uncharacterized compound.

Concepts

functional groups • electromagnetic spectra • resonance

Objective

Interpreting spectroscopy is like detective work. This part of the *Inquisition* obliges the people to understand and interpret clues from IR spectra.

B Origin Of IR Absorbance

Quanta in IR transitions are *more / less* energetic than those associated with ultraviolet (UV) transitions. NMR (nuclear magnetic resonance) involves *higher / lower* frequency quanta than changes in IR states.

Fourier transform IR (FTIR) is *smoothed / accumulated after multiple scans* to increase signal-to-noise.

IR is sensitive to changes in *polarizability / dipole* so it provides a way of observing functional groups, particularly *symmetrical / unsymmetrical* ones like C=O, N-H, N=O.

Energies in IR are *greater / smaller* than in NMR and fall in the wavelength range 10 – 100 nm.

Strong bonds between the same atoms vibrate *faster / slower* than weaker ones, *ie* at *higher / lower* wavenumbers, for which the units are s^{-1} / cm^{-1}.

Bonds between carbon and heavy atoms tend to vibrate (symmetrical stretch unless otherwise indicated throughout) *slower / faster* than those between carbon and lighter ones, *ie* at a *higher / lower* wavenumber.

Rank bonds of carbon to the isotopes of hydrogen (-H, C-D, and C-T) bond according to increasing wavenumbers of their vibrations:

write C-H, C-D, and C-T
above the appropriate lines

—————   —————   —————

- ➤

increasing wavenumber

Rank the following bonds between carbon and oxygen in order of vibrations with increasing wavenumbers:

write

C≡O   C–O   C=O

above the appropriate lines

—————   —————   —————

- ➤

increasing wavenumber

Wavenumbers in IR spectra *are / are not* proportional to frequencies.
Transmission in IR is *directly / inversely* correlated to absorbance. Vibrations of the same energy generally have *the same / different* absorbances in IR spectra.

The wavenumber axis in IR spectra is *linear / expanded below 2000 relative to the 4000 – 2000 cm⁻¹*.

A bond can stretch in various ways (*eg* symmetrical and unsymmetrical stretches) so each bond *can / cannot* be associated with more than one IR peak.

In the following diagram, put:

•   an **A** at a point that would correspond to minimum absorbance at 1600 cm⁻¹
•   a **B** at a point that would correspond to maximum transmission at 2400 cm⁻¹
•   a **C** at a point that would correspond to maximum frequency at about 50 % absorbance
•   a **D** at a point that would correspond to the minimum energy vibration at about 50 % absorbance

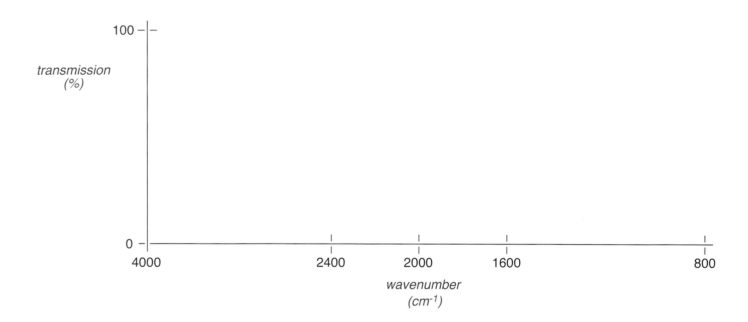

Between 4000 and 2500 cm⁻¹ is a region that corresponds to C-H, N-H, and O-H stretches; draw a straight line labeled with an **E** to represent this on the diagram above.

C-H stretches occur at about *3000 / 2000* cm⁻¹. H-C(sp²) tends to be a little above 3000 cm⁻¹, H-C(sp³) is a little below (*eg* 2950 cm⁻¹), and H-C(sp) is much above (*eg* 3300 cm⁻¹)

N-H stretches tend to occur around *3600 / 3300* cm⁻¹. NH₂ groups have two vibrations in a tooth-like pattern, R₂NH groups have just one.

O-H that are not strongly H-bonded stretch at around *3500 / 3900* cm⁻¹; if they are strongly H-bonded they can stretch between 3400 and 2500 cm⁻¹.

The strongest bonds between carbon and non-hydrogen atoms, *eg* CC and CN triple bonds tend to stretch in the 2500 – 2000 cm⁻¹; draw a line labeled with a **F** to represent this on the diagram above.

Aromatic C=C vibrate around *2000 – 1800 / 1600 - 1500* cm⁻¹; draw a line labeled with a **G** to represent this on the diagram above.

C=O bonds stretch between *1900 – 1500 / 2100 – 2000* cm⁻¹.

C=C bonds vibrate around *1640 / 1800* cm^{-1} and absorb much *more / less* strongly than C=O because they are more symmetrical. Aromatic C-C bonds vibrate at *higher / lower* frequencies because those bonds are stronger than C-C but less strong than C=C.

NO$_2$ groups give two intense bands at about *1850 & 1650 / 1550 & 1350* cm^{-1}.

Sulfoxide S-O bonds absorb at *1600 – 1650 / 1030 – 1080* cm^{-1}.

Single bonds like C-O, C-N, C-Cl vibrate below 1500 cm^{-1}; draw a line labeled with a **H** to represent this region on the diagram above. This is called the _____ region because overall it is unique to each organic compound.

C Functional Group Assignments

One or more IR stretching frequencies are associated with each of the following compounds. Circle one *bond* (not necessarily the whole functional group) characteristic of each wavenumber, and label it with the corresponding letter.

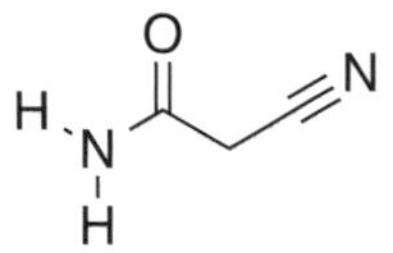

A 3300; **B** 2300; **C** 1690 cm^{-1} 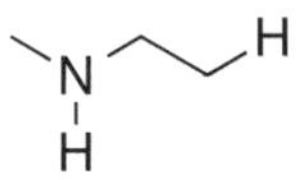   **A** 3300 cm^{-1} 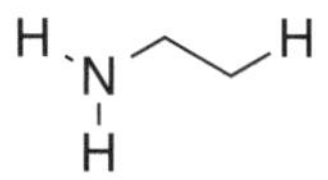   **A** 3300 and 3250 cm^{-1} 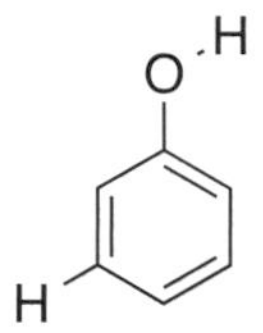   **A** 3400; **B** 3050 cm^{-1}

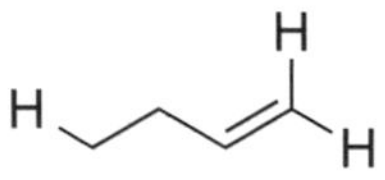

A 3050; **B** 2950 cm^{-1} 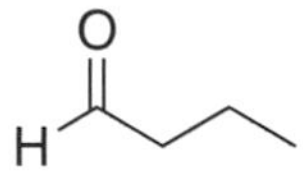   **A** 1730 cm^{-1} 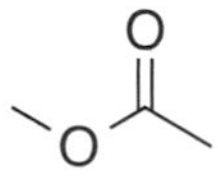   **A** 1735; **B** 1250 cm^{-1} 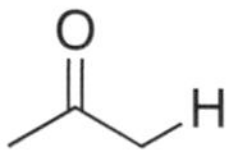   **A** 2950; **B** 1715 cm^{-1}

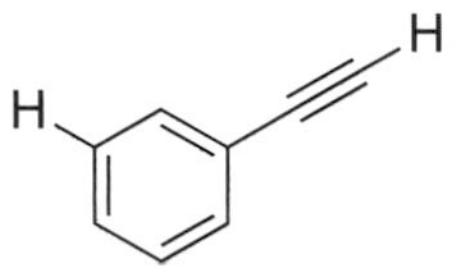

A 3050; **B** 2100 cm^{-1}    **A** 2950 cm^{-1} 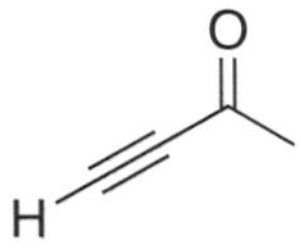   **A** 3300; **B** 1680 cm^{-1} 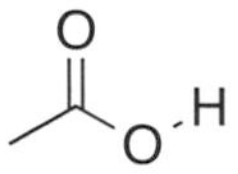   **A** 2900 (br); **B** 1690 cm^{-1}

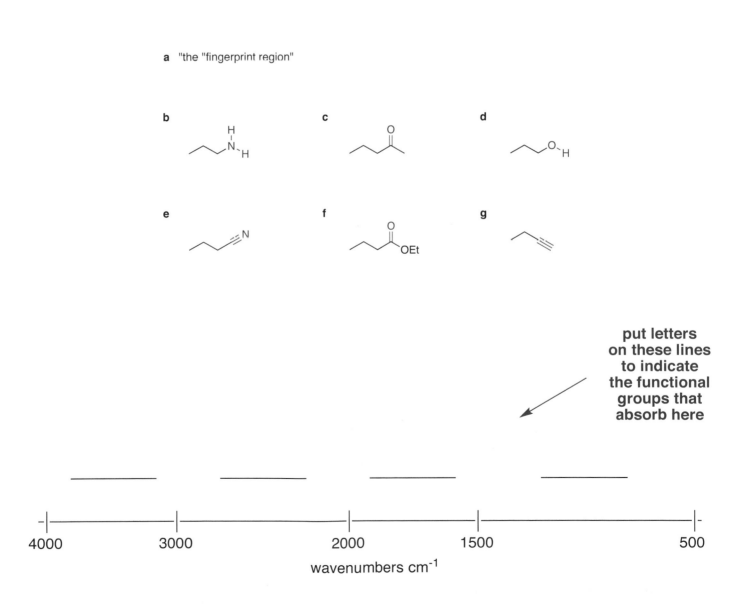

A 3400 (br); **B** 1100 cm⁻¹   **A** 1100 cm⁻¹   **A** 1560 and 1380 cm⁻¹   **A** 1770; **B** 1100 cm⁻¹

Throughout, br = broad.

Use the letters **a** – **g** to represent approximate regions of the IR spectrum where the following absorb (for **b** – **g** just indicate the most conspicuous absorbance associated with the functional group in red).

a "the "fingerprint region"

b

c

d

e

f

g

put letters
on these lines
to indicate
the functional
groups that
absorb here

4000   3000   2000   1500   500

wavenumbers cm⁻¹

D Assigning Structures From Spectra

Draw structures of the following six compounds.

_____

acetone

_____

acetonitrile

_____

DMF

_____

DMSO

_____

n-propyl alcohol

_____

pyridine

One of these compounds has only two significant IR stretches: a strong one at 1715 cm^{-1}, and a weak one at around 2950 cm^{-1}.

That compound is _____ .

The absorption at 2950 cm^{-1} is due to a _____ bond.

The absorption at 1715 cm^{-1} is due to a _____ bond.

Another one of these compounds has only two significant IR stretches: one at 2954 cm^{-1}, and one at 2267 cm^{-1}.

This compound is _____ .

The absorption at 2954 cm^{-1} is due to a _____ bond.

The absorption at 2267 cm^{-1} is due to a _____ bond.

IR spectra for four of the six compounds specified above are shown below. Draw the compound that corresponds to each spectrum, and show a bond that is associated with each numbered IR stretch. Each one was taken as a liquid film, and contains typical impurities.

spectrum 1 (assign all three peaks that are numbered)

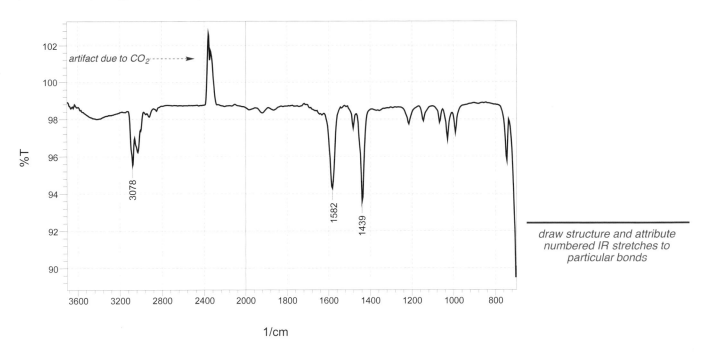

draw structure and attribute numbered IR stretches to particular bonds

spectrum 2 (assign only peaks at 3337, 2967 and 1057 cm^{-1})

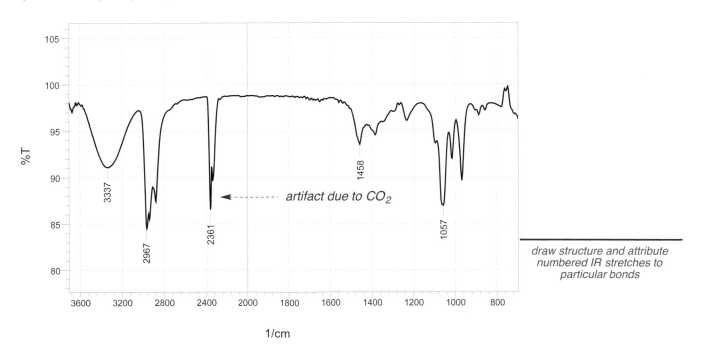

draw structure and attribute numbered IR stretches to particular bonds *spectrum 3 (assign only peak at 1670 cm^{-1}; the one at 3534 cm^{-1} is probably water in the sample)*

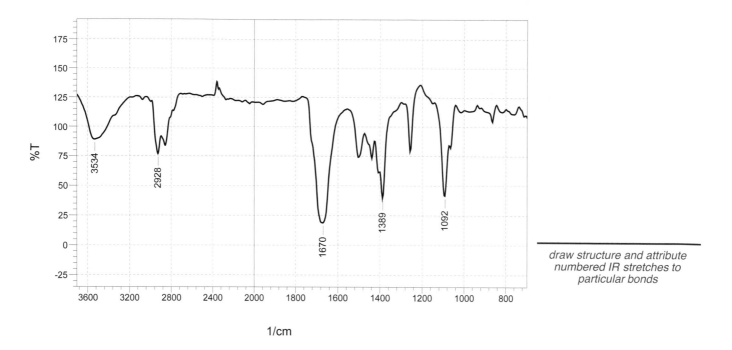

draw structure and attribute numbered IR stretches to particular bonds

spectrum 4 (assign only peaks at 1049 and 2997 cm^{-1}; the one at 3441 cm^{-1} is probably water in the sample)

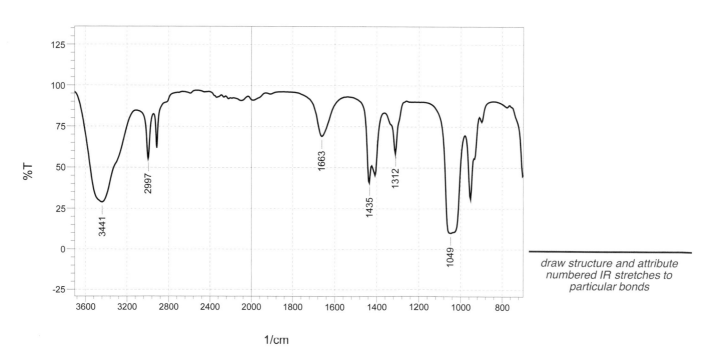

draw structure and attribute numbered IR stretches to particular bonds

The following are IR spectra of glucose, thymine, and BOC-Ala (all solid state IR). *Draw the structures of these molecules* next to their IR spectra.

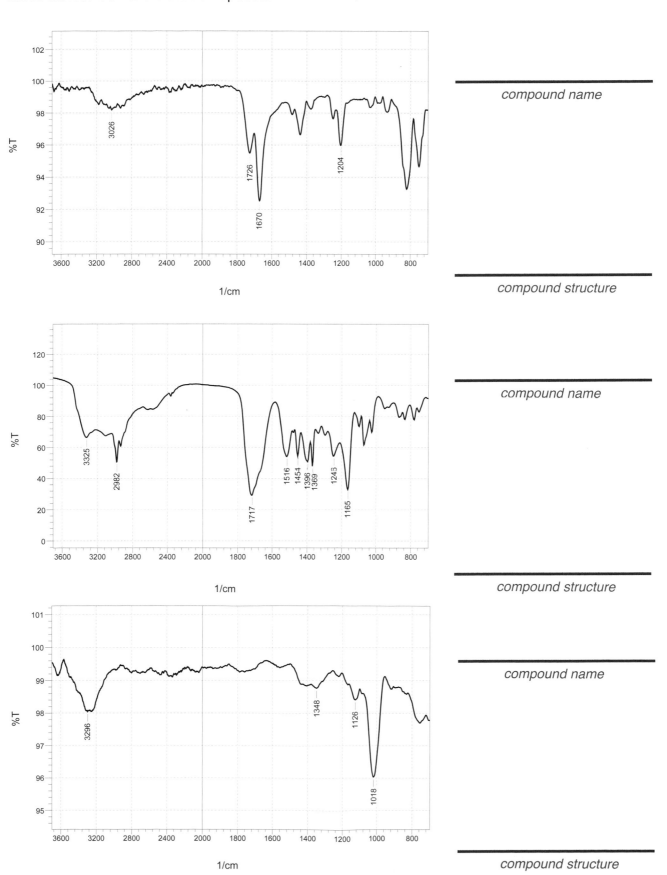

compound name

compound structure

compound name

compound structure

compound name

compound structure

On the following FT-IR of compound "cml-1-52", write **A** on the absorbance corresponding to the azide, **E** on that for the ester CO stretch, and **O** on that for the phenolic OH (taken as a thin film on a NaCl plate).

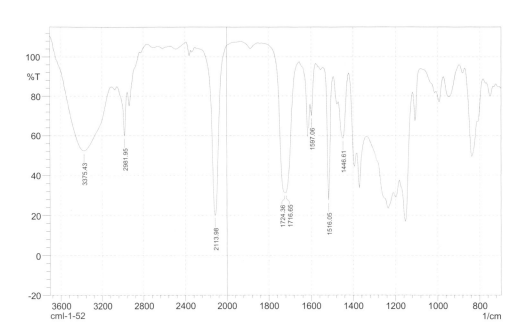

cml-1-52

On the following FT-IR of "boc-tyr-OtBu-OH", write **A** on the absorbance corresponding to the carboxylic acid OH, **C** on that for the CO stretches, and **CH** for the C-H stretches. (Taken as a thin film on a NaCl plate. Look up the structure of a BOC group).

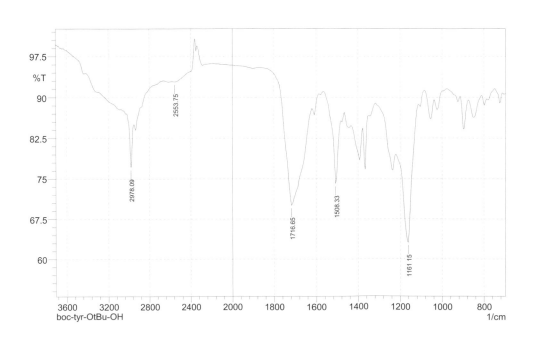

boc-tyr-OtBu-OH

On the following FT-IR of "cml-1-52-sm", write **A** on the absorbances corresponding to the amine N-H stretches, **C** on that for the CO stretches, and **CH** for the C-H stretches (taken as a thin film on a NaCl plate).

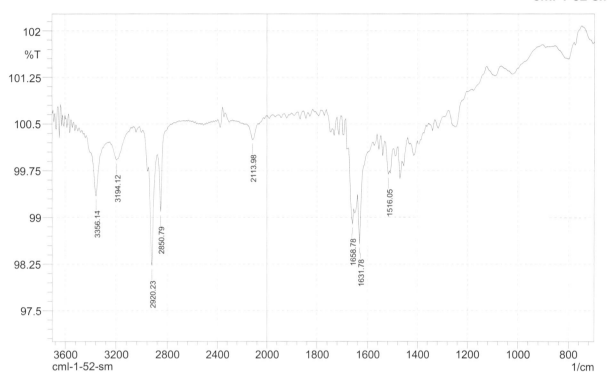

cml-1-52-sm

21 ^{13}C NMR Spectroscopy

from chapter(s) _____ in the recommended text

A Introduction

Focus

In the *same* magnetic field, ^{13}C nuclei often are in *different* environments because of magnetism induced by atoms in their intramolecular environment. Organic compounds that are not isotopically labeled show little magnetic interaction between adjacent ^{13}C nuclei, because the statistical probability of two ^{13}C nuclei being adjacent is only about 1 in 10^4 (the natural abundance of ^{13}C is 1.11 %). Protons attached to ^{13}C atoms perturb (*ie* couple with) the carbon resonances dramatically, but this coupling is nearly always completely suppressed by NMR techniques (saturating the proton spins). Consequently, in most ^{13}C spectra there is one signal per carbon atom environment. Incomplete suppression of coupling to protons (or other techniques like DEPT and HSQC) can be used to reveal how many protons are coupled to each carbon. The focus of this section is on determining how many signals to expect in ^{13}C NMR spectra, the origins of coupling, and the effects of incompletely suppressed coupling of ^{13}C NMR signals to protons.

Reasons To Care

^{13}C NMR spectroscopy is used primarily for characterization of compounds (confirming their structures). Suppose, for example, a new compound was isolated from a sponge because solutions of this compound were highly cytotoxic to cancer cells. ^{13}C NMR spectroscopy would be a "go-to" technique to help find the molecular structure of the compound.

Carbon NMR is not widely used for determination of the structure of proteins, or for magnetic resonance imaging (MRI of animals including humans) because its only NMR-active nucleus, ^{13}C, is not abundant or sensitive to the magnetization applied. However, the concepts outlined here can be extrapolated to ^{1}H NMR where the inverse is true.

Concepts

electromagnetic spectrum • interactions of magnetic and electric fields • penguins with compasses sitting on magnetic dipoles

Objective

There are three irresistible messages in this phase of the *Inquisition*, concerning:

- the origins of magnetic resonance signals;
- how to determine the expected number of uncoupled ^{13}C NMR signals for different molecules;
- why protons near (3 bonds or less away from) ^{13}C nuclei cause ^{13}C NMR signal splitting; and,
- why coupling of ^{13}C NMR signals with ^{1}H nuclear spins is useful.

B Fundamental Physics Of NMR (Nuclear Magnetic Resonance)

Nuclear / electronic spin is the property that defines NMR active nuclei.

Some nuclei have spins that align in a magnetic field; NMR is caused by *flipping / pairing* these spins between aligned and counter-aligned states by applying a *radiofrequency / X-ray* pulse.

NMR spectroscopy therefore corresponds to the *high / low* energy range of the electromagnetic spectrum, *ie high / low* frequency and *high / low* wavelength.

For ^{13}C and ^{1}H the nuclear spin is *½ / ¾*, and for ^{12}C the nuclear spin is *0 / 1 / 2*.

The natural abundance of ^{1}H is *high / low*, but that of ^{13}C is *high / low* (*11 / 1.1* %), and this is one of the reasons that it takes more time to accumulate ^{13}C NMR spectra.

FT-NMR spectra are *taken in one scan / averaged over multiple scans* to increase *sensitivity / signal-to-noise / both these parameters*.

The energies required for NMR transitions are much *less / more* than those between vibrational states in IR, and *less / more* than the quanta required to promote electrons in UV spectra.

On a macroscopic level, NMR active nuclei *are / are not* sensitive to large external magnetic fields like those applied in NMR machines.

In the absence of an external magnetic field the energy difference between nuclear spins is *zero / small / about the same as X-ray quanta*.

The larger the applied magnetic field, the *smaller / larger* the energy gap between nuclear spin states.

Numbers of nuclei that adopt spin states that are aligned and opposed to an external field is governed by *the energy gap between the nuclear spin states / Boltzman distributions / both these parameters / neither of these*.

On a molecular level, NMR active nuclei *are / are not* sensitive to the electron density and proximal NMR active nuclei in the same molecule, hence these nuclei in different parts of the molecule flip when *different / exactly the same* field strength(s) are/is applied.

Spectroscopists may say that electron environment and NMR active nuclei "*ignore / shield* each other to varying degrees".

The scientific term for a NMR active nucleus that is more exposed to an applied magnetic field is *deshielded / somewhat naked* relative to one that is insulated but neighboring NMR active nuclei.

C Chemical Shifts In General

In NMR spectroscopy, a scale is defined relative to a signal in some reference compound; for ^{1}H the reference is *SiMe$_4$ / PMe$_3$*.

Chemical shift δ / α on this scale reflects how much less the frequency is for an NMR active nuclei to flip, or *resonate / tremble*, relative to that standard set at 0 on that scale, or:

$$\frac{\text{frequency of 0 on scale - frequency for nucleus}}{\text{frequency of 0 on scale}}$$

Most chemical shift values are *positive / negative*.

Nuclei with positive chemical shifts are *shielded / deshielded* relative to the zero point.

By convention, 0 in ^{1}H NMR corresponds to *the operating frequency of the machine / no magnetic field at all* so a 200 MHz NMR spectrometer sets 0 at *200,000,000 / 0* Hz. One millionth of this is *200 / 0* so on a 200 MHz machine a chemical shift of one part per million (ppm) corresponds to *200 / 200,000,000, ie 200 / 0* Hz.

on a 250 MHz machine, 1 ppm corresponds to _____ Hz in proton NMR spectra

on a 400 MHz machine, 1 ppm corresponds to _____ Hz in proton NMR spectra

on an 800 MHz machine, *10 ppm* corresponds to _____ Hz in proton NMR spectra

Two ^{1}H resonances on a 500 MHz machine separated by 0.05 ppm are separated by a frequency of _____ Hz.

If two peaks are separated by 60 Hz on a 600 MHz machine, that corresponds to a chemical shift difference of _____ ppm.

If two peaks are separated by 6 Hz on a 60 MHz machine, that corresponds to a chemical shift difference of _____ ppm.

The chemical shift separation of two resonances that are 60 Hz apart will be *greater / less* on a 60 MHz machine than on one operating at 600 MHz.

The chemical shift separation of two resonances that are 100 Hz apart will be *greater / less* on a 100 MHz machine than on one operating at 1,000 MHz.

Frequency differences between resonances *at fixed frequencies* appear to be *less / more* as the operating frequency of the NMR machine is increased. This point is important when thinking about *coupling*; (dealt with later in this *Inquisition*).

D Chemical Shifts In ^{13}C Spectra

Place the letter **H** on the end of the spectrum below where *most* magnetic field (or highest radiofrequency) is required to flip a NMR active nucleus; this is called the *upfield / downfield* region and corresponds to *shielded / deshielded* nuclei.

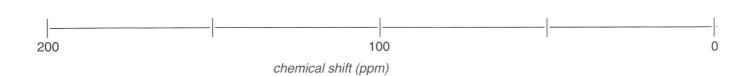

200   100   0

chemical shift (ppm)

Place a **L** on the end of the spectrum below where *least* magnetic field (or lowest radiofrequency) is required to flip a NMR active nucleus; this is called the *upfield / downfield* region and corresponds to *shielded / deshielded* nuclei.

Non-perturbed saturated carbons in ^{13}C NMR spectra tend to occur between 0 – 50 ppm; mark this range and label it "Csp^3-*H* and Csp^3-*C*" in the spectrum.

Saturated carbons next to an oxygen atom tend to occur between 50 – 100 ppm; mark this range and label it "Csp^3-*O* in the spectrum below. From this we can deduce electronegative atoms that *repel / attract* electron density tend to *shield / deshield* adjacent ^{13}C nuclei, and other electron withdrawing groups will also tend to *shield / deshield* adjacent ^{13}C nuclei.

Non-perturbed unsaturated carbons tend to occur at about 100 – 150 ppm; mark this range and label it "Csp^2-*H* and Csp^2-*C*" in the spectrum below. We may conclude from this that sp^2-hybridized carbons tend to be *more / less* shielded from magnetic fields than ones that are sp^3-hybridized.

Unsaturated carbons next to oxygen, *ie* carbonyl groups C=O, tend to resonate at about 150 – 200 ppm; mark this range and label it "Csp^2=*O*" in the spectrum.

If a very small person sat on two or more carbons in a molecule and saw non-identical views of the rest of the molecule, then those carbons are *inequivalent / equivalent* except if the molecular environments were mirror images.

Equivalent carbons in ^{13}C NMR spectra resonate at *the same / different* chemical shifts, and inequivalent ones usually resonate at *the same / different* chemical shifts.

272

Indicate how many types of carbons, *ie* the number of inequivalent carbons, in the following molecules; this is *the same as / different to* the number of resonances that are expected in the ^{13}C NMR spectrum. Use your deductions from the previous page to also predict the regions of the ^{13}C NMR spectra where these resonances will occur. (It is hard to get all the chemical shifts exactly correct).

inequivalent C

number of resonances (ppm):
0 - 50 _____
50 - 100 _____
100 - 150 _____
above 150 _____

inequivalent C

number of resonances (ppm):
0 - 50 _____
50 - 100 _____
100 - 150 _____
above 150 _____

inequivalent C

number of resonances (ppm):
0 - 50 _____
50 - 100 _____
100 - 150 _____
above 150 _____

inequivalent C

number of resonances (ppm):
0 - 50 _____
50 - 100 _____
100 - 150 _____
above 150 _____

inequivalent C

number of resonances (ppm):
0 - **40** _____
40 - 100 _____
100 - 150 _____
above 150 _____

inequivalent C

number of resonances (ppm):
0 - 50 _____
50 - 100 _____
100 - 150 _____
above 150 _____

inequivalent C

number of resonances (ppm):
0 - 50 _____
50 - 100 _____
100 - 150 _____
above 150 _____

inequivalent C

number of resonances (ppm):
0 - 50 _____
50 - 100 _____
100 - 150 _____
above 150 _____

inequivalent C

number of resonances (ppm):
0 - 50 _____
50 - 100 _____
100 - 150 _____
above 150 _____

inequivalent C

number of resonances (ppm):
0 - 50 _____
50 - 100 _____
100 - 150 _____
above 150 _____

inequivalent C

number of resonances (ppm):
0 - 50 _____
50 - 100 _____
100 - 150 _____
above 150 _____

inequivalent C

number of resonances (ppm):
0 - 50 _____
50 - 100 _____
100 - 150 _____
above 150 _____

inequivalent C

number of resonances (ppm):
0 - 50 _____
50 - 100 _____
100 - 150 _____
above 150 _____

inequivalent C

number of resonances (ppm):
0 - 50 _____
50 - 100 _____
100 - 150 _____
above 150 _____

inequivalent C

number of resonances (ppm):
0 - 50 _____
50 - 100 _____
100 - 150 _____
above 150 _____

inequivalent C

_number of
resonances (ppm):_
0 - 50 _____
50 - 100 _____
100 - 150 _____
above 150 _____

inequivalent C

_number of
resonances (ppm):_
0 - 50 _____
50 - 100 _____
100 - 150 _____
above 150 _____

inequivalent C

_number of
resonances (ppm):_
0 - 50 _____
50 - 100 _____
100 - 150 _____
above 150 _____

inequivalent C

_number of
resonances (ppm):_
0 - 50 _____
50 - 100 _____
100 - 150 _____
above 150 _____

inequivalent C

_number of
resonances (ppm):_
0 - **40** _____
40 - 100 _____
100 - 150 _____
above 150 _____

OMe

OEt

OMe

ᶦPr

inequivalent C

_number of
resonances (ppm):_
0 - 50 _____
50 - 100 _____
100 - 150 _____
above 150 _____

inequivalent C

_number of
resonances (ppm):_
0 - 50 _____
50 - 100 _____
100 - 150 _____
above 150 _____

inequivalent C

_number of
resonances (ppm):_
0 - 50 _____
50 - 100 _____
100 - 150 _____
above 150 _____

inequivalent C

_number of
resonances (ppm):_
0 - 50 _____
50 - 100 _____
100 - 150 _____
above 150 _____

inequivalent C

_number of
resonances (ppm):_
0 - 50 _____
50 - 100 _____
100 - 150 _____
above 150 _____

MeO   OMe

MeO   OMe

OH   OH

Cl   Cl

inequivalent C

_number of
resonances (ppm):_
0 - 50 _____
50 - 100 _____
100 - 150 _____
above 150 _____

inequivalent C

_number of
resonances (ppm):_
0 - 50 _____
50 - 100 _____
100 - 150 _____
above 150 _____

inequivalent C

_number of
resonances (ppm):_
0 - 50 _____
50 - 100 _____
100 - 150 _____
above 150 _____

inequivalent C

_number of
resonances (ppm):_
0 - 50 _____
50 - 100 _____
100 - 150 _____
above 150 _____

inequivalent C

_number of
resonances (ppm):_
0 - 50 _____
50 - 100 _____
100 - 150 _____
above 150 _____

inequivalent C

_number of
resonances (ppm):_
0 - 50 _____
50 - 100 _____
100 - 150 _____
above 150 _____

inequivalent C

_number of
resonances (ppm):_
0 - 50 _____
50 - 100 _____
100 - 150 _____
above 150 _____

inequivalent C

_number of
resonances (ppm):_
0 - 50 _____
50 - 100 _____
100 - 150 _____
above 150 _____

inequivalent C

_number of
resonances (ppm):_
0 - 50 _____
50 - 100 _____
100 - 150 _____
above 150 _____

inequivalent C

_number of
resonances (ppm):_
0 - 50 _____
50 - 100 _____
100 - 150 _____
above 150 _____

The ^{13}C NMR spectrum of the soccer-ball-like molecule C_{60}, has _____ ^{13}C resonances.

The intensities of peaks in ^{13}C NMR spectra tend to be dependent on several factors, so they usually *can / cannot* be reliably used to ascertain the number of equivalent carbons involved.

Draw the structure isomers of C_7H_{16} with the following numbers of inequivalent carbons in their ^{13}C NMR spectra:

_____   _____   _____

       7 inequivalent C   *4 inequivalent C*   *3 inequivalent C*

E Coupling In ^{13}C NMR

Imagine a small penguin holding a compass, sitting on the ^{13}C atom of ^{13}CHCl$_3$ in a magnetic field. The compass is influenced by the magnetic field, but also by the magnetic spins of adjacent NMR active nuclei. Ignore the nuclear spins of chlorine atoms throughout.

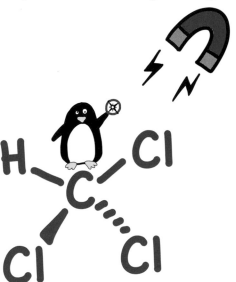

^{13}CH Spin Systems

The ^{1}H nucleus *is / is not* NMR active so at any instant the ^{13}CHCl$_3$ proton could have a nuclear spin that is aligned or opposed to the magnetic field.

If the penguin happens to be sitting on a molecule with the proton nuclear spin aligned then the magnetic effect on her compass would be *the same / different* to another molecule where the spin is opposed to the applied magnetic field.

Statistically, the population of ^{13}CHCl$_3$ molecules for which the proton spin is aligned is only a little bit different to that for the misaligned ones, hence the ^{13}C NMR signal for ^{13}CHCl$_3$ splits into *two / three* peaks of almost equal intensity; this is called a *triplet / doublet*.

The chemical shift of that carbon is *exactly at the center of / 1 ppm away from* these resonances.

In ^{13}C NMR spectra the effects of *coupling / matching* with protons in the molecule are completely or mostly removed (via NMR instrument magic) to make the spectra simpler.

If the effects of *C – H* coupling are mostly removed then some splitting will still be seen (this is called *partial decoupling*). If this were done for ^{13}C spectra of ^{13}CHCl$_3$ and ^{13}CCl$_4$ then we would see a *doublet and a singlet / singlet and a doublet*, respectively.

In that experiment it *would / would not* be possible to distinguish between ^{13}CHCl$_3$ and ^{13}CCl$_4$ without thinking about chemical shifts. In general, it is sometimes useful to retain some coupling information.

$^{13}CH_2$ Spin Systems

If the penguin sat on the C in $^{13}CH_2Cl_2$ in a magnetic field then the proton spins could be *aa, ao, oa, oo* (*a*= aligned and *o* = opposed). Energetically, the effect is *different / the same* for the *ao* and *oa* cases. (This diagram should help answer that question because it has the answer in italics).

I stand here   *and experience.....*   *magnetic effect feels same*

3 different magnetic field strengths influence that ^{13}C, ratio 1:2:1

Statistically, the penguin's compass could be experiencing *two / three / four* different magnetic fields and the relative probability is *1:2:2:1 / 1:2:1 /1:1*.

A partially decoupled ^{13}C NMR spectrum of $^{13}CH_2Cl_2$ would show a *doublet / triplet / quartet* for the carbon and it *could / could not* be differentiated from $^{13}CHCl_3$ and $^{13}CCl_4$ on this basis alone.

$^{13}CH_3$ Spin Systems

A partially decoupled ^{13}C NMR spectrum of $^{13}CH_3Cl$ would show a *quintet / quartet / triplet / doublet* for the carbon and it *could / could not* thus be differentiated from $^{13}CHCl_3$, $^{13}CH_2Cl_2$ and $^{13}CCl_4$.

Complete the following diagram:

put arrows on all H atoms to indicate spins (as above)

_____ *different magnetic field strengths influence that ^{13}C, ratio* _____

The relative probabilities for finding the spins in *a* or *o* states is *1:2:1 / 1:1 / 1:3:3:1 / 1:4:6:4:1*.

In conclusion, ^{13}C with *n* hydrogen atoms attached to it will be split into *n / n + 1* peaks.

In this situation, the number *n* refers to the number of nuclei *doing the splitting / being observed* and not those *doing the splitting / being observed*.

The relative intensities of these peaks *have to be deduced out from first principles / follow Pascal's triangle*.

Given the low natural abundance of ^{13}C, molecules with two ^{13}C atoms adjacent to each other in a chain are *rare / common* and *can / cannot* be ignored.

Differentiating CH, CH$_2$, And CH$_3$ In ^{13}C Spectra

Circle *s*, *d*, *t*, *q* on the end of each arrow in the following diagram to indicate *singlet*, *doublet*, *triplet*, or *quartet* for the ^{13}C resonances observed in a ^{13}C NMR spectrum where the proton couplings are not totally removed.

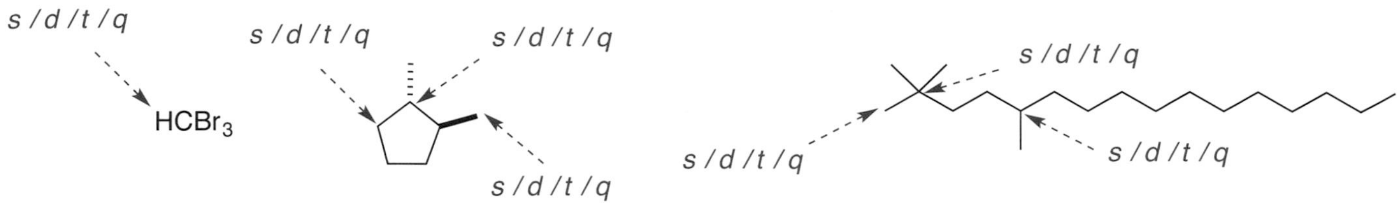

s / d / t / q

s / d / t / q   *s / d / t / q*

HCBr$_3$

s / d / t / q

s / d / t / q

s / d / t / q

s / d / t / q

s / d / t / q

The difference between peaks is called the *matching / coupling* constant and it is expressed in *ppm / Hz*.

Couplings expressed as chemical shift differences would be the *same / different* on machines operating at different field strengths, so they are *always / never* quoted in this way.

DEPT Spectra To Differentiate Quaternary, Methine-, Methylene-, and Methyl-Carbons

As stated above, effects of proton coupling are almost always removed in ^{13}C NMR spectra (partial decoupling experiments are relatively rare). DEPT is a special ^{13}C NMR technique to differentiate between CH$_2$, CH & CH$_3$ together.

Carbons with no hydrogen atoms on them, *tertiary / quaternary*, *do / do not* show up in DEPT spectra.

DEPT 135 spectra are usually presented with CH & CH$_3$ *negative / positive* peaks, and resonances for CH$_2$ carbons *negative / positive*.

DEPT 90 spectra only show *CH / CH$_2$ / CH$_3$* peaks.

Variations of DEPT *can / cannot* allow CH & CH$_3$ groups to be differentiated, but this takes more effort.

DEPT is a *more / less* effective way of differentiating methyl, methylene, methane, and quaternary carbons than partial decoupling, because the spectra are quicker to accumulate.

A few assignments have been made for the DEPT spectra of compound **1**. Complete the assignment process using the numbering scheme indicated.

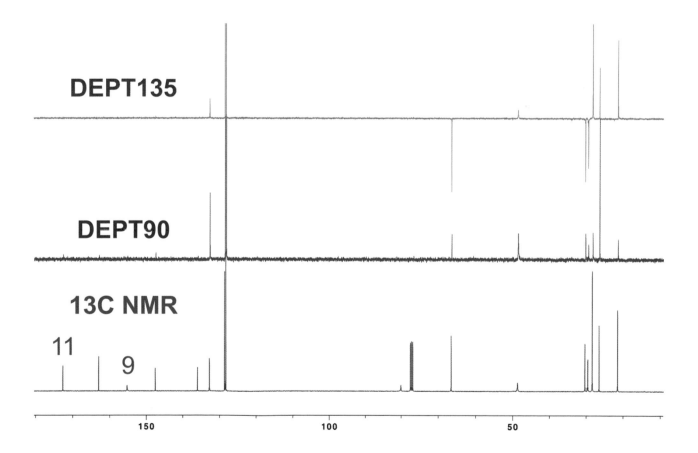

Whereas couplings of C with H are usually suppressed in ^{13}C NMR spectra, proton-proton couplings in ^{1}H NMR spectra are *also usually suppressed / nearly always shown*.

As an alternative to DEPT, the NMR technique called HSQC (Heteronuclear Single Quantum Correlation) spectroscopy can correlate ^{13}C- with the *^{1}H-NMR signals of the protons attached to them / ^{13}C atoms that are close to each other*.

F Some Problems Involving Interpretation Of ^{13}C Spectra

Look up the structures of citric acid and 1-propanol, write the structures near the corresponding ^{13}C NMR spectra below, and assign the peaks.

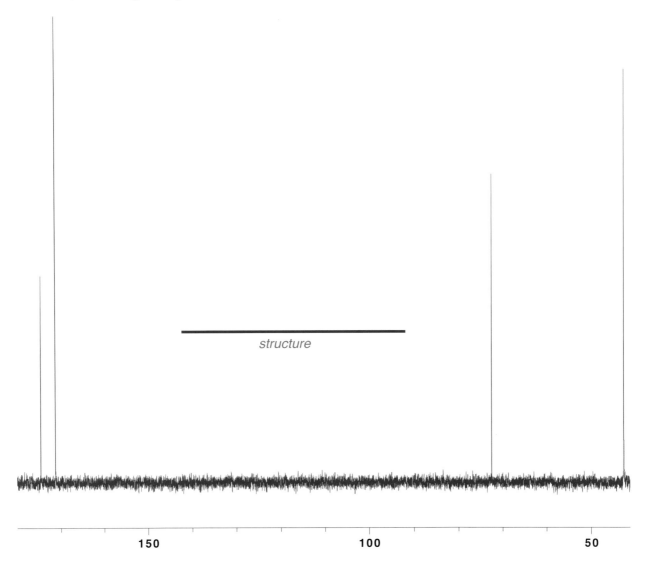

structure

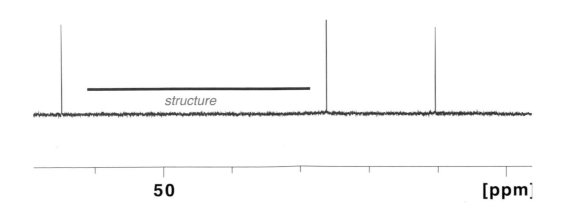

structure

[ppm]

One of the ^{13}C spectra below is of adenosine and the other is of tryptophan. Draw the structures of these near the corresponding spectra, and assign one peak in each spectrum.

structure

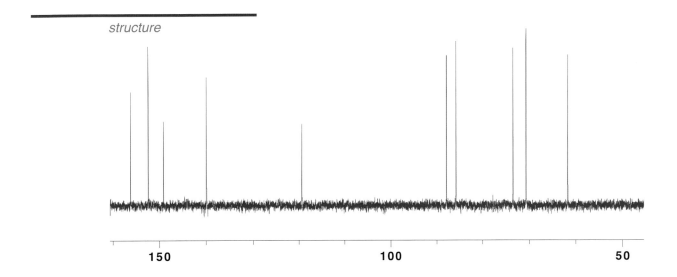

150   100   50

structure

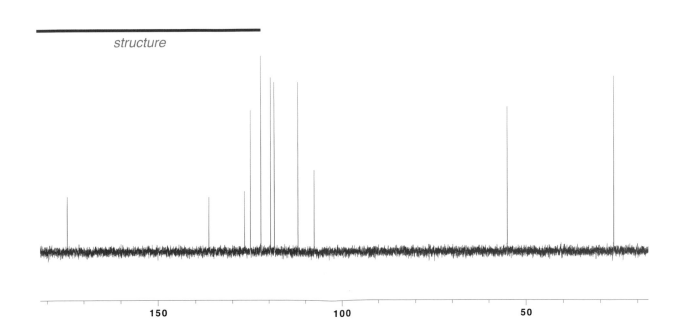

150   100   50

Look up the structures of guanine and the anti-cancer drug 5-fluorouracil. Below are the relevant parts of the ^{13}C NMR spectra of these molecules. Draw structures of guanine and 5-fluorouracil next to the corresponding spectra, and assign the ^{13}C NMR peaks. ^{19}F is an abundant NMR active nuclei, nuclear spin ½; both 2- and 3-bond couplings to ^{19}F are seen in the 5-fluorouracil ^{13}C spectrum.

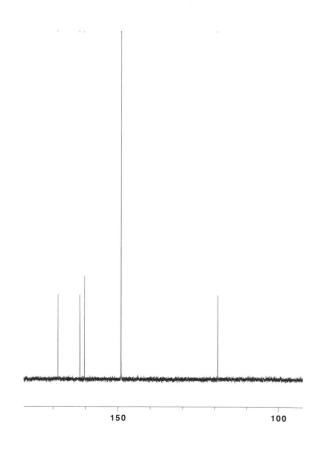

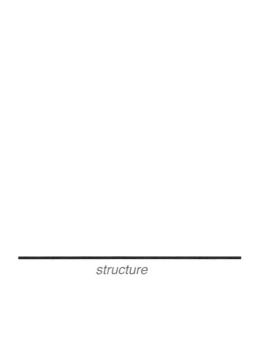

structure

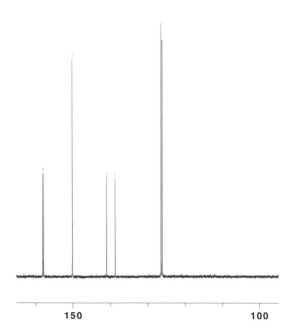

structure

22 ¹H NMR Spectroscopy

from chapter(s) _____ in the recommended text

A Introduction

Focus

¹H nuclei have magnetically sensitive nuclei at >99.9 % natural abundance. Like ¹³C nuclei, protons can have different intramolecular environments. Proton chemical shifts are characteristic of their local environments, *ie* the functional groups they are part of and which are immediately adjacent to them. Chemical shift and proton-proton coupling data alone, make ¹H NMR the most informative spectroscopic technique in organic chemistry. ¹H NMR is the focus of this section.

Reasons To Care

Whereas ¹³C NMR spectroscopy is largely a tool for chemistry, other disciplines have built such specialized expertise in ¹H NMR they tend to "own" it. For instance, ¹H NMR is used in determining the 3D structures of proteins, how proteins interact with ligands, and for imaging organs in the body via MRI. This introduction will *not* discuss those applications in the biological sciences; at this stage it is only important to recognize the wide range of applications of proton NMR in the biological and health sciences.

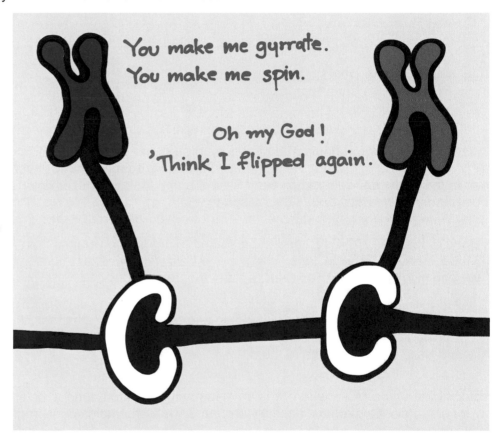

Concepts

electromagnetic spectra • magnetic equivalence and inequivalence • chemical shifts • coupling constants

Objective

This section is a first step towards understanding of proton chemical shifts, ¹H-¹H couplings, and how these parameters can be used in structure determination.

B Chemical Shifts In ¹H Spectra

On the chemical shift axis below, write **TMS** at the point you expect the protons of SiMe₄ to resonate, **H** on the high field region, and **L** on the low field region.

The relevant chemical shift range in ¹H NMR is much *smaller / larger* than in ¹³C NMR.

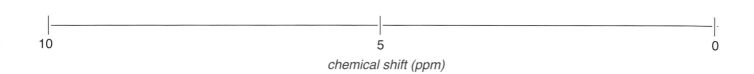

chemical shift (ppm)

Unperturbed hydrogen atoms attached to saturated, sp³-hybridized, carbon atoms tend to resonate in the *high / low* field region from 0.5 – 2.5 ppm, while those attached to sp²-hybridized carbon atoms tend to be seen in the *high / low* field region from 5 – 6.5 ppm. Indicate these regions with lines on the spectrum above and write *H*-Csp³ and *H*-Csp² above them.

Protons of the type *HC*-Csp² tend to be shifted to *higher / lower* field than *HC*-Csp³ atoms; for instance, C*H*-alkene and C*H*-aryl protons, *ie allylic and benzylic / benzylic and allylic*, tend to resonate at *higher / lower* chemical shifts than *HC*-Csp³, *eg* 2 – 3 ppm.

Protons *directly* attached to an aromatic ring tend to resonate at *higher / lower* chemical shifts than *H*Csp² protons in alkenes, around 7 - 8. Indicate these regions with lines on the spectrum above and write *HC*-Csp² and *H*-aryl above them.

Protons of the type *HC*-X where X is an electronegative atom tend to be shifted to significantly *higher / lower* field than *HC*-C atoms, typically around 3 – 4 ppm. Indicate this region with lines on the spectrum above and write *HC*-X above it.

Assign the ^{1}H NMR resonance of the following compounds based on the chemical shifts indicated. Also indicate the number of different types of *H* resonances, the number of proton environments.

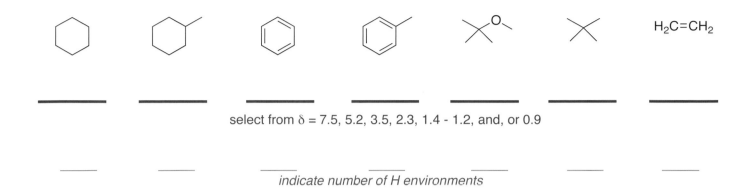

select from δ = 7.5, 5.2, 3.5, 2.3, 1.4 - 1.2, and, or 0.9

indicate number of H environments

If there are *x* unique *H* environments the number of NMR signals will be *0.5 x / x / 2 x.*

Write the structures of the compound from the choices shown above that best corresponds to the following ^{1}H NMR spectra.

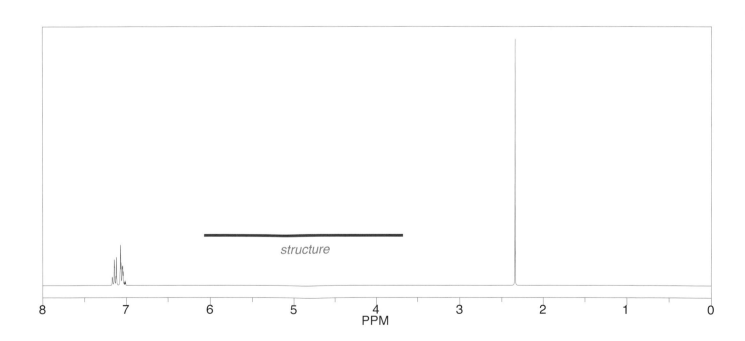

structure

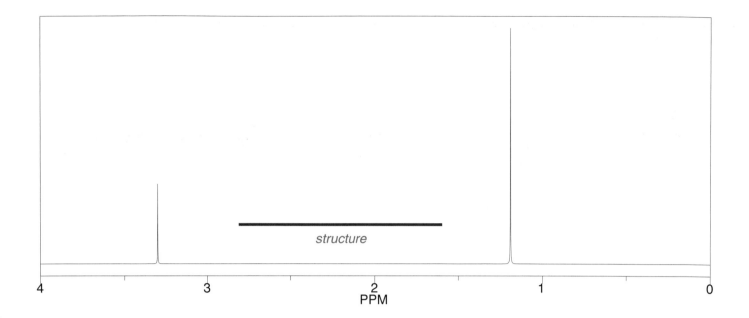

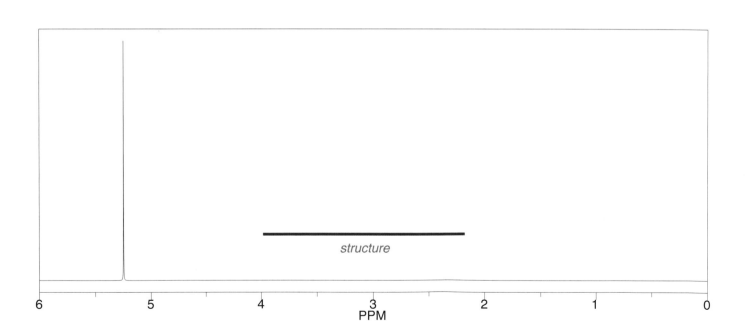

Predict ^{1}H chemical shift regions and numbers of different resonances for the following compounds.

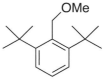

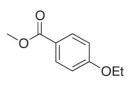

OMe

inequivalent H	

number of
resonances (ppm):
0 - 2 _____
2 - 3 _____
3 - 4 _____
4 - 7 _____
7 - 9 _____

inequivalent H

number of
resonances (ppm):
0 - 2 _____
2 - 3 _____
3 - 4 _____
4 - 7 _____
7 - 9 _____

inequivalent H

number of
resonances (ppm):
0 - 2 _____
2 - 3 _____
3 - 4 _____
4 - 7 _____
7 - 9 _____

inequivalent H

number of
resonances (ppm):
0 - 2 _____
2 - 3 _____
3 - 4 _____
4 - 7 _____
7 - 9 _____

inequivalent H

number of
resonances (ppm):
0 - 2 _____
2 - 3 _____
3 - 4 _____
4 - 7 _____
7 - 9 _____

inequivalent H

number of
resonances (ppm):
0 - 2 _____
2 - 3 _____
3 - 4 _____
4 - 7 _____
7 - 9 _____

inequivalent H

number of
resonances (ppm):
0 - 2 _____
2 - 3 _____
3 - 4 _____
4 - 7 _____
7 - 9 _____

inequivalent H

number of
resonances (ppm):
0 - 2 _____
2 - 3 _____
3 - 4 _____
4 - 7 _____
7 - 9 _____

inequivalent H

number of
resonances (ppm):
0 - 2 _____
2 - 3 _____
3 - 4 _____
4 - 7 _____
7 - 9 _____

inequivalent H

number of
resonances (ppm):
0 - 2 _____
2 - 3 _____
3 - 4 _____
4 - 7 _____
7 - 9 _____

inequivalent H

number of
resonances (ppm):
0 - 2 _____
2 - 3 _____
3 - 4 _____
4 - 7 _____
7 - 9 _____

inequivalent H

number of
resonances (ppm):
0 - 2 _____
2 - 3 _____
3 - 4 _____
4 - 7 _____
7 - 9 _____

inequivalent H

number of
resonances (ppm):
0 - 2 _____
2 - 3 _____
3 - 4 _____
4 - 7 _____
7 - 9 _____

inequivalent H

number of
resonances (ppm):
0 - 2 _____
2 - 3 _____
3 - 4 _____
4 - 7 _____
7 - 9 _____

inequivalent H

number of
resonances (ppm):
0 - 2 _____
2 - 3 _____
3 - 4 _____
4 - 7 _____
7 - 9 _____

286

inequivalent H

number of
resonances (ppm):
0 - 2 _____
2 - 3 _____
3 - 4 _____
4 - 7 _____
7 - 9 _____

inequivalent H

number of
resonances (ppm):
0 - 2 _____
2 - 3 _____
3 - 4 _____
4 - 7 _____
7 - 9 _____

Ph Ph

inequivalent H

number of
resonances (ppm):
0 - 2 _____
2 - 3 _____
3 - 4 _____
4 - 7 _____
7 - 9 _____

Ph Ph

inequivalent H

number of
resonances (ppm):
0 - 2 _____
2 - 3 _____
3 - 4 _____
4 - 7 _____
7 - 9 _____

inequivalent H

number of
resonances (ppm):
0 - 2 _____
2 - 3 _____
3 - 4 _____
4 - 7 _____
7 - 9 _____

MeO   OMe

inequivalent H

number of
resonances (ppm):
0 - 2 _____
2 - 3 _____
3 - 4 _____
4 - 7 _____
7 - 9 _____

MeO   OMe

inequivalent H

number of
resonances (ppm):
0 - 2 _____
2 - 3 _____
3 - 4 _____
4 - 7 _____
7 - 9 _____

inequivalent H

number of
resonances (ppm):
0 - 2 _____
2 - 3 _____
3 - 4 _____
4 - 7 _____
7 - 9 _____

OH   OH

inequivalent H

number of
resonances (ppm):
0 - 2 _____
2 - 3 _____
3 - 4 _____
4 - 7 _____
7 - 9 _____

Cl   Cl

inequivalent H

number of
resonances (ppm):
0 - 2 _____
2 - 3 _____
3 - 4 _____
4 - 7 _____
7 - 9 _____

inequivalent H

number of
resonances (ppm):
0 - 2 _____
2 - 3 _____
3 - 4 _____
4 - 7 _____
7 - 9 _____

inequivalent H

number of
resonances (ppm):
0 - 2 _____
2 - 3 _____
3 - 4 _____
4 - 7 _____
7 - 9 _____

inequivalent H

number of
resonances (ppm):
0 - 2 _____
2 - 3 _____
3 - 4 _____
4 - 7 _____
7 - 9 _____

inequivalent H

number of
resonances (ppm):
0 - 2 _____
2 - 3 _____
3 - 4 _____
4 - 7 _____
7 - 9 _____

inequivalent H

number of
resonances (ppm):
0 - 2 _____
2 - 3 _____
3 - 4 _____
4 - 7 _____
7 - 9 _____

C Coupling In ^{1}H NMR

Recall in ^{13}C NMR, coupling of ^{13}C signals to directly attached protons, *C*-H, is sometimes important when considering ^{13}C NMR spectra; these are called *one bond* couplings. Protons further away, *eg C*-C-H, do have an influence via *two bond / three bond* couplings, but it is not important to consider them now.

Heteronuclear Coupling To ^{13}C Is Unimportant

In ^{1}H NMR the natural abundance of ^{13}C in organic molecules is *100 / 11.1 / 1.11* %, so most protons attached to a carbon atom *are / are not* split by the one bond ^{13}C nuclear spins.

Splitting of proton NMR signals by natural abundance ^{13}C in organic compounds (*ie* not isotopically labeled with extra ^{13}C) can usually be ignored (*cf* the major isotope of carbon, ^{12}C, is *NMR active / silent*).

Coupling between ^{13}C and ^{1}H are examples of *hetero- / homo*-nuclear couplings.

Homonuclear ^{1}H Coupling

The most useful coupling information found in ^{1}H NMR spectra tends to arise from protons splitting other protons. Homonuclear coupling information usually *is / is not* removed when processing proton NMR spectra.

Organic molecules tend to contain lots of valuable information from H^a-C-H^b and H^a-C-C-H^b couplings, *ie 2 and 3 / 3 and 4* bond *hetero- / homo*-nuclear couplings.

Couplings of the type H^a-C-C-C-H^b, *ie 1 / 2 / 3 / 4* bond homonuclear coupling can sometimes be observed, but these effects are small and can be ignored at this level.

For example, the inequivalent protons in ClCH$_2$CH$_2$Br **A** are separated by *3 / 4* bonds and *do / do not* give significant couplings.

Conversely, the inequivalent protons in ClCH$_2$OCH$_2$Br **B** have *3 / 4 / 5* bonds between them and *do / do not* give significant couplings.

Equivalent protons in NMR spectra *do / do not* appear to be split.

Resonances in molecules like CMe$_4$, MeOMe, MeCOMe, and MeCOCH$_2$Cl are *singlets / doublets*.

Circle methyl groups that appear as singlets in the ^{1}H NMR spectra of the following molecules.

Draw three other, structurally dissimilar, molecules that would have a methyl group not coupled to any other protons.

molecule 1	*molecule 2*	*molecule 3*

Spin Systems

Spin systems are sets of protons that are only coupled to each other. They consist of *2 / 3 / any number >1 NMR* active nuclei.

Lasso the various proton spin systems in each of the following molecules, assuming only 2- and 3-bond couplings can be observed.

In general, if a proton is magnetically impacted by n non-equivalent protons then its resonance will be split into n / $n + 1$ signals.

It *does / does not* matter how many protons *are being split* but it *does / does not* matter how many protons (n) *are causing the splitting*.

The relative intensities of the peaks in the split signal *must be deduced out from first principles / follow Pascal's triangle*.

H^a-C-H^b Spin Systems

If we sit on H^a in an H^a-C-H^b system (throughout, assume no other NMR active nuclei coupled to these) when a magnetic field is applied, then the field that reaches us *will / will not* depend on whether the spin of H^b is aligned or opposed (*a* or *o*), and H^a will appear as a *singlet / doublet / triplet*.

Protons on the same carbon atom of a CH_2 group can *never / sometimes / always* be inequivalent, and if they are then they *will / will not* appear to split each other.

If we sit on H^a in a H^a-C-CH^b system when a magnetic field is applied, then the field that reaches us *will / will not* depend on whether the spin of H^b is aligned or opposed (*a* or *o*), and H^a will appear as a *singlet / doublet / triplet*.

If any of the following molecules have a methylene (CH_2) group where the two protons are inequivalent, circle those carbons.

If any of the molecules above have a methylene with two inequivalent protons that are also *not coupled to any other proton* via 2- or 3-bond couplings, put a square around that carbon.

H^a-C-C-H^b Spin Systems

The magnitude of the H^a-C-CH^b coupling will be *larger / smaller* than in the H^a-C-H^b system because the magnetic effects of the two atoms are more removed from each other.

A molecule with an isolated H^aC-CH^b spin system is shown below; draw two more.

isolated H^aCCH^b	*molecule 1*	*molecule 2*

The field that reaches H^a in an H^a-C-CH^b_2 system when a magnetic field is applied *will / will not* depend on whether the spin of H^b is aligned or opposed (*a* or *o*).

In this system, H^a will appear as a *singlet / doublet / triplet / quartet* due to coupling with H^b.

Conversely, H^b will appear as a *singlet / doublet / triplet / quartet* due to coupling with H^a.

H^aC-CH^b_2 Spin Systems

A molecule with an isolated H^aC-CH^b_2 spin system is shown below; draw two more.

isolated $H^aCCH^b_2$	*molecule 1*	*molecule 2*

H^{a}C-CH$^b_3$ Spin Systems

The field that reaches H^a in an H^a-C-CH$^b_3$ system *will / will not* depend on whether the spin of H^b is aligned or opposed (*a* or *o*).

In this system, H^a will appear as a *singlet / doublet / triplet / quartet*, and H^b appears as a *singlet / doublet / triplet / quartet*.

A molecule with an isolated H^{a}C-CH$^b_3$ spin system is shown below; draw two more.

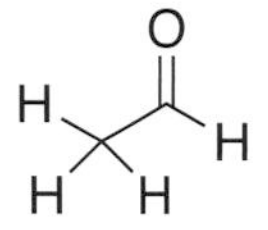

isolated H^{a}CCH$^b_3$ *molecule 1*   *molecule 2*

H$^a_2$C-CH$^b_3$ Spin Systems (Isolated Ethyl Groups)

In a H$^a_2$C-CH$^b_3$ system, it *does / does not* make any difference to the splitting of H^a that there is another H^a because equivalent protons in NMR spectra *do / do not* split each other.

Let's sit on some H^b protons in these systems, and look around. An isolated H$^a_2$C-CH$^b_3$ system, *ie* an ethyl group not coupled to anything else, always appears as a triplet quartet pattern where the methyl part is a *triplet / quartet*, and the methylene is a *triplet / quartet*.

Circle all the *isolated* H$^a_2$C-CH$^b_3$ spin systems in the following molecules (*ie* only those that appear as triplet-quartet combinations.

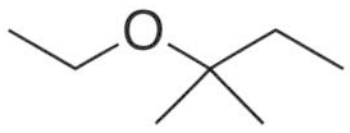

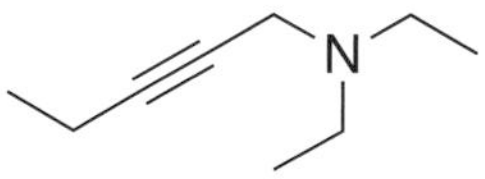

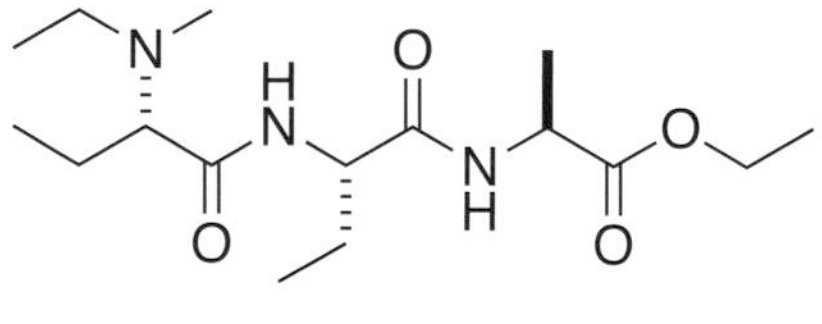

(H$^a_3$C)$_2$CH^b Spin Systems (Isolated ^{i}Pr Groups)

In a (H$^a_3$C)$_2$C-H^b system, the H^b resonance "feels" a magnetic field perturbation by six H^a nuclei, hence H^b will appear as a *singlet / doublet / triplet / quartet / pentent / hextet / heptet* with a relative intensity of _____ whereas the methyl groups will be split into *singlets / doublets / triplets / quartets*.

Circle the isolated ^{i}Pr spin systems in the following molecules.

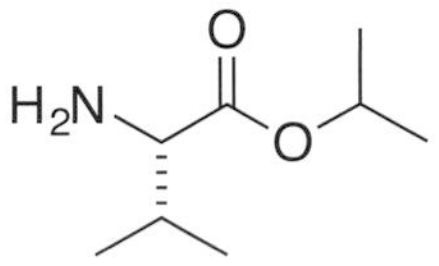

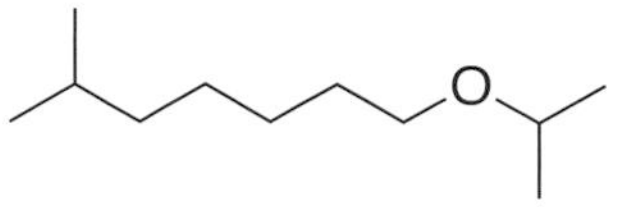

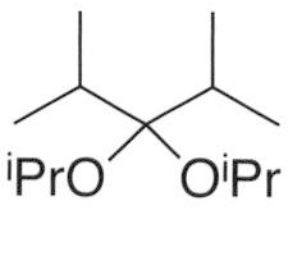

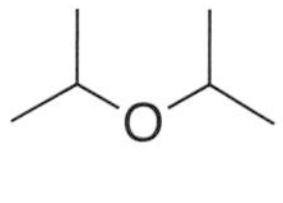

Common Splitting Patterns In Organic Molecules

For each of the following molecular fragments, indicate the splitting of the $\underline{H}$ proton caused by the other protons around it. On the same diagram, name each of these fragments (one name is used twice).

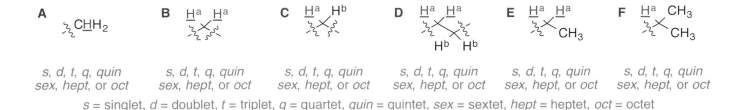

A $\ce{CHH_2}$

B H^a H^a

C H^a H^b

D H^a H^a / H^b H^b

E H^a H^a / CH_3

F H^a CH_3 / CH_3

s, d, t, q, quin
sex, hept, or oct (for each A–F)

s = singlet, d = doublet, t = triplet, q = quartet, quin = quintet, sex = sextet, hept = heptet, oct = octet

fragment name   possible fragment names: ethyl, ethylene, _iso_-propyl, methyl, methylene

Below are six compounds that together represent all six situations outlined above (**A – F**). Match the compound with the fragment it contains, then with the spectra below.

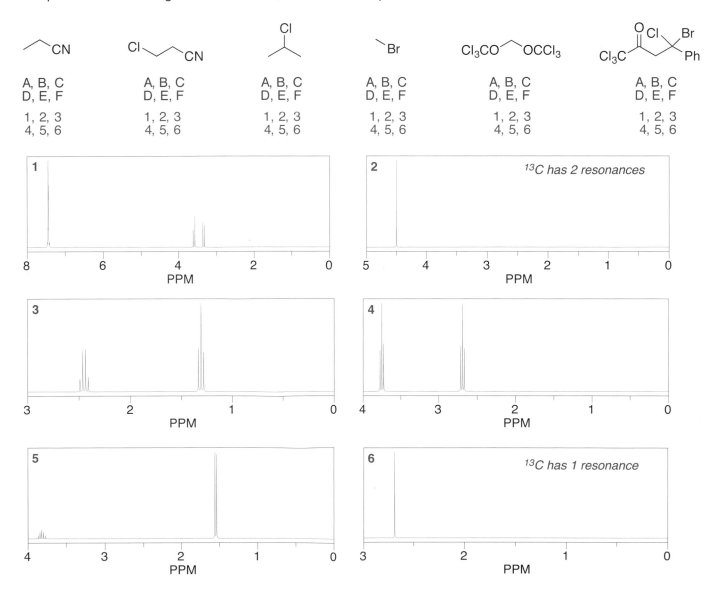

$\ce{CN}$ — A, B, C / D, E, F — 1, 2, 3 / 4, 5, 6

$\ce{Cl{-}CN}$ — A, B, C / D, E, F — 1, 2, 3 / 4, 5, 6

(iso-propyl chloride) — A, B, C / D, E, F — 1, 2, 3 / 4, 5, 6

$\ce{Br}$ — A, B, C / D, E, F — 1, 2, 3 / 4, 5, 6

$\ce{Cl_3CO{-}OCCl_3}$ — A, B, C / D, E, F — 1, 2, 3 / 4, 5, 6

$\ce{Cl_3C{-}...{-}Ph}$ — A, B, C / D, E, F — 1, 2, 3 / 4, 5, 6

Spectrum 1

Spectrum 2 — ^{13}C has 2 resonances

Spectrum 3

Spectrum 4

Spectrum 5

Spectrum 6 — ^{13}C has 1 resonance

The following are proton NMR spectra of chloroethane, 2-chloropropane, and 2-chloro-2-methylpropane. Indicate which one is which by drawing the structures in the spaces provided.

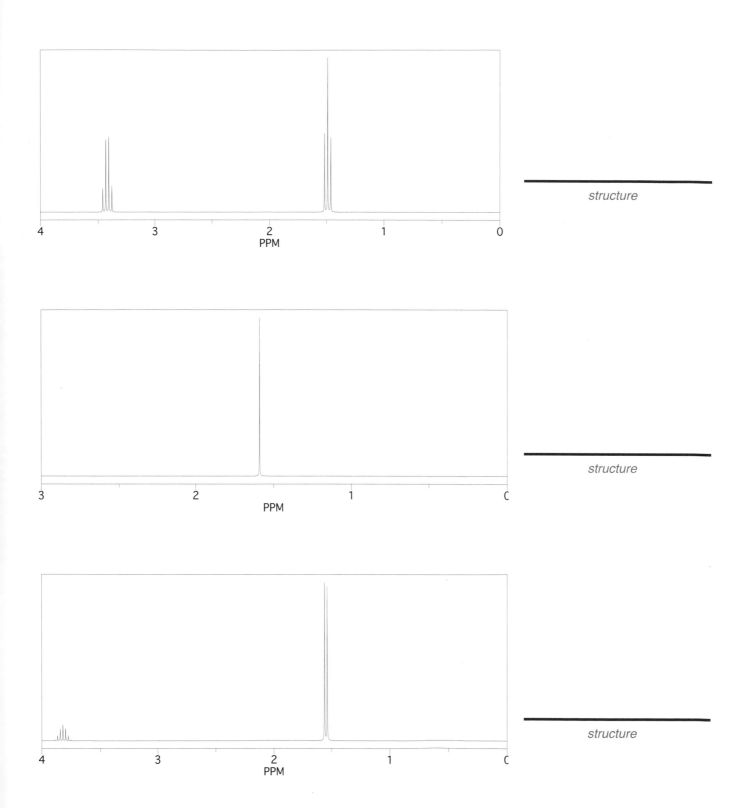

structure

structure

structure

Assign the peaks in the NMR spectra of the following compound by labeling them with the letters indicated on the structure. Indicate peaks from equivalent atoms by putting more than one letter on that peak.

¹H NMR

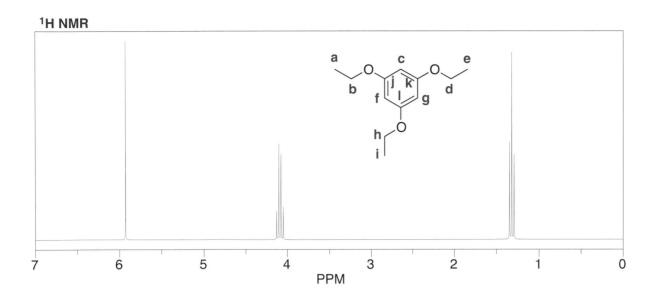

¹³C NMR

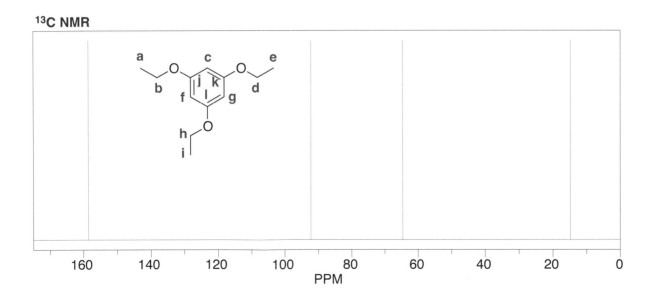

D Diastereotopic Protons

Draw Newman projections of the following molecules from the perspective indicated, and deduce whether or not H^a and H^b are equivalent.

..... can be represented as

where H^a and H^b are / are not equivalent

..... can be represented as

where H^a and H^b are / are not equivalent

..... can be represented as

where H^a and H^b are / are not equivalent

..... can be represented as

where H^a and H^b are / are not equivalent

..... can be represented as

where H^a and H^b are / are not equivalent

..... can be represented as

where H^a and H^b are / are not equivalent

Protons on a methylene group are *equivalent / inequivalent* when the methylene is in a chiral environment.

Predict the splitting pattern of the methylene groups in the following molecules (*eg* singlet, doublet, doublet of triplets). In the last example, it is relevant that ^{19}F is both abundant, and has a nuclear spin of ½ (like a proton).

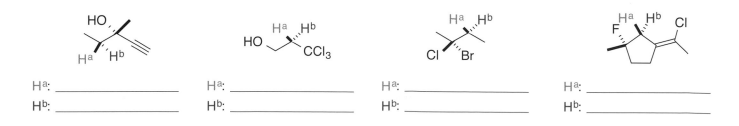

H^a: _____

H^b: _____

H^a: _____

H^b: _____

H^a: _____

H^b: _____

H^a: _____

H^b: _____

E Some Problems Involving Spectral Interpretation

Below are ^{1}H NMR spectra of acetonitrile and ethyl acetate (both in CDCl$_3$). Draw the structures of these molecules next to the spectra and assign the peaks.

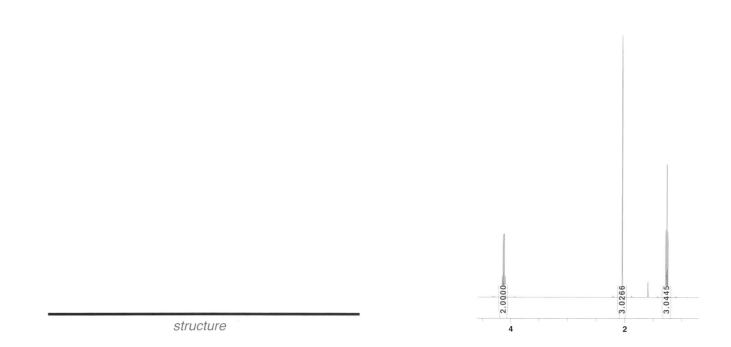

structure

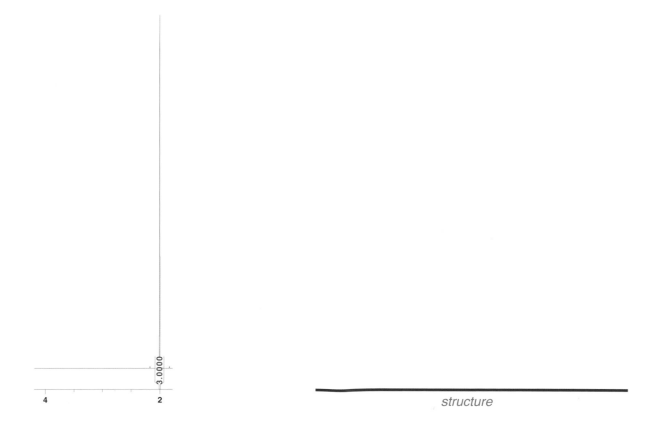

structure

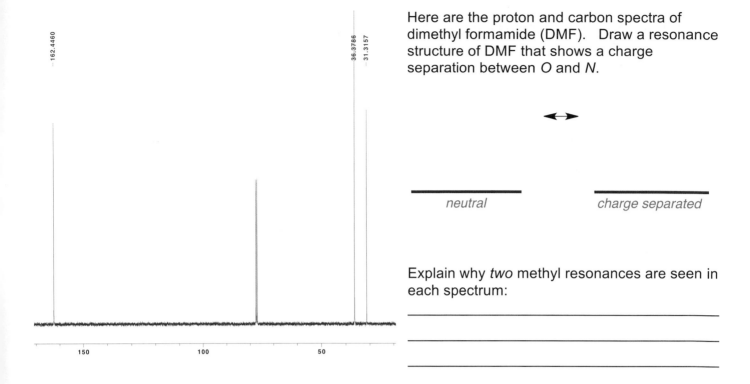

Here are the proton and carbon spectra of dimethyl formamide (DMF). Draw a resonance structure of DMF that shows a charge separation between *O* and *N*.

$\longleftrightarrow$

neutral   *charge separated*

Explain why *two* methyl resonances are seen in each spectrum:

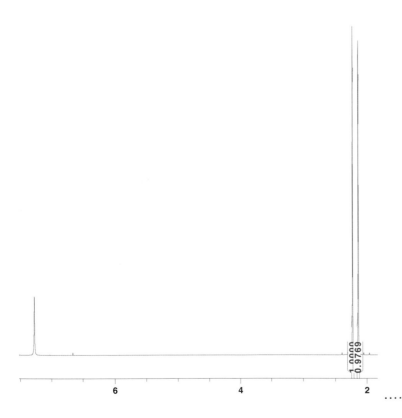

23 Mass Spectrometry (MS)

from chapter(s) _____ in the recommended text

A Introduction

Focus

Mass *spectrometry* (*note:* not spectroscopy) is the science of "weighing" molecules, molecular fragments, and molecular complexes. This section focuses on the different ways of ionizing and detecting molecules, and information that can be obtained by observing molecular ions and their fragments in MS.

Reasons To Care

A few decades ago the dominant method for ionizing molecules in MS was by firing electrons at them (electron impact, EI). EI is a sufficiently destructive ionization technique that often the molecular ion is not observed, only fragments of that ion.

In the last 20 – 30 years, practical "softer" ionization techniques like MALDI and ESI have emerged, that allow molecular ions to be observed even for large, non-volatile, biomolecules. These techniques have displaced much EI equipment, so it is easier to observe molecular ions of small molecules, but much of the fragmentation information that was unavoidably collected is not obtained using softer ionization techniques. One exception is where ESI is coupled to gas chromatography (GC-MS), where ESI is still the norm; consequently, the questions on fragmentation are included here.

MS instrumentation has evolved rapidly in the last 20 years to match the demands of proteomic studies. Thus, there are innovations to increase the sensitivity and resolution of MS. Methods can be combined so that, for example, a protein molecular ion can be observed and, in parallel, deliberately fragmented to obtain amino acid sequences. Applications of MS in pure chemistry research tend to be simplistic relative to sophisticated approaches used in proteomic and health related studies, but the core concepts introduced here are the same.

Concepts

ionization • isotopic abundances • curly arrows to depict fragmentation of radical cations

Objective

To introduce what MS is and what it can do in efforts to characterize small molecules, and to appreciate that the cutting-edge applications of MS in biomedical sciences require sophisticated, specialized equipment.

B Components Of Mass Spectrometers

MS separates ionized atoms, molecular fragments, or molecules on the basis of the ratio of *mass-to-charge / charge-to-mass / mass only*.

The primary objective of MS is to determine the *mass / charge* of that entity, usually the molecular ion (the ion derived from the complete molecule *with / without* fragmentation).

Most mass spectrometers are able to (circle those that apply):
- create ions in solution
- create ions in the gas phase
- separate ions on the basis of *m/z* (*ie* an analyzer)
- separate neutral fragments on the basis of *m/z*
- detect the number of carbons in the molecule
- detect the number of ions of each *m/z*
- detect the size of quanta absorbed, making this a form of spectroscopy

There are three basic components to a mass spectrometer (circle all that apply): *an ionization source / an analyzer / a sonicator / a detector*.

Electrospray (ESI) is a form of *ionization / analysis / detection*.

Quadrupoles are components used for *ionization / analysis / detection*.

Time-of-flight (TOF) is a form or *ionization / analysis / detection*.

Quadrupole ion traps are components used for *ionization / analysis / detection*.

Matrix assisted laser desorption (MALD) is a form of *ionization / analysis / detection*.

Fourier transform (FT) is a form of *ionization / analysis / detection*.

Electron Impact (EI) is a form of *ionization / analysis / detection*.

Detectors in MS are usually *electron multipliers / UV / IR*.

MS instruments can be described in terms of either the ionization or analysis method. Thus *MALDI-TOF / ESI-MALDI* is a valid description but *MALDI-TOF / ESI-MALDI* is not.

c Primary Ions Formed In Different Ionization Techniques

In *matrix-assisted lased desorption ionization*, or _____ the sample is adsorbed into a "matrix compound" (2,5-dihydrobenzoic acid is a typical one) and ionized by a burst of laser light. The matrix transfers energy to the sample and mainly *protonates* it to give a cation, *ie* $[M]^+$ / $[M + 1]^+$ / $[M + 2]^+$.

In *electrospray ionization*, or _____ the sample in a solvent (*eg* water) is sprayed from a tube at a high voltage, causing it to be protonated by the solvent giving $[M]^+$ / $[M + 1]^+$ / $[M + 2]^+$ and ions with more than one proton.

For each of the following, show the primary ions (*eg* the first formed ions) for each technique. Multiple protonation events are possible in MALDI and ESI, but show only monoprotonation. Show protonation on the most basic atom in the sample, where appropriate.

	MALDI	ESI	EI

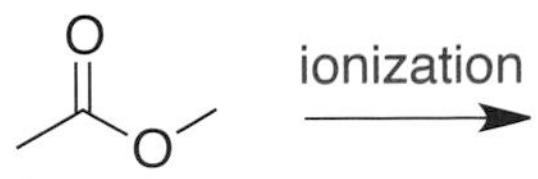

ionization

_____   _____   _____

ionization

_____   _____   _____

ionization

_____   _____   _____

Electron impact, removes *an electron / a proton* from molecules to give *radical cations / radical anions* which have the same MM as the sample, provided there is no fragmentation, *ie $[M]^+$ / $[M + 1]^+$ / $[M + 2]^+$*.

Resolution / sensitivity is important in MS when trying to distinguish two materials of similar molecular weights.

Observation of signals when working with tiny amounts of substrate is a question of *resolution / sensitivity*.

Fourier transform ion cyclotron resonance (FT-ICR) relies on detecting m/z values in an ion trap based on angular momentum. It is one of the *most / least* sensitive forms of MS.

D Isotopes In Mass Spectrometry

For each of the following molecules, calculate the *exact masses* of the most prevalent molecular ion, given the following mass data (take the most abundant isotope):

Element	Isotope	Abundance (%)	Mass number	Exact mass
hydrogen	^{1}H	99.99	1	1.00783
carbon	^{12}C	98.89	12	12.00000
carbon	^{13}C	1.11	13	13.00335
nitrogen	^{14}N	99.64	14	14.00307
oxygen	^{16}O	99.76	16	15.99492
fluorine	^{19}F	100	19	18.99840
phosphorus	^{31}P	100	31	30.97376
sulfur	^{32}S	95.00	32	31.97207
chlorine	^{35}Cl	75.77	35	34.96886
chlorine	^{37}Cl	24.23	37	36.96590
bromine	^{79}Br	50.69	79	78.91835
bromine	^{81}Br	49.31	81	80.91635
iodine	^{127}I	100	100	126.904468

CO C_2H_4 $C_2H_5{}^{35}Cl$

_____   _____   _____
exact mass   *exact mass*   *exact mass*

$CH_3{}^{79}Br$ $CH_3{}^{81}Br$ $C_2H_5{}^{37}Cl$

_____ _____ _____
exact mass   *exact mass*   *exact mass*

A *high resolution* mass spectrometer *can / cannot* distinguish carbon monoxide and ethene.

Even at low resolution, molecular ions of compounds containing natural chlorine are separated by _____ atomic mass units (amu's) in a ratio of _____ , and compounds containing natural bromine are separated by _____ amu's in a ratio of _____ .

A compound containing *two* bromines will have _____ molecular ions in a _____ ratio; and a compound containing *three* bromines will have _____ molecular ions in a _____ ratio (assume this is the only atom present with different abundant isotopes).

Illustrative Interpretation Of Isotopes In MS

Three EI mass spectra are shown below. One corresponds to a chlorine-containing compound **A**, another compound **B** contains bromine, and the third one **C** has no halogen atoms but it contains nitrogen.

the chlorine-containing compound A is number: _____

the bromine-containing compound B is number: _____

the non-halogenated compound C is number: _____

1 (m/z = 170 and 172):

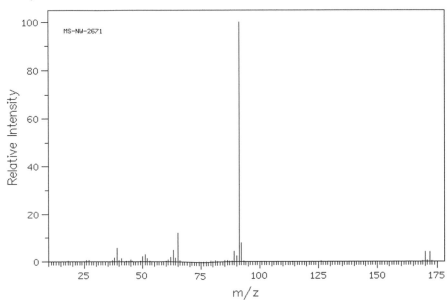

2 (m/z = 112 and 114):

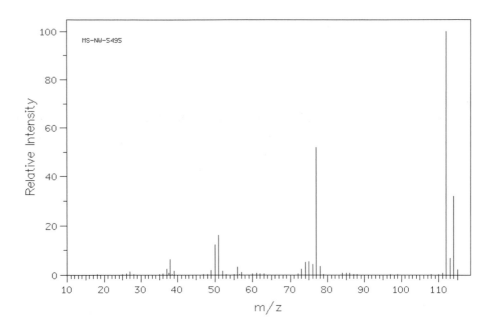

3 (m/z = 107):

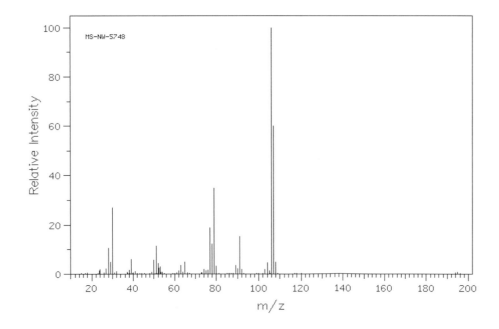

Compounds containing odd numbers of nitrogen atoms (1, 3, 5 *etc*) *never / always* have odd molecular ion m/z values.

E Fragmentation

Radical cations formed via some forms of ionization can dissociate into smaller cations and *anions / radicals*.

Where more than one cation could be formed it is the *least / most* stable one that is most likely to be observed.

Electrospray / electron impact methods *usually* show fragmentation, but *ESI / EI* does not.

ESI / EI is very widely used in contemporary MS, but *ESI / EI* instruments are becoming less important.

Fragmentation is usually *desirable / undesirable* because observation of the molecular ion is the most important information that is sought. Nevertheless, fragmentation patterns can give information on molecular structure, and this *is / is not* useful when complementary methods for molecular characterization are unavailable.

A way to combine the advantages of observing molecular ions *and* fragmentation patterns is *MS/MS / fast atom bombardment (FAB)*. In this approach ions are formed in ways that do not induce fragmentation, captured, then ionized in ways that do.

Perpendicular / tandem mass spectrometry allows observation of molecular ions from peptides and proteins and other biomacromolecules, then fragmenting them to observe their amino acid sequence.

Fragmentation pathways in MS can be complicated. Draw the predominant cation formed by dissociation of methyl radicals from the following radical cations.

C_2H_6]$^{\bullet+}$ $\xrightarrow{-Me\bullet}$ _____

$\xrightarrow{-Me\bullet}$ _____

$\xrightarrow{-Me\bullet}$ _____

$\xrightarrow{-Me\bullet}$ _____

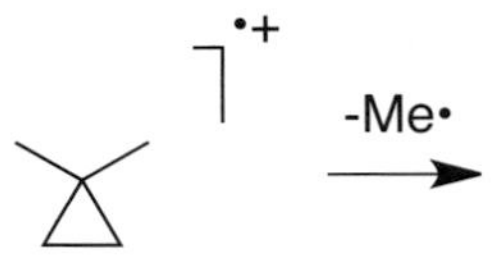
-Me•

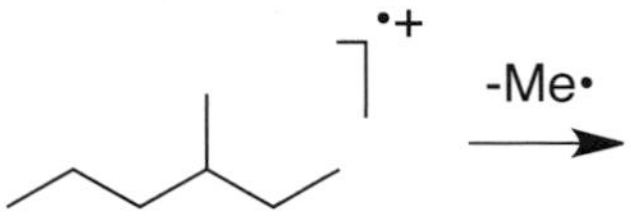
-Me•

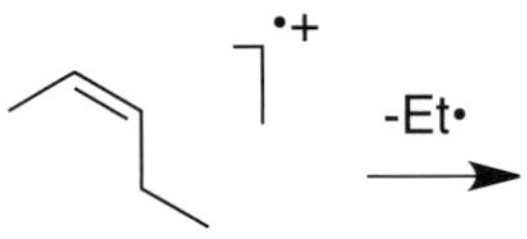
-Et•

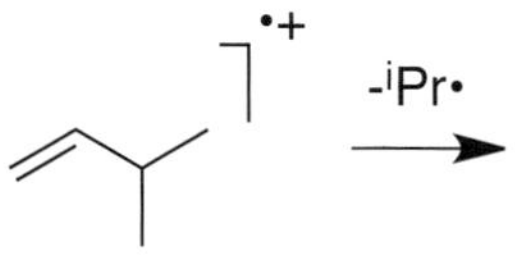
-iPr•

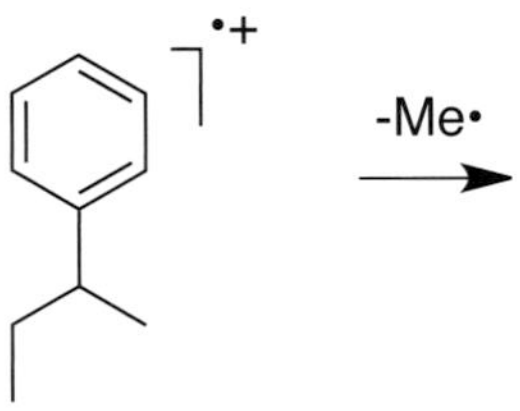
-Me•

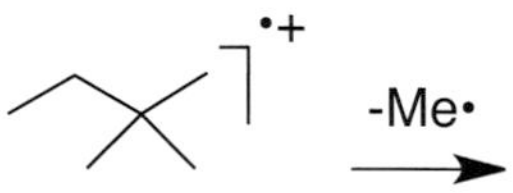
-Me•

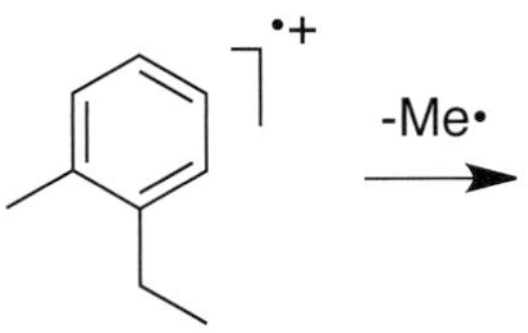
-Me•

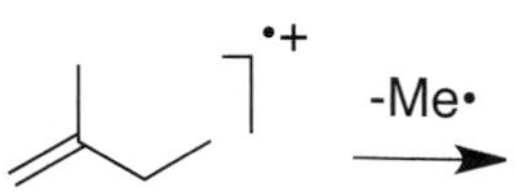
-Me•

Draw the predominant cation formed by dissociation of chloride radicals from the following:

C_2H_5Cl •+   -Cl• ⟶

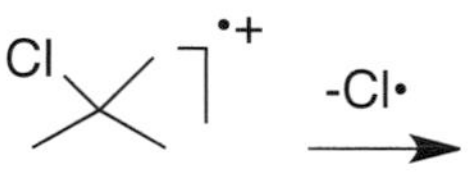

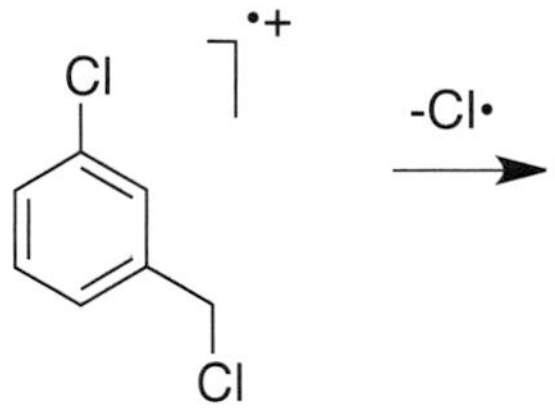

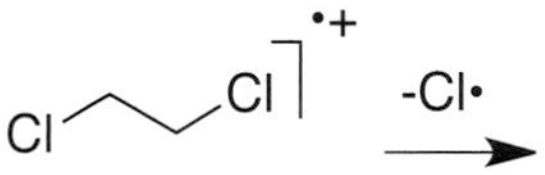

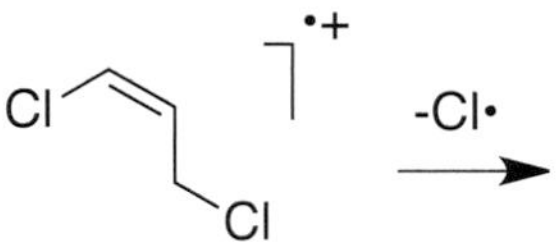

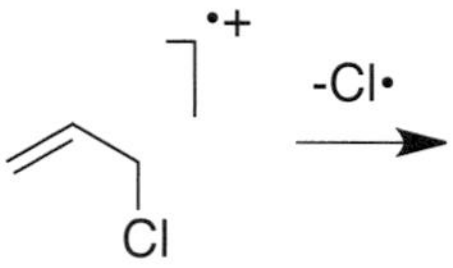

Cl—C(X)—• +   -Cl• ⟶

(3-chlorophenyl)CH₂Cl •+   -Cl• ⟶

Cl–CH₂CH₂–Cl •+   -Cl• ⟶

Cl–CH=CH–CH₂–Cl •+   -Cl• ⟶

CH₂=CH–CH₂–Cl •+   -Cl• ⟶

α-Cleavage

Alcohols can fragment by rupture of C-C(OH) bonds (α-cleavage) or via loss of water (dehydration). Show the *cations* resulting from both fragmentation pathways.

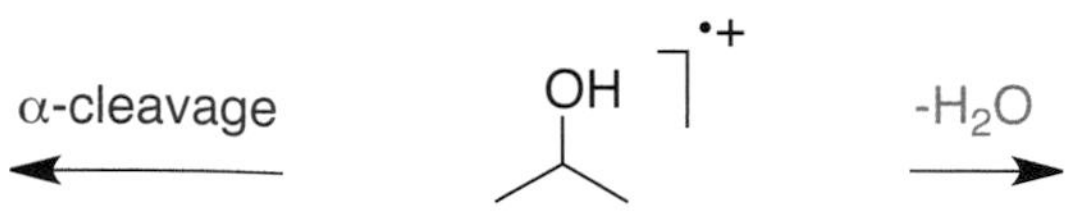

α-cleavage ⟵   (CH₃)₂CH–OH •+   -H₂O ⟶

α-cleavage ← 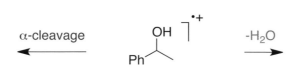 → -H₂O

α-cleavage ← -H₂O →

α-cleavage ← -H₂O →

Draw all the possible cations formed by α-cleavage of C-C bonds or dehydration of the following alcohols.

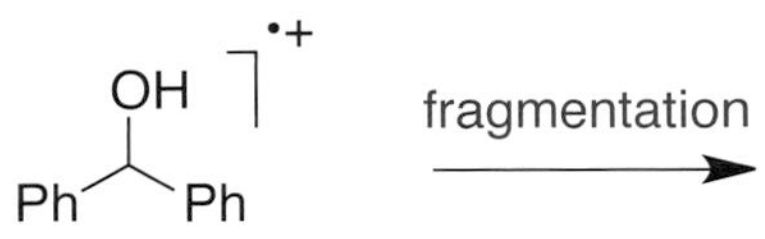
OH
Ph
Ph
•+
fragmentation

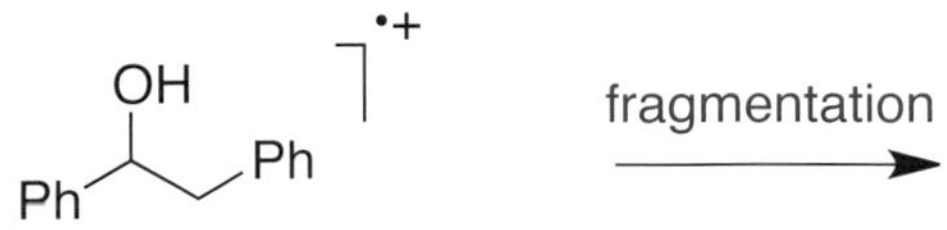
OH
Ph
Ph
•+
fragmentation

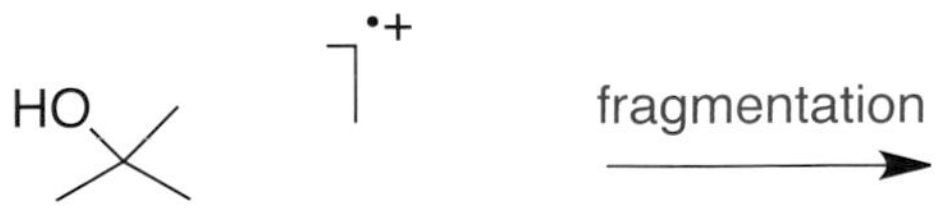
HO
•+
fragmentation

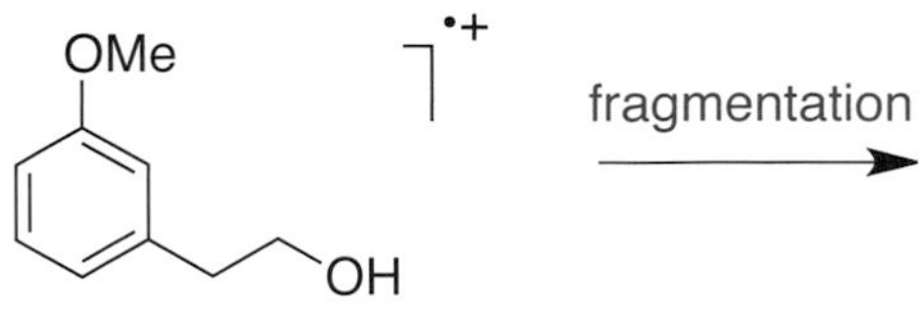
OMe
OH
•+
fragmentation

Amine radical cations can undergo α-cleavage fragmentation like alcohols; draw the product cation fragments from the following examples:

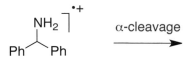

α-cleavage

_____

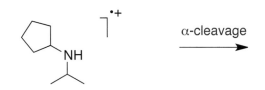

α-cleavage

_____

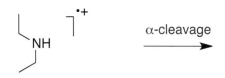

α-cleavage

_____

NEt₃

α-cleavage

_____

Carbonyl-containing radical cations can also fragment via α-cleavage; draw that pathway for the following (show both possibilities if more than one exists):

Ph—C(=O)—Ph]•+   α-cleavage →

Ph—CH₂—C(=O)—H]•+   α-cleavage →

cyclohexanone]•+   α-cleavage →

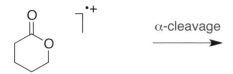

α-cleavage

The McLafferty Rearrangement

Draw in the Cγ-H atoms in the following molecules *if they have them*.

Carbonyl compounds with γ-hydrogens can also fragment via a 6-membered transition state: *The McLafferty rearrangement.* This gives cleavage of the bond between the α and β / β and γ / CO and α fragments in the diagram above on the left.

Show the products of these rearrangements for the following molecules. If the relevant hydrogen is not shown then it is useful to draw it in, and students who draw clear curly arrows for the fragmentation make less mistakes.

McLafferty
rearrangement

+

---

alkene   *radical cation*

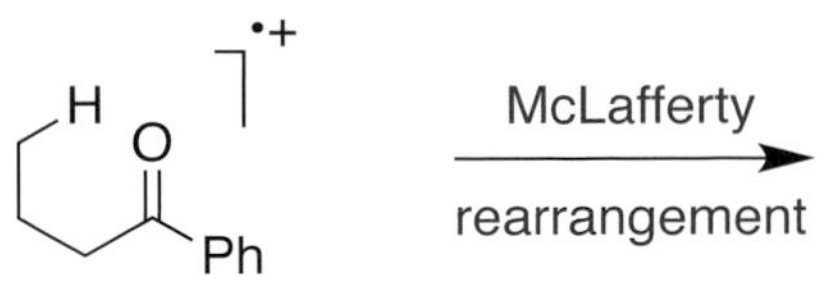
H
O
Ph
•+
McLafferty
rearrangement

+

______________ ______________

alkene *radical cation*

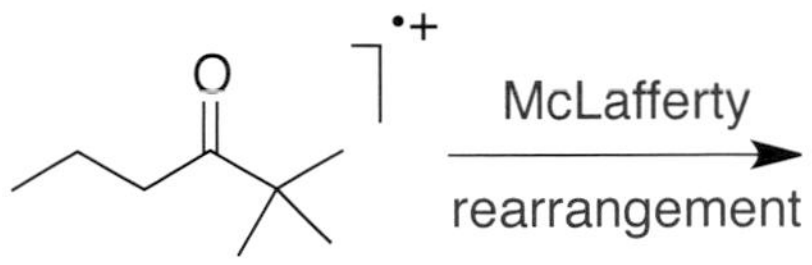
O
•+
McLafferty
rearrangement

+

______________ ______________

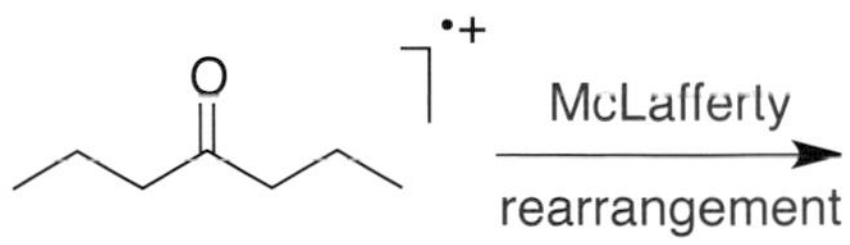
O
•+
McLafferty
rearrangement

+

______________ ______________

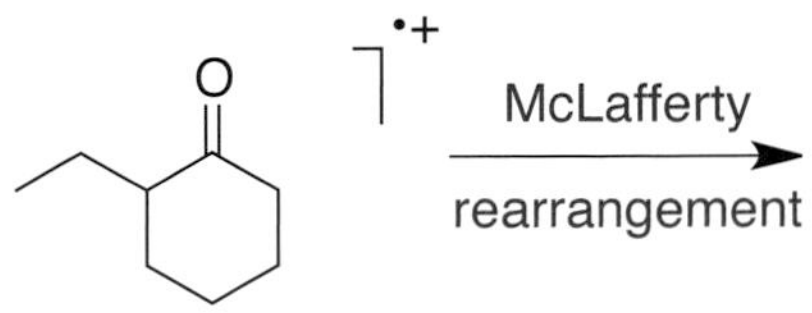
O
•+
McLafferty
rearrangement

+

______________ ______________

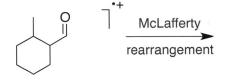

McLafferty
rearrangement
→

Summarize differences in EI-MS of these two molecules: